BEYOND ALL HORIZONS

Charles Stacey

ARTHUR H. STOCKWELL LTD
Torrs Park, Ilfracombe, Devon, EX34 8BA
Established 1898
www.ahstockwell.co.uk

British Library Cataloguing-in-Publication Data.
A catalogue record for this book is available
from the British Library.

ISBN 978-0-7223-4563-4
Printed in Great Britain by
Arthur H. Stockwell Ltd
Torrs Park   Ilfracombe
Devon EX34 8BA

DEDICATION

I dedicate this book to a very brave young girl, Charlotte, who lives in Oxford, and to all those brave children worldwide who bring to us that supreme happiness so beloved of that superb French writer, Victor Hugo.

ACKNOWLEDGEMENTS

Too many to list individually but each and every one proved of great personal value during the period under review – 1920 to date. But of special importance Juliet Gardiner, author of *The Thirties* (my formative years) and two other very fine authors – Claire Tomalin and Prof. Michael Slater, both of whom have shared with me their enjoyment of the works and life of that inimitable complex genius – Charles John Huffam Dickens (1812–1870).

PREFACE

As that well-known literary lawyer, C. D. Jaggers Esq. – he of the wagging, admonishing forefinger, phrased it – I have been informed, rather than told – that this earthly world we inhabit is but a speck of dust in the vast, mainly unchartered, universe of which we are a part.

This may be so, and prompts the question – are there possibly other worlds similar in many respects to our own world?

I first had this thought when, at about nine years of age, I became an unwilling member of a group of small boys of a similar age in a Shaftsbury Home for Boys, situated in Beulah Hill, South Norwood, London SE15. My mother, then thirty-one years of age, took me there by bus from our small flat in Manor Park, North London. I was the last of four siblings to be placed in care. My two brothers, aged seven and five years, and my sister, aged three years, had together been placed in a Dr Barnardo's home, at an earlier date. I had, I think, a small brown paper shopping bag containing my few personal items of clothing, and perhaps a toothbrush. It was a long time ago in 1929 and memories fade with time and age. My mother must have wept when she left me, for I saw her bowed head and her flustered fingers groping for a handkerchief in her handbag. I have since been reminded by a poem, written by S. Sassoon, of the bowed back of the Prince of Darkness who laughed as he walked away from the Cenotaph in Whitehall, London, in November 1920 when the Unknown Warrior was laid to final rest in Westminster Abbey. But, there was one difference – the Devil laughed – my mother and I wept. She openly, and since I was told boys do not cry – I wept inwardly and, often, still do, when memories come briefly to life.

I missed my two brothers, my sister and my mother. Perhaps I missed the father who had abandoned us, but with reservations. He, like many of us at that time, was a belated victim of the First World War, in which he had served as an infantryman – aged seventeen to eighteen years of age in the Somme battles between July and November 1916. His unit, the 5th Bn East Surrey Regiment comprised many of the young volunteers of Kitchener's 100,000 men, and his clarion call "Your country needs you". My father was wounded and gassed, and I became his first son when he was twenty-two years of age and my mother was twenty-one. When left unsupported, and with we four young children, she worked in a 'sweat shop' in North London as a sewing machinist. Naturally at that time of the Great Depression, her wages on piecework were meagre, to say the least.

But, back in the boys' home, in which I had been left, I coped as best I could with the strong religious fervour, so much in evidence at that time – grace said at every meal, daily prayers, church visits (two in different directions and different creeds – Anglican and Methodist), visits by trainee missionaries waiting to go to China to convert the Chinese. I suppose trying out their newly acquired skills on us as a passive party of possible converts.

But on the whole, we were fed and watered to satisfactory standards of the time. Naturally I absconded one rainy night and walked as far as Wood Green, North London, in order to find my mother, but equally naturally as a small boy alone at night, was apprehended by a policeman on his night beat. A very pleasant walk to the local police station, relevant details of my starting point given, a cup of tea and a piece of currant cake were provided, and after phone calls made, the home master, a Mr Arthur Potts – a terribly religious man – arrived, adopted a kindly parental attitude and conveyed me in public transport back to the home. Here, he took off his thick leather belt (much preferred to braces at that time) and in the downstairs kitchen lashed out at me. I crawled under a large table near one of its stout wooden legs and yelped as the belt hit part of the table leg. A sensible and cunning move on my part, I later thought, when assessing the bruises acquired during his brief but furious onslaught. My yelps must have influenced his wife to come to my aid as she too was highly religious but in a more kindly way. When older, I realised what a blow to the ego my leaving without authority must have caused him. But it must have cut deep, as shortly afterwards he escorted me to the Gordon Boys' Home (a national memorial to General Gordon, killed in Khartoum, Sudan, on 25 January 1885). Here, I remember him saying to the Lt Col. officer in charge of the home, 'This is the boy we spoke about on the phone.'

He then left and I stayed as a very small oboeist in the military band. The military school was run on strict military lines, bugles, parade ground, two uniforms (one weekday with shorts, one on

Sundays and high days in trews – Gordon tartan colours of course). A glengarry as headgear, barrack blocks with dormitories housing us in age groups. By the time we were sixteen and ready to go elsewhere, (usually to HM Forces) we would, if we were good, have acquired a row of good-conduct chevrons on the left sleeve of our walking-out uniform. I believe I was awarded one for every six months' service.

Having also acquired a reasonable level of playing the oboe, and a love of music that has never left me, after three years at this establishment I absconded. Same reason for doing so, but it was not rainy on that coldish night in late October 1936 when I set off on foot from West End, Nr Woking, Surrey, to Woking Station. I hoped to find a place to hide in one of the carriages of a milk train going to London.

Waiting for such an opportunity to put my plan to the test, I hid behind several full milk cans on the platform. Naturally my hiding place was at the back of the lined-up cans, as each one was trundled noisily aboard the train. I was finally discovered as the last one was removed. The train driver, a very kindly man, and obviously a father, asked me where I intended to go and when I told him, he took me on the firing platform of the train with his stoker. I was given some tea from his flask and half of a banana sandwich. The warm glow from the train's fire (steam-driven) warmed me as I was wearing my daily short shorts uniform and only the ragged coat I had found on a scarecrow near Brookwood Cemetery on my way to the station.

When we reached London, I was given a two-&-sixpenny piece (the size almost of my small palm) to pay for my fare to North London where I hoped to find my mother's address.

When I asked the driver how I could repay him the money, he said, 'You don't, Sonny Jim, you just pass it on,' which I have been trying to do ever since, but not always with success.

He told me, before I set off on my mission that he was called 'the Fat Engine Driver from Chertsey, Surrey' and that would always find him. He was my first mentor, and when, after the war, I tried to find him, I was told he had been killed by a bomb from a German plane during the air raid on the railway station.

I found my mother's address just before Fireworks Day in 1936, and as I received no answer from my knocking, I lay down on the tiled doorstep. Here I was found asleep by my mother who first thought I was a guy left by children asking for a 'penny for the guy' which was the soliciting phrase of the time, used by the youngsters exhibiting their home-made guy.

I think my mother was pleased to see me, for we had not seen each other for six long years between 1929/30 and 1936.

She made a bed up on a sofa for me and a couple of coats as blankets. And, as a happy abscondee, who at last had achieved his boyhood aim, went to sleep.

The next day, I was placed with my aunt in her house in Goodwyns Vale, Muswell Hill. Here, several days later, I was collected by two bailiffs, male representatives of some authority, and taken back to the military school in West End, Cobham, Surrey.

Having tasted freedom, I was anxious for its return – so, to hasten that day when placed in a cell on my own, I went on hunger strike.

I believe this stubbornness on my part hastened the school authorities to expel me into the custody of my mother and her sister, my aunt.

So, in these six formative years of my life, I had always consoled myself by the thought that a world existed somewhere so different to the one I was in. Out there in that unlimited dimension of space of which our sky is the first horizon.

Since I never found this world in terms of reality, it has become the theme of this book. It is but a modest attempt at authorship, and probably would be much improved without this preface – who knows? The things of this world are temporal – so, perhaps the things of other worlds may be spiritual? Hence the title of this book *Beyond All Horizons*.

CHAPTER ONE

Charles Easton, Principal Minister of the Pre-Inquiry Branch, at Headquarters, Nimbus 9, pressed the Cojoin switch of his desk console, connecting him with his chief secretary, David Edwards.

'David, has the report from Chief Investigator Holmes come in yet?'

'It is coming in as we speak, Minister, but since it appears a rather lengthy one, I can progress it to you as I receive it.'

"Yes please, David, you know we are being chased up on this one by the superior officer of Guardian A Branch. Apparently, he has employed too many of his Guardian Angel strength of late. Current world events, of course, to blame and CI Holmes was tasked to pre-antecedent enquiries of some 200 potential recruits and some fifty other candidates for accelerated promotion to GA Status One. I believe it all relates to a very special mission, Highest Celeste HQ is planning in the immediate future.'

'I understand, Minister. I've put it on immediate transmission code.'

'I'm reading it now. The usual plus marks for your section for its efficiency, David.'

'Thank you, Minister. Much appreciated.'

THE REPORT

Security Classification:
None needed at this stage of the Inquiry
Ref: Principal Minister
        Pre-Inquiry Branch
HQ   Nimbus 9
To: Principal Minister
        PI Branch

I have to report that on 31st Nov '85 information was received at this branch from Supreme Minister Guardian Angel Branch, that a pre-acceptability check was required urgently on several subjects/persons to determine their suitability for GA recruitment purposes. Also, a more detailed inquiry in respect of likely personnel to be chosen for GA Status One, if found suitable subject material.

All these inquiries were made satisfactorily except one subject, hereinafter referred to in this report as GAP/CS/1. The required investigation forms of all (save GAP/CS/1) have been forwarded in advance of this report (all marked ES/Exceptional Suitability).

Further inquiries established that subject GAP/CS/1 was resident in a small guest house in Newquay, South West Anglo Quarter. He had recently moved there from his former place of residence in Wiltshire (SW Anglo Quarter) following a marital mishap – several such apparently occurring in his life. In view of the number of tenants in the house in question, thought it advisable to assign the task of observation/abstraction of antecedent materials, etc., to sleeper GA Ingrid Peterson, of Holvk, Norway (NE Europe Quarter), who was able to conveniently acquire a room as a tenant for about a terres month. Their respective rooms were on the same floor.

It may be recalled that sleeper GA Ingrid, following an unrequited love affair in that locality, attempted and almost succeeded, when distraught in taking her own life by leaping from one of the dangerous and unstable cliffs in that area. Her pre-exit permit was revoked and a sleeper GA in the immediate vicinity on the night in question prevented her from completing her action.

The sleeper GA later received his own pre-exit permit, and is now a full-time GA and sleeper GA Status Nine was allowed to Ingrid. Ingrid is now fifty-two years of age, intelligent, and possesses those classic good looks of those from the Scandinavian NE area, is bilingual in her native tongue and in the English language. Has never left the idealism of her youth and is fond (excessively so) of all children for whom she writes stories (several of which being published). She is unmarried has no family – all pre-exit permit holders, and longs to be part of a loyal loving partnership – preferably marriage, of course. Both she and subject CS (nomenclature for easier referencing) became close, but not intimate friends, in a short time, she considered themselves as soulmates). Mindful of her task, she obtains all the relevant material necessary for qualification for the rank of GA Status Nine, including two small books he had written she thought that when read would provide indications of his philosophical outlook on life and his ethical and moral beliefs.

At this stage a brief account of subject CS is pertinent. He is a Caucasian male, 5' 10" in height – weight 10 st 6 lb, fair complexion, clean-shaven, sparse hair (was auburn in colour), eyes blue, seemingly sound in mind . . . and usual age-related indispositions. Born in North London in 1920, active war service, regular soldier, several medals relating to battles, Middle East, Italy, and six years in the Far East, Malaysia, Singapore and Hong Kong, twice sustained gunshot wounds. Married blissfully and happily a young widow of twenty-three, he then twenty-five, a widower in 1948, wife died age twenty-five of acute myeloid leukaemia. Resumed in forces, several overseas tours of duty, several marital mistakes, not too happy a childhood, six years in quasi orphanages, of average intelligence, acquired a BA degree (in humanities) with Open University, loves children and hoped to get employment with his degree as an art teacher to children but was too old for such employment, until recently an avid reader and a would-be painter. Landscapes, etc., rather than doors and windows.

My initial assessment was such that Higher Authority would approve his advance status as when pre-exit permit was allowed.

However, at this point in my investigation, subject CS and Ingrid – under the latter's guidance and persuasion, no doubt – left the European theatre of operations. Inquiries showed he had obtained a small loan from his bank, and she had acquired additional income to augment the sum she possessed personally.

They travelled to the Far East, apparently in search of a fabled Eastern equivalent of Nimbus 9. This place, allegedly in the higher region of the Tibetan mountain range, is referred to in current literature as 'Shangri-La'.

I understand that in the early 1930s a Member of Parliament was involved in a flying accident in that region. He was on a trade mission to the Far East and had a small party of advisors and businessmen with him, in addition to the plane's crew. Due to severe weather conditions, the plane failed to gain the necessary height to cross the mountainous barrier and crashed in a snow-filled valley. No one was injured but the plane's undercarriage was severely damaged. An SOS signal was sent out before the plane's transmission ceased to function. Both crew and passengers (all unhurt) left the plane and made their way on foot to what they thought to be a village in the vicinity. After an arduous journey they were met by a small party of men, they thought to be from some religious order. And, taken through a concealed mountain pass, they found refuge in an extraordinary monastery-like place they were told was named Shangri-La. Several air searches were made in the area, but no trace of the plane or its passengers was found.

It was not until several years later that the MP returned to England with the intention of writing a book about his experiences. The book was given the title *Lost Horizon* and Shangri-La was first mentioned. It became a name linked to an idyllic utopian place and the name is in current use to this day.

The book was widely read and one can but presume its reading by Ingrid and subject CS considerably influenced their altruistic thinking processes, and led them to undertake their mission for such it was as my further inquiries showed. After obtaining what they thought was suitable clothing for the mountainous region, they set out, at first by various kinds of transport, and then finally on foot for their fabled destination. A remarkable, and possibly, a foolish undertaking. They appeared to make reason the slave of their passionate commitment – shades of David Hume, the Scottish philosopher there, it seems, and his classification of reason. The weather conditions varied considerably at this time, and with the aid of my thought-transference spray, I was able to obtain details of their ordeal.

They were initially seen by local villagers ascending a steep path towards a severe, snow-covered rock face and a sudden snowstorm obscured them. In better conditions on the following day, a rescue party from the village set out to try to locate them at the place where they were first seen. It was noticed then that one was carrying the other and making their staggered progress for some form of shelter near the rock face. Eventually the two bodies were found – clasped in each other's arms, in an improvised snow shelter. It was established that the woman (Ingrid) had sustained a severe injury to her back, indicating why her companion had carried her, until they found such shelter as was possible. The bodies were placed on a sledge and as the party prepared to leave, a snowstorm with blizzard-like severity suddenly occurred. They found shelter in a crevice-like cave in the rock face and as space was limited, left the sledge with the two bodies outside. However, the storm lasted several hours and it was not until dawn the following day that they left the cave and found no trace of the sledge or the bodies. With the heavy snowfall during the night, no sledge marks, footprints or other signs of human activity could be seen.

On their return to the village, the matter was reported and their account was that I obtained. I thought it advisable to visit the location concerned and at the rock face I noticed its surface was warm to my ungloved touch. Also, I sensed a scent of some kind that reminded me of those wonderful orchids grown on Nimbus 9. An impossible conjecture really since the cold air could never have favoured the growth of such blooms.

Despite other further detailed inquiries, I found no trace of Ingrid and subject CS – and presumed both were dead – their deaths caused, no doubt, by hypothermia in the severe weather conditions. I had, therefore, no other option than to forward all antecent history of those potential Guardian Angel recruits, and attached thereto the appendices A and B in respect of subject CS. It is with regret that I close this report. I had higher hopes of a completely successful investigation, but the defection of the two parties previously mentioned, and full details lacking as to their present whereabouts, precluded it.

Much later, after the publication of his book, the MP wearied of the treadmill-like quality of his political activity also of the symbols of impending imbecility, such as rearmament, air-raid shelters and gas masks, all suggestive of yet another disastrous random harvest of millions of casualties.

He resigned as an MP and sought to find that haven of peace and tranquillity he had once known, all too briefly, in Shangri-La.

He had been a widower for several years before the plane flight that ended so drastically. It is possible that, in the daughter of the head of Shangri-La Monastery, he found again that person without whom in his life his heart would know no peace.

This may have been a telling factor in the decision of Ingrid and her companion to seek such peace and happiness themselves.

When last seen by a party of mountaineers in the area in question, the MP was seen before a smooth rock face. A sudden cloud of a rosy-pink colour obscured all vision and when the cloud drifted away, he was seen no more. The assumption being he had found his Shangri-La and his heart would forever be at peace.

I regret that this inquiry did not have the successful result such as I have had on all my previous investigations. But, should any evidence come to hand further inquiries will be made and a report duly submitted.

Signed Conan Holmes,
Chief Investigating Officer, PAB Branch,
HQ, Nimbus 9
Copies: HCHQ Nimbus 9
             Prime Minister, PAB Branch
             PR Minister, GA Branch
             Archives
             File

'Report ends, Minister.'

'Thank you, David. When CI Holmes returns, would you kindly ask him to call in to see me?'

'Certainly, Minister. He is with me at present, tired, but still the same eager beaver of old, he overheard your request and is on his way to you, no doubt.'

'Thank you, David.'

CHAPTER TWO

'Hello, Holmes. Thank you for coming to see me so soon after your many travels. I have read your report – very interesting and, there may be yet a satisfactory ending to your enquiry, but first a few of your observations on the current views of those in positions of authority in that "speck of dust" world as it was recently dubbed by some unwise person.'

'I share your view, Minister. It is far from being a mite in our dimensional extended universe – in various articles in newspapers and horoscopes and magazines, there is constant mention of Guardian Angels, and cosmic influences. A recent letter published in one such newspaper from a very intelligent Mr T. W. K. Davies from Wellingborough, Northants, was about the question of alien visitors visiting this world. He wrote, "Why should aliens be interested in us?" A good question at that time of unidentified flying objects (UFOs), crop circles, references to Guardian Angels and much else of a similar nature. Perhaps Mr Davies' remarks were highly relevant to the issue in question, but I wonder if Mr Davies had given thought to the possibility that the visitors were not aliens but reflections of themselves (those being visited) – their better nature, better judgement of others and universal affairs, being unbiased and unprejudiced and possessing a very human need and a harmonious relationship with each other – irrespective of race, colour or creed. Even centuries ago, the Prince of Denmark, aided of course by that Prince of the English language, William Shakespeare, told his companion Horatio: "There are more things in Heaven and Earth, Horatio, than are dreamt of in your philosophy," an indication, even then, that a world other than this, was of interest to the Bard, himself. I noticed, Minister, that many had turned away from orthodox religious beliefs, some were heavily involved in fringe movements, sects, etc., but most were seeking a spiritual alternative. And that what they seek, we provide in our Guardian Angel concept and, one day, Minister, in the not too distant future, they will understand and the tasks taken on for so long will have produced a peaceful, contented world. For another observation I made shows, I think, that the legal section of their establishment long ago gave thought to brain-cortex tasks.'

'Really, Holmes, a bit whimsical perhaps?'

'Not really, Minister, for in the definition of a fact – namely: any physical event perceived by one of the five senses; sight, hearing, taste, touch or smell, or any mental event of which one feels himself conscious. The concluding part of that definition suggests what Hamlet told Horatio: About that special somewhere between heaven and earth, might be true, a spiritual entity perhaps?'

'You really believe that, Holmes, don't you?'

'I certainly do, Minister.'

'In that case, Holmes, H.C.'s decision to assign to you a mission, long thought of, and very close to his heart.'

'Details? Facts? Minister?'

'It is a mammoth task and you will be given all possible aid – including two specially selected aids, who have asked to be part of your team. You may recall that H.C. nearly lost his only granddaughter, Jess, in that ideological conflict with warring factions in the Middle East. Before her expected death she made a plea to H.C., no doubt you could quote it offhand, Holmes?'

'Yes, Minister, I've seen it in the archives many times on occasions when I have set out on missions on his behalf – I think she said, "Dear wonderful, loving Grandfather, please forgive them for they do not understand what they are doing."

'Also, Holmes, as an archives-reading zealot, you read of the efforts he made to bring peace to that troubled planet, where he caused the truce on Christmas Day in 1914, on the Western Front, in that horrendous war of 1914–1918? His efforts were ruined by blinkered incompetent military leaders on all sides of the conflict.'

'Yes, and I've always wondered why that stupid war began and why the various crowned heads failed completely to stop the slaughter at its outset and on many later occasions.'

'Well put, Holmes. I see you still hold those strong pacifist views of yours.'

'I've had them I think, from the day I was born. After all, all monarchies originally came from that symbol to the heavens for a good harvest – the corn dolly.'

'Placed on top of sheaves, I believe, Holmes?'

'Quite so, Minister, and then I well remember H.C.'s eventual intervention in that second horrendous conflict, 1939–1945 – when he finally gave the thunderclap nuclear details to those most anxious to avoid the possible obliteration of Japan by its war-prone authorities and the people themselves. A terrible decision was made by H.C. – but I believe in the circumstances, it was the correct one – providing it was used judiciously first on an unoccupied area or region within vision of those responsible for the continuation of hostilities. Yes, Minister, even the person responsible for all the destruction and suffering caused, said to H.C. afterwards, "It was an immoral act," but any war is totally immoral.'

'General Le May, I believe, Holmes, was the man in question?'

'Indeed he was.'

'Well, that's the introduction to H.C.'s long-held hope – that the peace all long for, will come about, through your efforts on this mission. I understand that H.C. had as but two of his advisors – Thomas Hardy and W. Owen.'

'Yes, I think Hardy's hopeful lines in his poem *"When shall the saner policies whereof we dream, hold sway in each proud land"* influenced H.C., and so he wants to implement the saner policies, preferably by using inducements or blandishment – as a last resort (and you must contact HQ, Nimbus 9, before resorting to their use), "natural" disasters of a non-injurious kind but extremely impressive in their magnitude.'

'I understand, completely, on that point, Minister. But the other two suggested methods to obtain compliance of his wishes.'

'There are many – I have listed them, not necessarily in order of sequence of importance. They are:

1. A constant fuel and power supply provided by secret areas of both polar regions
2. Elimination of all forms of cancerous growth
3. Limb replacements
4. Vision restoration – to be passed to the appropriate authorities
5. Cessation of floods and earthquakes for a period as long as peace holds good
6. Controlled perpetual motion (only 50% of our research to be provided, again subject to full compliance with non-aggressive policies)
7. The facility of a world currency means of communication.

'A Guardian Angel will be allotted to the prime authority in every country with warlike activity potential or otherwise – these I think for . . . purposes once an inducement/blandishment has been made and agreed.'

'It is a task that, I believe, Holmes, with all your background knowledge of that planet your uncanny investigational skills both home and abroad, as they say, can bring to a worthy and just conclusion.'

'Do you think you can manage it, Holmes?'

'It has been a long-held hope of mine to be given such a task, since I first came to Nimbus 9, and as such I can see the wise decision to give me two assistants.'

'You will have them now, Holmes, they will come in to meet you. Just press the Cojoin switch on your portable console, whenever, I suppose, debriefing is finished.'

'A few last questions. I am told that in the light air of mountainous regions the thought-transference spray did not operate as efficiently unless a booster phial was inserted.'

'Yes, the Nitro-vax seems to dilute too quickly but I noticed it brought about a cardiac-related enhancement. It seemed to enhance what we call "The holiness of the human heart" and magnified considerably the truth of the imagination. Not bad side effects, Holmes, there is a poetical quality about that enhancement.'

'Yes, I believe it was a remark Keats made to a friend. I know that my old comrade, the poet Vernon Scannell, once said that he had an unshakeable belief in its veracity. I realise that you were disappointed at not establishing the whereabouts of your two defectors, but on their return to us they provided much useful information.

'In their hibernated state on being left on the sledge, a pre-exit permit was authorised at HQ here with a mortalic protection coverage addition. Thus, on the night, they were rescued by monastery personnel and placed in the children's hospital annexe they were resuscitated. When fully recovered they were employed, at their request, in the research laboratory. The climate within the monastery and its environments was pleasantly warm – an atmosphere of peace and tranquillity pervaded almost everywhere. It was a place they found lived up to all their expectations. They memorised details of the various medical/surgical/mental research techniques, enjoyed every moment of their stay there. On both sides, when they left as merger/hostages (a meaningless term really) were sad to leave each other. This I think was an indication of their worth as industrious and reliable volunteers. They are to be your two additional aides and, possibly, you could find them suitable employment in a minor research lab capacity, where they can discreetly pass on their acquired Shangri-La knowledge. In the medical sense only, naturally, Great Ormond Street Children's Hospital has good research facilities and projects of real worth at the present time.'

'I think I can arrange that for them, Minister – perhaps a mutual re-approachment first, to enable a new and this time, a successful partnership.'

'Well, give them time to redeem themselves, give them time. Yes, you are right. I suppose there must have been something before "time" became a word in everyday use. I like W. H. Auden's use of it in his poem. You'll quote it, no doubt, Holmes, in your current poetical mood?'

'Yes – "In time, all wrongs are righted
        All evils made good
        Befriend us time
        Love's gaunt executioner."'

'Rather with tongue in cheek, I had in mind a different last line.'

'And, Holmes?'

'"Love's forgiving redeemer."'

'Not quite as poignant and sharp as Auden's'.

'Probably not, but perhaps the adjectival use of "comely" redeemer?'

'I think not, Holmes.'

'Well, I'll stick to my own favourite poem. Very short, but to my mind, beautiful.'

'And again, Holmes, it is?'

> 'Not for me all the roses of the world
> But only the wee white rose of Scotland
> That smells so sweet
> And breaks the heart.'

'And on that splendid poetical example we shall have an introduction of your two aides, Ingrid and subject CS – both now Guardian Angels,

Status One. Just one more observation, Holmes, they have so much in common, and have formed a close and loving relationship. He is fourteen years her senior, but I suppose it will work out satisfactorily in the end?'

'You are probably right, Minister. In fact, I'm inclined to leave out "probably". Time will tell.'

'No more poems please, Holmes. I thought writing detective novels your forte. You might care to write one about your two new assistants.'

'What title might it be given?'

'*The Case of the Lost and Found Horizon*, I think might be applicable?'

'You are probably right, Holmes.'

'Oh, just a few final observations on my part, I have read the copies of the two books you forwarded and I do think that with training, he could have been a successful portrait painter. He is a bit of a romantic, but I suppose all his marital mishaps were later caused by a good deed in the first place, going wrong – as Oscar Wilde wrote, "No good deed ever goes unpunished" – a bit cynical, but true in many cases, I suspect.'

'He has an obvious aversion to any activity of a warlike or aggressive nature. His religiosity is a problem, though.'

'Well, Minister, he was an infantryman and when bullets scythe through the air near their head or body, they still any possible agnosticism very speedily. I think his constant searches for domestic contentment, stem from his abandonment in his formative years. Such persons sometimes take it out on others, the fact that they lost out somewhere along the line. I think society has yet to realise fully the consequences; a child suffers from an absent parent or parents. It cuts deep into their soul and its effects last a lifetime – even the aged continue to weep inwardly at their earlier loss of emotional security.'

'Yes, Holmes, I agree. The future of any world lies with its youth, so every care should be taken to safeguard that precious future.

CHAPTER THREE

Much later, as Principal Minister, Charles Easton, left his office, he saw CI Holmes, ahead of him in the corridor. Quickening his pace he caught up with him.

'Holmes, I was hoping to catch you up as I hoped we might get a table together on the balcony of the cafeteria. I'm a bit out of this scurrying business, but H.C. has requested me to inform you that he is well pleased with all you accomplished on your recent mission and that it was completed so successfully and quickly.'

When seated to their satisfaction with their chosen 'tasse de Twinings' as they dubbed it, to hand, Easton continued.

'There is a degree of concern about the lack of cooperation on the part of PM X of Y as you styled him and his country in your report, in respect of his involvement in the supply of the new drug "Detenus" of which you obtained details during your enquiries in his domain.'

'Yes, Minister. I thought at the time he was overeager to obtain fuller details of the promise of the Belgium Government to supply 50% of their "Flanag" poppy quota.'

'Well, it appears that you had every right to be wary of his intentions. You know that the research that went into the blending of the Flanders poppy crop and that grown in the upper regions of the Afghanistan border produced the present worldwide usage of the prescription for the treatment of almost all mental illnesses and indispositions. Apparently, there are those who wish to divert the research made and cause the drug to become what they classify, as a "docility drug", with extremely harmful consequences both to its individual use and in its wider influence on world affairs. In short, Holmes, yet another attempt at world domination. A very serious and sinister situation that would push back our efforts for world peace, to a degree H.C. is not prepared to countenance.'

'But surely, Minister, massive efforts will be made by other countries to counteract the effects of such a drug? An antidote drug?'

'It would take time, Holmes, and there is no guarantee of it being successful. Tests on animals have been abolished for many years now. There are stringent rules on the employment of human volunteers.'

'Yes, I appreciate that. But if such volunteers were used, it would help, would it not?'

'Yes, it would, but H.C. is determined not to sanction it. He is ever mindful of the evil ways in which human beings were used in allegedly, pursuance of medical science in the recent world war. Much useful information was obtained in those diabolical tests by those so-called doctors, but even now the use of such information is considered unethical. And the would-be perpetrators of this docility drug must have some protection from the drug's effects – excluding perhaps, certain minions necessary for its success.'

'It's quite possible that small experiments with the drug have been made already.'

'Such as, Holmes?'

'The judiciary in several democratic countries. Weak and ineffectual sentences being passed on offenders, clearly seen to have blatantly committed very serious offences. A public outcry well publicised by the media occurs, the matter is referred to an appeal court – the sentence altered to reflect the seriousness of the crime, another appeal to the Court of Human Rights – and the appeal court's decision overruled. Result – public confidence in the judiciary undermined. So this is not a case of world domination by the usual aggressive means – mass armaments, etc. – but an insidious way of undermining the confidence of entire nations to defend themselves successfully.'

Then, presumably, there will be no casualties, unlike in previous wars, only mere submission to the will of the power using the docility drug?'

'Correct, Holmes, and we need to know the degree of effectiveness of this drug, how it is to be administered – details of its changed composition. It is no doubt an ingenious plan to secure the passive acceptance of domination other than by the accepted warlike means. And this is why H.C. wishes to employ your well-known investigational skills and original lines of inquiry.'

'And, Minister, method or methods to be chosen and used to inflict this diabolical plan upon the world at large – are they known?'

'No, but one might presume by air or water or a form of gas?'

'Or biological means, of course?'

'Yes, that is also a possibility – using the known air currents and climate effects, etc., both air and water are needed for human survival.'

'Agreed, Holmes, and food is essential too, and the staple diets of many countries are known.'

'Yes but distribution of such items would take time in its contaminated drug condition, and its delivery and distribution.'

'True, Holmes, but there must be a way to prevent its worldwide distribution.'

'For this plan to succeed, there must have been small attempts in the beginning to assess the efficacy of the drug on a small scale of course. Whether its influence was of short duration or longer-lasting. Its effect on different classes, particularly members of the elite establishment. The great and the good as they are called.

'Thus, if members of the judiciary are used in test runs – weak sentences encourage the criminal class (or fraternity, as they too are called), in the commission of crimes to the detriment of the members of the law-abiding public where personal views are advanced by those sitting in judgment – a form of masking the legal consequences of inadequate sentencing. It is but a possibility, I admit, likewise the use of the drug causing persons in parliamentary positions to take part in reality shows (widely publicised) or situations bringing them into public contempt and ridicule them to such an extent that a by-election is called and an opposition candidate of different political opinion secures the votes necessary to obtain the seat. Just personal views, Minister, but if such practices were on a larger scale, they could become highly effective in influencing public opinion.

'There is additionally, the need to protect the larger section of the community using the drug from its full consequences, or is it yet again, a case of so-called legally acquired authority to rule the country – without means of physical force or intimidation, but a form of brainwashing drug techniques. We just do not know the answer to so many questions. The countries' borders are certainly not open to all and sundry. So, there appears to be an entry difficulty, am I correct?'

'Indeed you are and a docile and compliant population will prove of little help to you once we have decided on your method of entry. We need to know how this well-organised plan came into existence without the population being subjected to physical injury, or threats of same, incarceration or total elimination. Its application must have been top secret, known only to a few – all others are but willing and subjected collaborators. It is a mammoth and dangerous task we are asking you to undertake in the very heartland itself. I know you are said to be the very master of disguises, but it is thought you might be allotted an embassy post or trade advisor or any other role you may consider, say a quasi-military attaché?'

'No, Minister, that's too obvious that last suggestion, for it is a well-known fact in nearly all countries warranting ambassadorial status that the role of such attachés is merely to cover spying activity. It is a well-known and accepted fact and all nations employ it as a cover for such dubious, political activities.'

'Have you any ideas as to your own choice of means of entry?'

'Yes, several, in fact. For in a professional ambassadorial capacity I should be carefully watched in my duty and off-duty moments. Subjected to close observation by professional and highly trained state security personnel. So might I suggest a form of culturally concealment background?'

'Such as, Holmes?'

'A musical entry – my violin concerto and lyrical choral work "Ode to Nimbus", are considered by all Nimbus 9 musical critics to be worthy examples of current musical developments – especially the piece for the piano – rivalling, they say, the difficult solo piece of Maurice Ravel's "Gaspard de la Nuit" with its complexity and musical structure.'

'Really, Holmes, when did you last hear Ravel's work?'

'Oh, a long time ago – but the musical structure involving double notes scored in major seconds gave me much food for thought. I realised that such music codified its usage for the conveyancing of information of a secret or confidential nature obviously of use to intelligence branches worldwide.'

'To transmit intelligence material in such a way – somewhat original, Holmes, surely?'

'Well, not really, it had been used in a political way in June 1944 to apprise French Resistance forces of the impending invasion under the "title" Operation Overlord always known as the D-Day Landings.'

'Yes, but that was vocal – the poetical use of a few lines from a French poem.'

'Admittedly so, Minister, but – musically transmitted information was used in overseas broadcasts. The opening bars of a Beethoven symphony preceded the news set in a format understood only by the recipients, who were anxious to avoid radio detection by their oppressors. Severe penalties for listening to foreign broadcasts, was the order of the day.'

'Oh yes, Holmes, and the military victories, in the recent war and there were many in the beginning, were heralded by Wagnerian boastfulness. Also, if I remember rightly, a particular piece was played by the Berlin Symphony Orchestra in April 1945, notifying an underground organization not to proceed with major demolitions to vital industrial infrastructures, the flooding of mineshafts, blocking essential canals, etc., these were one-off situations, of course, so different from what you are suggesting as operationally of valid use.'

'I agree, but my musical structured codification uses musical definitions such as scherzo, glissando, forte, pianissimo, allegro, andante, con brio, and many others and notes of a particular piece of music played in alphabetical sequence. It requires of course a sender and a recipient – both of high musical and tonal ability to function correctly.'

'Yes, but it seems that if you are the sender, we shall need a well-trained musical receiver here.'

'In fact, Minister, there is one such who has the necessary musical knowledge and has compiled his own codification manual. It is in its embryonic stage but is workable.'

'I see now, Holmes, your cover as a cultural figure, conducting your own composition might deflect any suspicion of your ulterior motives – I use the word ulterior carefully of course. The national orchestra might be willing to tackle your composition. It would be ideal.'

'I think that is quite possible, Minister, for it is a very musically conscious country.'

'Am I to know the details of this code, Holmes?'

'Yes, why not – musical puzzles are just as enigmatic as those deciphered at Bletchley Park, long ago.'

'Such as?'

'In the rudiments of music we have the trill defined as "a note to the note above played as rapidly as possible according to tempo".'

"Yes, I follow you.'

'So, there are many ways to employ or use a trill – sharps, flats, the common scale of C. The examples of trills being exchanged between various instruments – say oboe and flute as in the *William Tell* overture – or Beethoven's Rural Symphony. They can be played, in sequence by first, second and third violins – and other stringed instruments. Trumpet players usually excel at them with triple tonguing, etc., in fact the whole orchestra can be used including the percussion section. All can be used in a musically based code. Phrased words indicated by tempo, pauses, or even individual words.'

'I suppose a musically phrased code book is necessary for decoding such information – am I right, Holmes?'

'Indeed you are. Much of this work has been prepared – at present in its infancy, so to speak. But I have a small example of its effectiveness in these two sealed envelopes. I wish you to hold them while I go to the canteen piano and play a small piece of Ravel's work. Your watch has second and minute hands. So, if you listen to the trills I play at various times – click the second-hand control for the duration of such musical embellishments and note them numerically and note them quickly – don't be too obvious in doing so. Do it as casually as possible, so as not to attract undue attention of, shall we say, a trained security observer.

'Do not worry if you do not get the timing exactly right – this is but a minor test. In the normal run of things the music will be recorded, slowed down if necessary and decoded for translation purposes. It will be but a short piece, specially chosen as an example of how foolproof and secure as a code it can be. Say, two minutes at the most. Write the duration time of a trill and then the first letter of the word = viz T – if played loud write "F" for forte, or if played softly "P" for pianissimo – the duration time of another trill (same written action again, and the duration of a note played three times). I shall play the piece twice just in case of a possible error in notation. To assist you I have brought along a newspaper

– *The Chronicle* – with its usual crossword page. If this is left open your jottings will give the impression of doodling while thinking up the answers to the clues. So a pen in hand will not be a cause for suspicion or observation.'

'Yes, I see.'

When his brief musical offering ended, he returned to the table to find his companion had a small piece of paper on which was written 5 TF 4 TN. Holmes then asked for the envelope marked 2 to be opened and its contents read. 'They are identical' was the Minister's reply upon reading the note enclosed.

'Amazing, Holmes.'

'Now, Minister, if you open the other envelope marked 3 you will find the translation of the coded message and I think you will agree with what is written.'

The Minister did so and read, "Not to be disclosed as yet" – 'Do you agree?'

'Decidedly so, Holmes, and what means of entry to this country of would-be conquerors, do you have in mind?'

'I thought that initially as the celebrated composer/conductor of his own work – in respect of which the codified/receipt manual has been prepared I shall keep my intelligence report brief and a "return to coda" symbol is used at the end of the message(s). It will signify that the use of the docility drug on a vast scale is imminent.

'The manual contains translation and interpretation details to cover most contingencies and geographical locations.'

'A dangerous undertaking, Holmes. H.C. has made available all the physical and scientific aid you will need. All details are in a mission brief to be delivered to you personally at your office. I trust all will go well for your efforts, Holmes.'

'Don't have cause for worry, Minister. I have several contingency plans should a hitch occur.'

'Well, good luck, Holmes.'

'Thank you, Minister.'

"Your flight leaves from the usual veloss platform on the solar eclipse on Tuesday. Further mission documents with up-to-date last-minute information will be personally handed to you when boarding; your usual crew and trusted assistants will already be on board. Be careful, Holmes – we need you.'

'As I once heard said "likewise", Minister.'

'Go on, Holmes, off you go.'

A short time later, after Charles Easton had returned to his office, his chief secretary, David Edwards, contacted him on their Cojoin system.

'Yes, David, what is it?'

'I am sorry, Minister, to be the bearer of sad news, but Chief Investigator Holmes has had a cardiac arrest. He collapsed – a severe one it is believed. He fell when admiring those splendid orchids in the main garden. The usual emergency treatment was given.

'It is assumed that the hibernation system applied will bring him out of a coma, but the long-term prognosis is that it will be some time before he makes a full recovery.'

'In the meantime, David, his services will be greatly missed. Thank you for your prompt message. I shall pass the news to H.C. and will contact you later. So be at hand, David, there's a good chap.'

'I shall, Minister.'

'Oh, before you go, I believe you were once a stalwart member of Holmes' Investigation Branch and, I am told, were not too keen to leave it on your becoming my chief secretary – on promotion – and if I may say so, my very efficient right-hand man?'

'Yes, that is so, Minister – although promotion was slow in that branch, it was because there were so many brilliant investigators as competition for a promotional post. But, I am glad I made the move. It has most certainly broadened my knowledge of the internal organization of Nimbus 9.'

Easton's Cojoin system buzzed urgent red as Edwards left the room. He answered it, spoke intermittently at length, finally switched it and summoned Edwards' prompt return.

'Please be seated, David – we've got a great deal to discuss. How would you take to accepting my position and the promotion that goes with it?'

'Well, it's a challenge, Minister, but I am prepared to take it on. May I know your next appointment, for surely there is to be one?'

'It's in the hands of H.C. at present, but I think he will concur with my wish to undertake a special task on his behalf. That was his call to me earlier as you left, and if I am not mistaken, as his console buzzed red, that's his call for me with his decision.'

'And have you decided who is to be your Chief Secretary, David?'

'Yes, I thought GA Status Nine CS would be my substitute. He writes a logical report, is conscientious, and he and Ingrid have accepted two young survivors of that horrible Tsunami as in an adoption capacity. He is reliable, punctual and efficient.'

'Yes, David, a good choice. Meanwhile, I shall be endeavouring to take the place of our mutual colleague and friend, Holmes.'

'So, we shall both miss Holmes for a while, Minister?'

'Yes, David, and so too will that speck of dust of his, with its beautiful galaxy only 120,000 light years across. I believe they call it their Milky Way. Holmes referred to it as his "lost and found horizon". Rather an apt title, but then Holmes always had that poetical touch. Even in his reports.'

EPILOGUE

Holmes is making a good recovery in what he calls his LTC (long-term convalescence), but his carer, who is inordinately fond of him, calls it TLC (tender loving care).

With the help of members of the Degas and Tchaikovsky families, he is composing his music for the ballet he has named *Schmetterling Traumerei* (Butterfly Dreamland). It has captured the attention of many music lovers in Nimbus 9 – including Puccini who wishes Holmes to include his (Puccini's) "Humming Chorus" from *Madam Butterfly*.

Several well-known choreographers are advancing their views as to how the butterfly dancers should make their stage entrance – filtering from the left or right side of the stage – fluttering down from above – but Holmes considered that if they entered in globular transparent spheres that burst or opened on arrival on stage, the dancers could emerge safely to continue their opening dance routine. It all sounds very promising and Holmes is beginning to wonder if he chose the right vocation long ago. His two musical aides are both impressed with his musical talents. Charles Easton thinks Holmes is in no rush to return to his Natural Investigational Sphere.

Meanwhile, the combined efforts of the Nimbus 9 team have secured a worldwide peace and a ready willingness on the part of potential warring factions to comply with instructions and suggestions emanating from Headquarters, Nimbus 9.

There are settled democratic governments in most countries and the strength of the family unit is actively encouraged, even a world language cannot be too far off.

Holmes, ever the pacifist, admits there is still much to be done, but insists that with faith, just the size of a mustard seed, and hope (in abundance) there is every possibility of the emergence of a more charitable world.

In order to influence the previous warring nations, he proposes a visit to the vast wartime cemeteries in Flanders and France on occasions when they are visited by parties of schoolchildren and those accompanying them. He would like to erect a small sign at their leaving point reading:

You have visited the sleeping villages of those who fell in man's senseless inhumanity to man. Please, when you leave, promise to try to make this world a better place, where a German Mother, Kathe Kollwitz Weizz, pleaded, 'Nie mehr Krieg' (no more war) – thank you for your visit and a safe journey home.

A well-meaning gesture on his part but one wonders what the reaction would be?

Personally, as a peace lover, he deplores the vast areas covered with white memorial stones in their thousands and thousands – so sombre, so heart-wrenchingly still and silent – mute witnesses to a lost generation who might, just might, have made a better fist of those interwar years of long, long ago.

As his health improves he occasionally visits his two former defectors and the children in their care.

It is said that he is now their grandfather by proxy, and a wonderful storyteller and weaver of tales with happy endings, where the characters all live happily ever after.

It is hoped within Nimbus 9 that his services on that speck of dust will never be required again – as it enters its new Century of Hope.

Although he is ever ready to undertake his peaceful missions, it is believed that the very successful debut of his much-loved and appreciated ballet about the beautiful but so brief life of butterflies, has tempted him, with great encouragement, to attempt its sequel, *The Butterflies' Night Haven* – Peter Tchaikovsky admires his soaring opening chords and says it reminds him of his own scenic music in *Swan Lake* and Pathetique Symphony. I believe H.C. proposes to tell Holmes this one day – how nice it would be to eavesdrop on that occasion.

This is merely a fanciful tale, but, perhaps within its pages, lie traces of that supreme happiness that Charles Dickens so lovingly found for two of his favourite children, Philip Pirrip and David Copperfield, in Estella and Agnes respectively.

Sleeping Village
(Crete, 1941).

APPENDIX A

A MILITARY MISCELLANY

NOT MANY PEOPLE KNOW ABOUT MESSINES OR YNYSYBWL

Charles Stacey, born 1920, was a former Regular Soldier who had the privilege of serving under many fine British Officers. This small book is dedicated to their memory.

Charles lives in Bristol and his current hobbies are painting and reading German history

These four simple short stories about 'War and Peace' fall far, far short in content and concept of Tolstoy's classic book with the same title; at least, the length is different.

Cologne, Germany
May 1945

A MILITARY MISCELLANY

MORE THAN AN APOLOGY

In the midst of the Second World War, Douglas Stewart, a poet who was born in New Zealand but, since 1938, had lived in Australia, wrote the poem below – as one of his "Sonnets to the Unknown Soldier":

WE DID NOT BURY HIM DEEP ENOUGH;
BREAK UP THE MONUMENT, OPEN THE TOMB,
STRIP OFF THE FLAGS AND THE FLOWERS AND LET US
LOOK AT HIM PLAINLY, NAKED MAN.
GREET HIM WITH SILENCE
SINCE ALL SPEECHES WERE LIES,
CLOTHE HIM IN FRESH KHAKI, HAND HIM A RIFLE
AND TURN HIM LOOSE TO
WANDER THE CITY STREETS
WHERE EYES SO QUICKLY INURED
TO DEATH'S ACCOUTREMENT
WILL HARDLY SPARE HIM A GLANCE,
EQUIPPED TO DIE FOR US,

YOU SEE THAT FELLOW WITH THE GRIN,
ONE EYE ON THE GIRLS,
THE OTHER ON THE PUB,
HIS UNIFORM SHABBY ALREADY?
WELL, DON'T LET HIM HEAR US,
BUT HE'S THE UNKNOWN SOLDIER,
THEY JUST LET HIM OUT,
THEY SAY HE LIVES FOR EVER.
THEY PUT HIM AWAY WITH FLOWERS AND FLAGS
AND FORGOT HIM,
BUT HE ALWAYS COMES WHEN THEY WANT HIM.
HE DOES THE FIGHTING.

On the morning of the 7th November 1920, Major Ronald Hughes,

Royal Engineers, officer in charge of 79th Field Company, Royal Engineers, entered the adjoining office of his Company Sergeant Major Donald Miller in Belgium.

At his greeting – 'Good morning, Sergeant Major' – Miller rose easily from behind his desk.

'Good morning, sir,' he replied.

'Had this order from Brigade Headquarters this morning asking us to provide four wooden stretchers. Nothing elaborate required – just plain wood – deal possibly. What have we got left of that timber the chaps felled recently in the Ancre area?'

'More than enough for the job' was the reply.

'Well, I'll leave it to you, and by the way, when finished the items are to be collected by members of the 45th Field Ambulance, RAMC, who are arranging their disposal to the units mentioned in the order. Just give them a call and they'll come over and collect.'

'Right, sir,' Miller replied, glancing briefly at the order given to him.

When about to leave, the Major turned and said, 'My wife and I had an invite to a social do at Div HQ. It's tomorrow night and the maid's day off – I don't suppose there's a chance that you are free and could step in once again and help us out by being at our quarters and keeping an eye on Nicholas, is there? Shouldn't be late back, say 11 p.m. at the latest.'

Miller, who was awaiting the arrival on the station of his own wife and children, agreed at once . . . he had served as a corporal in the war recently over, in the 174th Tunnelling Company, RE, when Major Hughes had been a 2nd Lieutenant, in the same unit. In the Fricourt area of the Somme in 1916, the unit had tunnelled to a depth of eighty feet in hard chalk beneath the German lines. It was dangerous, nerve-wracking underground warfare with the Germans counter-mining. Once, during a counter-explosion, he had been trapped and it was Hughes who had dug through and rescued him. It was a close bond, that both, as regular soldiers, valued greatly.

He liked Nicholas, the four-year-old son. At his bedtime, the boy had always asked for 'one of your stories' before he went to sleep.

The usual routine went 'Many years ago across the sea, there lived a King who had a very handsome and brave son called . . .'

'Nicholas' was the boy's swift interjection.

Having settled the nomenclature, Miller would continue with the story suitably embellished with deeds of bravery and adventurous activities, until the soft breathing of the boy drifted him away to a dreamland of his own.

The brigade order referred to by Major Hughes, had been issued by Brigadier General M. Black, General Officer Commanding British troops in France and Belgium, who was also deputy director of the War Graves Commission.

In early October 1920, he had been informed that the War Office had agreed to the proposal that a body of an unknown British soldier would be recovered from each of the four main battle areas, the Somme, Arras, Aisne and Ypres and that the body eventually chosen was to be subsequently interred with all the dignity the state could provide in Westminster Abbey.

The initial suggestion that such a tribute should be paid to the grand total of 3,049,772 casualties in the war was made by a regimental padre of the East Surrey Regiment, to Dean B. Sides of Westminster Abbey. The latter approached Field Marshal Sir William Graser, GCB, KCB, CB, DSO, MC and bar at the War Office who considered it a sound suggestion but added a rider to the effect that the words 'unknown soldier' were limited to the military and that, possibly, the word 'warrior' be used to cover the navy and air force. Dean Sides was then advised to contact the King on the latter's return from Balmoral.

When so apprised of the proposal, HM King George allegedly was none too keen on the idea but, on giving the matter serious thought, became greatly interested in the plan, going so far as to contribute one of his antique swords from his private collection at Windsor, to be affixed to the eventual coffin, as 'a soldier's gift to a soldier'. Actually, he was more of a naval person for he liked boats and sailing.

Company Sergeant Major Miller duly contacted 45th Field Ambulance, RAMC, and four field ambulances, each containing an officer and two other ranks, the latter having shovels and sacks, arrived and a wooden stretcher was placed in each vehicle. The ambulances were then driven to their designated region being the battle areas mentioned in the brigade order. Not one of the four parties of officers and other ranks were to be aware of the true reason for the work to be undertaken, that being to find an unknown British soldier's grave and exhume the body found there.

They were told also to make certain that the body exhumed was in a state of advanced decomposition. This instruction seemingly was so that the Unknown Soldier gave off no putrid or noxious odour from decaying flesh in the hallowed precincts of Westminster Abbey. Of course, this may be merely hearsay, but it was stressed that there should be no need to cremate the remains of the dead soldier.

There were other provisions such as the choice of a body of a soldier killed in the early part of the war – possibly a regular soldier of the original British Expeditionary Force – rather than a soldier of an equally catastrophic military disaster with appalling and tragic losses, for instance the inexcusable slaughter of the Somme battles of 1916 – men and boys, almost all civilian volunteers of Kitchener's New Army. Such nitpicking after such a conflict entailing so many casualties scarcely does justice to those who fought, died, were wounded physically and mentally in the Great War for Civilisation, or to those who survived the frightfully contested battle lines.

Whatever the views of senior army officers in their minuted discussion, their views were totally wrong and did no justice to themselves in their blinkered views or to the many grieving kith and kin of those servicemen who died subsequent to the 1914/15 battles.

However, the four parties, as instructed, confirmed from items of equipment, clothing, etc., on or in the immediate vicinity of the body, that it was that of a British soldier. Should any means of identification be found on the body, another corpse lacking such identification was to be found and exhumed. The chosen body was then covered in sacking, placed on the wooden stretcher and taken in the ambulance to Brigadier General Black's General Headquarters (GHQ), some forty kilometres west of Arras. Their arrival times were staggered and, once their task was completed, they returned immediately to their respective units, so that no possibility of a collusion regarding each task and location existed.

The Reverend William Dear at GHQ examined each corpse, determined it was a 'British soldier' and could not be identified apart from that fact. The four bodies were then placed on their stretchers in a small hut that served as a chapel, each covered by a Union Jack.

It is from this point on that many accounts of what later took place in the hut in question, have been aired, and, indeed, published. One account is that once the stretchers had been placed side by side, all those concerned with the operation up until the moment retired to a distance and that an officer who had never been inside the hut previously was then blindfolded and led to the entrance of the hut. He entered and, with his groping hand, touched one of the stretchers. It was the corpse on this particular stretcher that was chosen to lie in state in Westminster Abbey.

Another account (page 17, *British Butchers and Bunglers of World War One* by Dr John Laffin [published in 1988 by Sutton Publishing Limited]) relates, 'As the war ended there came the poetic idea of the "Unknown Warrior", the victim who would forever represent all the dead servicemen of the war. A blindfolded British Officer "of very high rank" – a general, in fact – was led into a hut containing the remains of six unidentified soldiers brought from the various battlefronts. He then groped about alone until he touched a coffin. This was the one taken back to Westminster Abbey and buried with all the honours that the nation could provide.' The event was a symbolism of sacrifice at its best, a magnificent idea. It was also entirely fitting. Blinkered generals, blind to the realities of war, had caused the shocking casualties. It was appropriate that they then should choose the man to represent all the soldiers who had been butchered.

And yet another account (pages 8–9 Chapter 1 *A Great Day for Westminster Abbey: The Age of Illusion* by Ronald Blythe, Oxford University Press).

' . . . After the coffins had been laid side by side, everybody concerned with the operation up until this stage retired to a distance and an officer who had never been inside the hut previously was blindfolded and led to the door. He entered and his groping hand touched a coffin. And so was chosen the poor nameless flesh which would be followed through the streets of London by George V, the King-Emperor, on foot, and interred with every pomp and dignity known to the State in Westminster Abbey.'

But another more detailed account – addressed to the editor of the *Daily Sketch* newspaper in November 1939 is that of former Brigadier General M. Black, who wrote as follows:

Sir,

From time to time accounts have been published purporting to relate how and by whom the Unknown Warrior's body was selected in France for burial in Westminster Abbey on November 11th, 19 years ago. I should like to give here the authentic account of what took place.

In October, I received notification from the War Office that King George V had approved the suggestion and the proposal that the burial should be in Westminster Abbey on November the 11th. I issued instructions that the body of a British Soldier, which it would be impossible to identify, should be brought in from each of the four battle areas – the Aisne, the Somme, Arras and Ypres – on the night of November 7th and placed in the chapel of St Pol. The party bringing each body was to return at once to its area, so that there should be no chance of their knowing on which the choice fell.

Reporting to my headquarters office at St. Pol, at midnight on November 7th, Col. Gell, one of my staff, announced that the bodies were in the chapel and the men who had brought them had gone . . . The four bodies lay on stretchers, each covered by a Union Jack; in front of the altar was the shell of the coffin which had been sent from England to receive the remains. I selected one, and with the assistance of Col. Gell, placed it in the shell; we screwed down the lid. The other bodies were removed and reburied in the military cemetery outside my headquarters at St. Pol.

I had no idea even of the areas from which the body I selected had come; no one else can know it . . . The shell, under escort was sent to Boulogne . . . The next morning, carried by the pall-bearers who were selected from NCOs of the British and Dominion troops it was placed on a French military wagon and taken to Boulogne Quay where a British Destroyer was waiting . . . six barrels of earth from the Ypres Salient were put on board to be placed in the tomb at Westminster Abbey so that the body should rest in the soil on which so many of our troops gave up their lives.

Then HMS Verdun moved off, a guard of honour of Bluejackets at 'the Present' carrying that symbol which for so many years, and especially during the last few months, has meant so much to us all.

Yours etc.
M Black

Kendal, Cumbria Nov. 1939

But there remains one more account, the one that follows:

In the Public Record Office are kept certain documents relating to this historic event. The Vehicle Work Tickets in respect of each of the four ambulances involved in the transporting of the remains of the four servicemen. These were authorised journeys to expressed locations:

(a) Bazentin Le Petit (Somme area) – St. Pol   RETURN
(b) Flesquie?es (Cambrau area) – St. Pol   RETURN
(c) Gheluvelt (Ypres area) – St. Pol   RETURN
(d) Monchy-le-Preux (Arras area) – St. Pol   RETURN

Thus, it can be assumed that all four ambulance parties involved knew of each other's destinations, at different times, since they belonged to the same unit, namely 45th Field Ambulance. One authorising officer signed all four work tickets.

Employed at the GHQ, St. Pol, were several other ranks employed on routine duties, such as the unloading of the plain coffin of English pine delivered on the 8th November 1920 and placed by them in the chapel. The two other ranks involved in this task were Cpl Alfred Beasley, formerly of the 2nd Bn Middlesex Regiment, and Pte Lionel McDermott, formerly of the 6th Cameron Highlanders; both regular soldiers, involved in the Battle of Neuve-Chapelle, Flanders 10–13 March 1915 and the Battle of Looe, northern France on 25 September 1915 respectively. After the removal of the three bodies of the servicemen not selected by Brigadier General Black, they were involved in the reinterment of these remains in the military cemetery at St. Pol. Then, later, told to dispose of the remaining wooden stretcher on which the remains of the chosen body had once lain. It was during this task that Cpl Beasley discovered a small blackened circular shaped piece of human bone from the body concealed in between the wooden slat cladding of the stretcher. He retained this find and told no one of it except Pte McDermott. They broke up the stretcher and believed it was subsequently used as firewood within the camp precincts.

The item found by Beasley was carefully wrapped by him in a piece of cloth and sealed in an empty oblong tobacco tin and kept by him as a memento of the historic occurrence.

47

Contrary to what Brigadier General Black and others thought about the impossibility of identification of the body chosen, later described by him, as being 'mere bones', many of the other ranks in the command were aware of the significance of the events set in motion by the various orders from Brigade Headquarters. Particularly, was this so in respect of the party selected to escort the coffin and its poor, sad, contents to Boulogne on the following day, the 8th November 1920.

Those forming this party were:

(i)   Company Sergeant Major Donald Bell, RASC, 2 Brigade, 8th Division

(ii)   Sergeant T. Keane, Royal Engineers, 54th Field Company. RE, 3 Brigade, Guards Division, 5th Army

(iii)   Lance Bombardier C. Braithwaite, Royal Field Artillery, 4th Brigade, 18th Division, 2nd Army

(iv)   Trooper L. Storre, Australian Light Horse, 4th Brigade, 4th Australian Division

(v)   Private L. Jessop, 18th (W. Ontario) Bn, 4th Brigade, 2nd Canadian Division

(vi)   Private G. Edwards, 97th Machine Gun Company, Machine Gun Corps

(vii) Rifleman J. Harvey, 1/21st London (1st Surrey Rifles), 142 Brigade, 47th (London) Division

As Ronald Blythe writes in his book *A Great Day for Westminster Abbey: The Age of Illusion*, these companions of the body were humble enough – but, once at Boulogne, the superb elevation of their charge began. However, what has remained unreported for so long are the details of the military background and wartime experience of the party chosen to accompany Brigadier General Black's 'mere bones' of a body to its final resting place.

Company Sergeant Major Bell, Military Medal, Mons Star, 1914–1919 War Medal, General Service Medal, a former member of the 11th West Surrey Regiment, 1st Division, British Expeditionary Force, later fought throughout the Somme battles from July to November 1916, after taking part in the battles at Mons and Ypres in 1914/15. Wounded and downgraded, but secured a transfer to the RASC.

In the battle of Gheluvelt, Ypres on the 31st October 1914, as a lance corporal, he was the sole surviving non-commissioned officer of 'D' Company, 1st West Surrey Regiment. Of the 850 members of the battalion, only one junior officer, and thirty-two other ranks survived.

Sgt Keane, in September 1916 moved with his unit to High Wood on the Somme and saw hundreds of the British infantry dead, lying in rows like corn that had been mowed down. The smell was awful and countless flies smothered the faces of the dead.

The dead lay so thick that the company horses could not avoid running over them. The sight of these troops mown down by machine guns remained constantly with him and convinced him of the utter futility of war and the egotism of the senior officers who bungled in their methods at the expense of the lives of countless brave men. Lance Bombardier C. Braithwaite RA had once been a member of a firing squad detailed to execute a young soldier who, allegedly, was guilty of cowardice for which death was the ultimate penalty. The offender shot had been a good soldier up to the point of his desertion, but could take no more after seeing several of his field gun team killed by a barrage of German 8" howitzer shells during counter-battery fire.

Trooper L. Storre, Australian Light Horse, had fought in the Gallipoli Campaign between 25th April 1915 and January 1916 where the casualties totalled about 205,000, including nearly 26,000 Australian casualties of whom over 7,500 were killed. The entire campaign achieved nothing.

Pte L. Jessop, 18th Bn, 2nd Canadian Division, took part in the capturing of Vimy Ridge, Passchendaele, when between 4th and 9th April 1917 the Canadian troops suffered 11,000 casualties, he being one of the less severely wounded.

Pte G Edwards 97th Machine Gun Company, 5th Division, served as a Vickers machine gunner on the Somme in July 1916 when five of the six-man gun team were killed. He, alone, survived wounded and dug out of a sap. Also served as a machine gunner in the tank attack on Fleur in the same battle.

Rifleman J. Harvey 1/21st London (1st/4th Surrey Rifles), 47th Division, took part in the Battle of High Wood on the Somme when his brother was killed on 15th September 1916. Subsequently, the 47th Division was officially criticised for its 'lack of push' and its GOC dismissed for 'wanton waste of men' entrusted to his command. The division had lost over 4,500 men to secure an advance of about 100 yards of the German trench – every inch had cost a life.

These, then, were the seasoned and disillusioned men chosen to accompany the remains of a fellow soldier in an army ambulance to Boulogne.

At Boulogne, the British destroyer, HMS *Verdun*, lay alongside the quay. The ship (during the night) had brought from England, a great oak coffin, weighing almost two hundredweight. Two British undertakers, Mr Noakes and Mr Sowerbutts, placed the plain pine coffin, unopened, inside the casket of English oak, then secured the lid and sealed it.

The casket was placed on a French military wagon, drawn by six black horses and, with great and moving dignity to the strains of Chopin's "Funeral March", taken to the dockside on the Quai Carnot and taken aboard HMS *Verdun* and accorded the naval honours normally accorded to an admiral.

Prior to the departure of the vessel, six barrels of earth taken from the Ypres Salient had been delivered to Westminster Abbey to be placed in the tomb so that the body should rest in soil on which so many troops had died. A man who had been nothing and was now to be everything had a funeral convoy of six destroyers with flags at half mast, to escort it to Dover where it received a field marshal's salute of nineteen guns fired from the castle. From Dover it travelled in a specially fitted saloon carriage to London where it rested overnight in a temporary chapel at Victoria Station. On the following morning, 11th November, pallbearers arrived to attend the corpse on its journey across the city. In attendance were Admirals Merex, Beatty, Jackson, Sturdee and Madden; Field Marshals French, Haig, Methuen and Wilson; and Generals Home and Byng. Air Marshal Trenchard followed alone.

At the abbey, the grave had been dug just inside the west entrance, and, after committal it was filled with the earth from the Ypres Salient. A very large slab of Tornai marble was laid over it.

For a brief time it bore a simple inscription 'An Unknown Warrior'. But, further nitpicking occurred, on this occasion by the Dean of Westminster. Dean B. Sides insisted 'that in future time (1970) people will want to know who the Unknown Warrior was' and so compiled the many-worded inscription that it has to this day.

But, still the nitpicking went on when, later in 1921, the present black marble slab from Belgium replaced the Tornai marble slab. Mr S. I. Levy, principal of the Liverpool Hebrew School, wrote to the Dean regarding one of the texts insisted upon by the Dean.

The text was 'In Christ shall all be made alive.' Principal Levy wondered if the Unknown Warrior might have been of the Jewish faith and, in which case, the line in question did not appear to meet the spiritual destinies of both Jew and Gentile.

The Dean replied that it was not outside the bounds of possibility that the Unknown Warrior might have been a Moslem – or a Mormon – 'We cannot hope to please everybody,' he wrote. It all came to nothing, however, High Anglican tact remained firm.

Some forty-one years after this correspondence between the Dean and Principal Levy, a Maurice Hugh Frederick Wilkins, born in 1916, a New Zealand-born British biophysicist who, with James Watson, Francis Crick and Rosalind Franklin, discovered the structure of DNA (deoxyribonucleic acid), shared the 1962 Nobel Prize with Watson and Crick (Franklin died before the award was presented). Genetic fingerprinting via DNA profile became possible. So there were still eight years to go before the Dean's prognostication about people wanting to know who the Unknown Warrior was. It now became, perhaps, possible to obtain a DNA profile from the remains of the Unknown Warrior if this was deemed necessary. There had been many voices raised in the 1920s deriding both Armistice Day and the interment of the Unknown Warrior.

George Bernard Shaw argued that the disabled drag down wages and the standard of work, and should not be employed at all industrially. The duty of the country is perfectly clear. These men were disabled in its service and should be supported unconditionally.

Another echoed view was 'I think all this business about the Unknown Warrior cheap and tawdry – I would rather have spent the money on employing some life warriors, I suppose I am not as sentimental as I ought to be.'

Beatrice Webb's acid comment was that Downing Street had been barricaded lest there should be yet another, and still more impressive public ceremony – the funeral of an assassinated prime minister!

Others thought that remembrance of the dead should be combined with positive action to aid the living.

Evelyn Waugh deplored the whole idea on principle and derided it 'as a disgusting idea of artificial nonsense and sentimentality'.

The *Daily Herald*'s comment was 'Who organised this pageant? The people who prolonged the war and grew rich out of it and now dope the people emotionally.'

Siegfried Sassoon, the poet, was one of those sickened by what they saw as the sentiment and hypocrisy of the proposed ceremonies at the Cenotaph and the grave of the Unknown Warrior. He wrote the lines 'The Prince of Darkness at the Cenotaph Bowed. As he walked away I heard him laugh.' And, W. H. Auden, in his poem, 'The Horizontal Man' contrasted the pious platitudes about honouring the returning soldiers – 'the vertical man' – with the reality of their post-war predicament. Britain gave honour – or so he claimed – only to the 'horizontal man' – the Unknown Soldier who had no further demands to make of the society he had died to protect. His still-living comrades were no longer needed and were now ignored.

Even in 1916 at a meeting of the French war-wounded, one of the number said, 'Today we are welcome, but after the war no one will speak of us and work will be hard to find.'

In so many cases this proved to be true and even during the fighting, H. G. Wells, in a letter to *The Times* had written of asserting the need to shake off 'the ancient trappings of throne and sceptre' and men who had seen 'cities pounded to rubble, men who with little aid or guidance from their own rulers have chased emperors from their thrones, are pretty fully disengaged at last, from the Englishman's old sense of immutable fixity in institutions which he may find irksome or worthless'.

Like the 'cities pounded to rubble' so were the lives of countless other survivors of the conflict. Widows, those who had lost their husbands, fathers, brothers, sons, those who had hoped to marry, those who supported and cared for the maimed in body and mind – the Great War did indeed exact a random harvest – little wonder it was called 'Great' and the casualties, too:

	Officers	Other Ranks
Killed	37,876	620,829
Wounded	92,644	1,939,478
Missing or Prisoners	12,094	347,051
TOTAL	3,049,972	

And warring nations, each suffered accordingly:

Killed		
	Frenchmen	1,380,000
	Germans	1,935,000
	Russians	1,700,000
	British Empire	1,081,952
	United States	48,909
	Austro-Hungarians	1,300,000
	Italians	615,000
	Romanians	335,000
	Turks	325,000
	Bulgarians	90,000
	Serbs	55,000

All the nations involved had civilian deaths, in some cases almost as high as the military ones – all nations had their widows and orphans – as a result of the inane conflict – and all nations had to learn their history afresh within the space of twenty years – mourning became almost commonplace – a national numbness at the senseless, needless slaughter.

It was against this background that those engaged in the conflict decided to go their different way – isolationism, revenge, communism, pacifism, republicanism – were but some of the names given to national policies, adopted to safeguard their interests.

In Britain there was one family, the two sons and one daughter of former Cpl Alfred Beasley, whose health had deteriorated as a result of his war service and wounds, who had watched him suffer a painful death. During his better days he had told his children about his find in St. Pol many years previously, and explained its possible connection to the Unknown Warrior buried in Westminster Abbey. His eldest son, Charles Beasley, was given the small metal tin and its contents as he hoped to study medicine and was considered to be its suitable guardian. Eventually, Charles completed his medical studies and obtained a post as an assistant to Prof. Hugh Mortice, a Dutch biophysicist and his staff at a well-known university. The team discovered the structure of deoxyribonucleic acid (DNA) and shared the Nobel Prize in 1962.

Charles mentioned his father's memento to others engaged in the discovery and it was decided to subject the bone and its adhered particles to a DNA profile test – perhaps the first genetic fingerprint. Initially, the tests were not altogether positive, but later it was established that the blood group obtained from minute blood specks and hair follicles, had a particular condition. The sickle-shaped red blood cells indicated a form of anaemia, termed sickle-cell disease. The disease often affects people of African descent.

Such a disease is thought to shorten life expectancy because of the chronic damage to the tissues. There was, therefore, a distinct possibility that the Unknown Soldier had been a West Indian member of the armed forces, and perhaps even, in a pioneer capacity, employed on the dangerous duties of conveying supplies, etc., – all part of the logistical demands of those in the front line. Such work was vital and the German artillery shelled many of the roads, tracks, paths used by general service wagons. Those killed were buried in the immediate vicinity and this entire area was later the scene of fierce fighting, before being captured by the Germans in their breakthrough in late March 1918.

It would be quite possible that the Unknown Warrior in Westminster Abbey is not 'a Mormon or a Moslem' but 'inside the bounds of possibility', might have been a West Indian member of the armed forces. Perhaps, if this is the case, the Church of England's High Anglican tact, as evidenced by Dean B. Sides' remark, can still remain firm. The involvement of the Church's missionary arm, the Society for the Propagation of the Gospel in Foreign Parts in its use of slave labour to run its Codrington estate on Barbados between 1710 and 1834, needed far more than the apology for its culpability. The burial of one descended from an ancestor, who was a slave of the Church of England, in the hallowed precincts of Westminster Abbey, might ease the soul-searching and help bury the chains of the first holocaust.

But, whether it excuses the arrogance and pathological pride of the various army commanders on all sides responsible for the great slaughter in the Great War, is indeed, another matter. An apology there is still to be forthcoming.

The *Daily Telegraph*, Saturday 11th February 2006 (reproduced below).

Church's slavery apology 'is not enough'

Descendants of plantation workers want more than just a word.
LISA Codrington knew her ancestors were Anglicans like her and
that, almost two centuries, ago, they were slaves. But she did not
realise until recently that they were slaves of the Church of England.

The clue is in her name: Codrington. Slaves of British planters often
took the name of their masters and, until 1710, Miss Codrington's
forebears lived on the Codrington plantation in Barbados.

After that date, as she discovered for herself a year or two before
the apology in this week's General Synod made it clear to the rest
of us, the Codrington lands, and the hundreds of slaves on them,
became Church property.

The Codrington slaves, men like Devonshire Codrington, born
in 1776 and Lisa's many-times great-grandfather, did not become
free until 1834, when the Church, like all slave-owners, was forced
to release them.

Anglican culpability in the Caribbean slave trade can be traced
back at least to 1710, when the planter Christopher Codrington died,

leaving his 300-acre Barbados plantations to the Church's newly-established Society for the Propagation of the Christian Religion in Foreign Parts (SPG).

So Miss Codrington and her family are well-placed to comment on the Church's apology. "It's a good start," said the twenty-eight-year-old actress and playwright, who was born in Winnipeg, Canada, of Barbadian parents and now works as an actress in Toronto.

"But is that all? I don't know how I feel about the apology until I hear everything about it. Is it involving reparation? Is it involving further work, further education by the Church?"

Mention of reparation will send shivers down ecclesiastical spines, because many institutions, including the British Government, have worried about apologising for slavery in case they are asked to put their money where their mouths are. "The more they do the better they do," she added. "Slavery is not something you can say sorry for and then be done with it."

Miss Codrington has been in Barbados for a month, researching a play about pre-emancipation life, with her mother Hughlene.

Mrs Codrington left Barbados for Canada in the 1970s, but her daughter has been back several times, fascinated by how much detail she can find about her slave ancestry.

She feels that the Church of England will have got away lightly if nothing more than words come from its bout of self-flagellation. "People have gotten worse [punishments] for doing less," Miss Codrington said. She started to think about her ancestry when a teacher at her drama school asked her to write a monologue "in an accent" and she chose to do it using her mother's native Bajan dialect.

But she has not leapt straight into a quest to lay the blame for her ancestors' sufferings. "I am at the investigative stage right now," she said. "I am the sort of person who likes to understand why things are the way they are.

"I realised that some of these things, like names and faiths, may not have been necessarily matters of choice. They may have been imposed. For me it's more important to figure out why and try to understand it than to get angry." In north-east London Miss Codrington's aunt, Devenish-Scott, 48, an educational consultant had not heard about the Church's apology until told by *The Daily Telegraph*.

Although a Pentecostalist rather than an Anglican, she inclines to be forgiving of the Church of England's past sins towards her family. "I know that the Church, unlike the rest of the plantocracy in Barbados, established the first schools for black children there. "I am not saying that excuses what they did though, and it would be right for them to provide more now for the families of people who suffered. I don't think a lot of people knew then, and would be appalled, but it seems like an appropriate time to apologise."

In Barbados, Woodville Marshall, emeritus professor of history at the University of the West Indies, said the Church's sins over Codrington were those of omission more than commission. "They had professional planters to run the place," he said. "The Church didn't play an active role, because they were more interested in the receipts."

After the plantation was left to the SPG, its slaves were branded on the chest with the word "society", to remind everyone that these were slaves of the Lord. In 1740, thirty years after the Church took over, four out of every ten slaves bought by the plantation died within three years. "Most people in Barbados are not too troubled by these issues," Prof Marshall said. "It was not so much the SPG that the Church should be apologising for as the activities of the individual parsons who kept plantations and slaves for sheer profit.

"The bicentenary of the abolition of the slave trade, which falls next year, has prompted an uncomfortable bout of soul-searching in the Church of England.

"While it has been at pains to highlight the role of reformers in ending the trade, it has been less anxious – until Wednesday's General Synod debate – to acknowledge its own involvement. Most obviously, the Church's missionary arm, the Society for the Propagation of the Gospel in Foreign Parts, used slave labour to run its Codrington estate on Barbados between 1710 and 1834. The society's governing body included Archbishops of Canterbury, one of whom wrote in 1760: 'I have long lamented that the Negroes in our plantation decrease and new supplies become necessary continually.'

"Surely this proceeds from some defect, both of humanity and even of good policy. But we must take things as they are at present." Not all clerics were so accepting. Dr Beilby Porteus, a Bishop of London, spoke out against the trade and attempted to improve conditions for the slaves.

But the Church's general attitude reflected that of the prevailing culture, which assumed that slavery was part of the order that God had ordained on earth for centuries. In the 18th century the onus was on opponents of the slave trade to show that it was against the will of God, and only when abolitionists were beginning to gain ground did supporters tend to respond.

One attempt was a 1788 pamphlet by Raymund Harris, a Church of England clergyman, entitled Scriptural Researches on the Licitness of the Slave Trade, Showing its Conformity with the Principles of Natural and Revealed Religion.

The abolitionist movement, which was largely inspired by Quakers, Methodists, and evangelical Christians, began to turn the tide when ideas of social justice became more widely accepted.

SELECT BIBLIOGRAPHY AND SOURCES

The Unknown Soldier – Neil Hansen, Transworld Publishing – Doubleday

British Butchers and Bunglers of World War One – Professor John Laffin, Sutton Publishing

The Somme – Peter Hart, Weidenfeld and Nicolson

Science Desk Reference – Macmillan, The New York Public Library, USA

A History of the Twentieth Century – Volume Two, 1933–1951, Sir Martin Gilbert, HarperCollins Publishers

Voices and Images of the Great War

Bury The Chains (The British Struggle to Abolish Slavery), Adam Hochschild, Macmillan

The Daily Telegraph, Sat. 11th February 2006, Page 4

LACHRYMA CHRISTI
(TEARS OF CHRIST)

PART ONE
LIFE

CHAPTER ONE

The invisible tendrils of a January wind explored the cold grey platforms of Rome Railway Station and found themselves rebuffed by the kitbag, field-service packs and other army equipment of Corporal Charles Easton who crouched in their centre. The year was 1945, the third year of the Italian Campaign and, Easton, one of the few persons on the station late that night, awaited the arrival of a troop train which was to take him to Florence to rejoin his infantry regiment fighting the German and Italian armies high up in the Apennine Mountains just below Bologna.

He had spent the better part of the previous day travelling up to Rome from the infantry base depot to which he had been posted after being wounded in a battle near Lake Trasimeno in late summer the year before. He was no stranger to the Rome area, having slogged along the dusty roads to reach the Eternal City after the bitter fighting beneath the brooding heights of Monte Cassino. Throughout the four long Cassino battles between September 1943 and June 1944 in muddy winter and arid summer, his battalion had attacked repeatedly only to be repulsed by the formidable enemy whose shock troops were from the German 1st Parachute Division.

His battalion had suffered severe losses and he wondered how he had endured the artillery bombardments, the freezing nights and the scorching heat of high summer when the dust and poisonous reek of high explosives clogged the nostrils and the mind itself. The courage and fortitude of his companions in his section had been a mutual link between them. Without it he felt certain that he would have been unable to cope in the frequent night attacks during the winter. He had detested slithering in the wet mud, like the overburdened mules accompanying them. Following dirty-ribboned tapes, marking the minefields laid by the enemy in pathways through the rocky outcrops, they had fought ever upwards over the flint-hard mountain face. Forever with them were the ear-splitting cracks of the detonating shells, echoing and re-echoing in the dark mountain vastness.

Cold, wet, often hungry and always scared and weary, they had eventually fought their way to victory. How long ago it all was, he reflected, and yet here again it was night with the cold winds of winter chilling his extremities. He disliked these shrivelling winds; harbingers of death he called them, when the defences of the frail and mortally sick were finally overcome. At twenty-four years of age, he had seen too much of death and the useless sacrifice of both the brave and the craven alike, to delude himself as to the meaning of life in wartime. It was merely a case of survival until the quiet days of peace returned.

His stay in hospital with a gunshot wound in the fleshy part of his right hip had not been excessive. Once the two bright red-lipped wounds had finished suppurating and began to heal, he was discharged to a convalescent camp to make room for the more recent casualties. The camp had been pleasantly situated near the Adriatic Sea and, by late winter, he had fully recovered to be passed medically fit for return to his unit.

He had arrived in Rome shortly before midnight and enquiries of the railway transport staff had elicited little information, save that the arrival of the northbound troop train was expected shortly after dawn on the following day.

Advised either to avail himself of the waiting rooms in the station, or to obtain overnight accommodation in one of the nearby transit barracks, he had chosen to remain in his military cocoon of equipment on the platform. Drawing the collar of his greatcoat up about his ears and pulling his forage cap further over his rebellious mop of hair, he snuggled down to try to get what rest he could before the travelling rigours of the morrow. He dozed rather than slept and frequently banged his army boots together to engender some warmth into his cold feet.

As if from a distance, he heard a voice calling to him. With his gloved hands he brushed his eyes, blinked himself into wakefulness, and saw the person addressing him. He saw a girl of about eighteen years of age, very small and delicate of build with a young, pinched face peering out from what appeared to be an old fur coat at least a size too big for her. Her brown hair had natural waves, one of which fell interrogatively over her forehead. Her flat-heeled, sandal-type shoes protruded slightly from the hem of the coat. In a mixture of Italian and English, she spoke to him.

'*Voi, soldata, niente* train this night.' She glanced up the empty ribbons of railway track as if to make him understand her remark.

His command of Italian, although not over-strong grammatically, was sufficient for him to explain to her that he was aware that there was no train at present, but that there would be one arriving in the morning. His fairly fluent command of her language and use of its pleasantries of speech when addressing her as 'a dear young lady', obviously delighted her, and her rewarding smile warmed him inwardly.

He knew instantly and instinctively that she was probably one of the many girls who, because of the appalling difficulties in wartime Italy and the distress of the civilian population, sought the companionship of the troops, whatever their nationality. In return for army rations or other foodstuffs which they took home to their families or relatives, they gave all they had to give – themselves. Many of the younger girls were without parents who had been killed in the fighting or bombing attacks, and were looked after, as far as possible, by a distant relative. In the hard, uncompromising times, he had seen even small children already skilled in the stealing and cadging arts and generally living on their wits. It was a side of war he loathed and hated, having been an orphan himself from a very early age. The army had proved to be a refuge of sorts for him and, although he had been a regular soldier for over six years and was a comparatively seasoned campaigner, he detested this part of the war. He was never indifferent to the plight of the refugees and the bombed-out families, whatever their nationalities. Invariably, he had doled out some of the army canteen purchases to the children, their profuse, genuine thanks and their broad grubby grins as they clutched the odd chocolate bar and bore it triumphantly off home, made the war bearable for him. Children always found the thin side of his soldierly cynicism and he minded it not one bit.

His thoughts returned to the present. The girl's small, white face with its wide brown eyes looking steadily at him – how often he had seen that look before and implied its meaning. Rummaging in his army pack, he found the rations he had drawn at the depot to last him the journey and offered them to her. She made as if to accept them but first asked if he had sufficient food left for himself.

'Oh, lots,' he replied, laughingly, to dissuade further enquiry.

'Let me see?' she said disbelievingly, peering childlike into his army pack. She glanced up quickly, having completed her inspection of its contents. 'You haven't any left,' she said, almost incredulously.

'Well, I can get some more tomorrow,' he replied quickly. 'Don't worry, you take these home to your family.' As he spoke, he stuffed the loaf of bread, small amounts of tea, sugar and coffee, two tins of corned beef and other items into a small sandbag, wrapped the bundle as securely as possible and placed it in her arms. He then pulled his greatcoat closely about him and prepared to settle down amidst his equipment. She remained still and quiet watching him and, without a word, walked away. He glanced at her retreating figure and she turned and smiled enigmatically before her small figure disappeared from his sight.

With a warm, contented smile on his face, he pummelled his place of rest into a state of semi-acceptability. The cold brass butt of his rifle made a dull clanking sound on the concrete platform every time it slipped down through his cradled arms. With his hands stuffed deep within his overcoat pockets, his cap pulled well down over his eyes, he endeavoured to doze away the waiting hours. Engrossed in his bedding-down activity, he failed to hear the returning footsteps of his former companion. Suddenly she appeared before him, dressed as before, but without the foodstuffs he had previously given to her.

'I haven't anything else,' he remarked, jocularly, turning himself away from her and squirming into a more comfortable position.

'No, no,' she protested vehemently, and continued, 'my aunt has sent me to tell you that you must come to our flat and not sleep in the cold in the railway station.'

"You must have a very understanding aunt,' he replied, making no attempt to accept the invitation.

She ignored his reply and tried to pull him to his feet. 'Come quickly,' she insisted, her features set quite determinedly.

'Do you want me to come?' he queried lightly.

'Of course I do, otherwise I would not have returned to fetch you,' she replied, crossly.

He rose suddenly, expertly slung the packs and equipment over his greatcoat, buckled his belt, hoisted his kitbag on one shoulder and slung his rifle sling over the other shoulder. The rapidity of his actions and his instant decision to do her bidding, obviously pleased his companion, for her look of pouted determination had been replaced by one of almost maternal concern.

He was at least a head taller than the girl and with his equipment festooned about him, he thought they must have looked an incongruous pair as they walked out of the station. She remonstrated at his fast pace, which he slackened as she placed an arm within one of his crooked elbows. He listened attentively to her directions, and, during their brief walk, he learnt that her name was Nicola and that she lived with her aunt in a small flat in the immediate vicinity of the railway station. After their mutual exchange of names, she thereafter called him 'Carlo', which, she solemnly informed him was the Italian for his own name. Although already aware of this fact, he made no mention of it, and permitted her to correct his frequent mispronunciation of various words he used conversationally during their journey.

The streets were silent and dark and he presumed that some form of curfew was in existence. He glanced down at her small face and saw there a compound look of a young, innocent girl and a very worldly aware young lady. He was amused at first by the possessive care she displayed for him, but he realised very suddenly that such concern for his welfare had an underlying cause. It was much like the feelings he displayed when treating the wounds of men in his section during a particular action. Compassion and tenderness were very much evident in her feelings for him. He did not fully understand their significance, and it puzzled him a little.

He supposed it to be a sense of belonging very briefly in a way of living outside army life, every nuance of the latter was known to him. This meeting was strange and unexpected – a brief strand of intermission in the web and warp of war – between a world-weary soldier and a young girl who had befriended him late on a cold winter's night and with whom he was now walking along still quiet streets beneath the vast darkness of the sky overhead.

CHAPTER TWO

Very quickly they reached a flight of a dozen stone steps which led to the block of flats in which she lived. The effects of previous bombing raids on the railway station and its locality were much in evidence. Doorways had been shored up with bone-white pieces of wood, positioned almost like a series of crucifixes. Large sheets of tarpaulin covered some of the bomb-blasted areas, but still to be seen were splintered windows, tile-less sections of the roof, mounds of brick and, everywhere, mortar dust. It was a depressing sight, but once they had entered the small kitchen of the flat with the welcoming glow provided by a wood fire and low-watt electric lighting, he experienced a profound change of feeling. The girl's aunt, a buxom woman of about fifty years of age, had prepared a meal of spaghetti and grated cheese and, on the white tablecloth, he saw spread out all the foodstuffs he had given to the girl. Nicola quickly removed her coat and helped him to take off his equipment. He was given hot water and a towel and sent into the small room leading from the kitchen in which to wash himself. As he combed his unruly hair into some semblance of order, he heard them talking together as to where he was to be placed at the table. He re-entered the room and tried to get them to eat without him for he knew how difficult it was for them to manage domestically day by day. His objections were tactfully and laughingly ignored and he soon found himself clean and glowing seated with them.

It was a simple meal made all the more pleasurable by the lateness of the hour and their ready acceptance of him. Towards the end of the meal, the aunt, who mothered him constantly, produced a bottle of strong red sweet wine which, she informed him, she had kept since Christmas. Three glasses were filled to the brim and they asked him to make a wish as it was a very special wine called 'Lachryma Christi'. He got to his feet and looked down on them warmly. 'I wish,' he said, and then paused and smiled, 'that after the war is over, I shall come back to Rome and meet you both again.'

'Bravo, Carlo,' responded Nicola animatedly, clapping her small hands. The meal, and especially the wine, had a mellowing effect upon him and a fluency in their language he had not thought he possessed. His tales of army life, its fortunes and misfortunes caused his companions much amusement as he assisted them to clear the table and wash and wipe the plates and glasses. Arrangements were then made for him to sleep in Nicola's room, and, since Nicola's aunt made the suggestion, he presumed he would find a couch or bed in the room, in addition to Nicola's sleeping place. On entering her small room, which was sparsely furnished, he found but one bed with Nicola's fur coat serving as a coverlet. Perched on the two pillows was a rather bedraggled cuddly toy rabbit. 'That's Nicola's lucky charm,' explained the aunt as she left the room, bidding them both a pleasant night's sleep.

The aunt's ready acceptance of the sleeping arrangements at first puzzled him. He supposed, however, that in wartime Italy, the normal strait-laced attitude to such situations was no longer rigidly held. When accommodation and the means to exist were scarce and difficult to find, possibly the moral implications possessed less significance.

Nicola had undressed quickly, slipped a nightdress over her head and was already snuggled down in the bed.

'Hurry up, Carlo,' she whispered, 'I'm cold.'

Despite his service background and the accepted vulgarity on occasion of barrack life, he was basically shy and reserved by nature and had never before in his life slept other than alone. The hard iron cots with equally hard mattresses had been his lot in the orphanages and in the various army barracks in which he had been quartered. In the Libyan Desert in previous campaigns, the hard unyielding sand had been his resting place beneath the velvet sky and, as an infantryman in Italy, usually a trench with a groundsheet spread for protection covered him from the elements.

To hide his shyness, he turned his back towards Nicola and quickly undressed. As he removed his underclothes, Nicola, who was peeping above the edge of the sheets watching his every action, saw the harsh, red, barely healed wounds on his hip.

'Oh, Carlo,' she cried, and clambered across the bed and

embraced him. Her arms about the tops of his shoulders held him protectively as she repeatedly brushed her lips and cheeks against his back. In one swift movement, she drew him into the bed and extinguished the light.

He lay still in the darkness, aware of the gradual warmth of their bodies so close together. He longed to hold her softness against him but, despite the wine he had drunk, he could not overcome his inhibitions. He found that his feelings for her, prompted by a sense of compassion and respect for her honesty and warm-heartedness, were such that he could not consider their relationship purely on a physical level. Something else was present – a tangible awareness between them that this was not simply a casual meeting in wartime between a soldier returning to the front line and a Roman girl, less virtuous perhaps than she might have been, had not the war occurred. Their meeting was to be far more than a mere fleeting romance – that he knew for certain.

In the close darkness, Nicola smiled knowingly. She, too, knew that something different had occurred in her life. Her previous existence with its casual affairs with unknown soldiers, never intense, never lasting and, sometimes, sordid and cheap, was never to return. She vowed it in her heart and mind and made a small silent prayer that her dream would, one day, come true. She turned away on her side and pressed herself warmly against him, her fingers lightly seeking and tracing his wounds as if to comfort the torn flesh and make it whole and smooth again. Her soft caresses made him tumescent and, although he tried to ease himself gently away from her, she pressed the more insistently against him, well aware of his unspoken need of her. Suddenly she turned and in an instant entered into his waiting arms, their lips meeting blindly and urgently. Much later he kissed her soft eyelids closed, brushed the spun strands of hair from her damp face and held her closely and fiercely until she slept – her face calm and free from passion. With the warmth and serenity of her presence he, too, slept, and her softness and love dispelled forever the cold previously ever present loneliness within him.

CHAPTER THREE

Towards dawn's first light, wakefulness came. It was for him a natural reaction, for in the front line he and his comrades had always stood to and manned their dugouts to repel any dawn attacks by the enemy. Very few such attacks had ever developed, since the Germans, in the main, were strongly defence-minded and committed themselves usually to counter-attack to regain lost territory, or launched their own attacks at last light. However, he mused, old habits die hard, and he lay awake watching the first suffused light of the coming day seeping into the room. He looked down tenderly on Nicola, breathing lightly in the crook of his arm. Through the thin nightdress he saw the roseate hue marking her breasts, and felt her thin young arms holding him captive as if she too wished the moment of happiness to be never-ending. Her beauty for him came from within herself, it was incapable of definition and he knew only that she was the person for whom, either consciously or otherwise, he had been seeking all his life. It was far from being a case of mother-substitution, he knew himself to be too self-sufficient for such a need. The fact that they were different nationalities mattered not – the nature of their respective lives previous to their meeting was for him totally irrelevant. One could know many women or men physically and yet retain an inner purity. It was, he thought, all very much relative and human needs, as he knew too well, manifested themselves in so many diverse ways – food, sustenance, shelter, ego needs, affection and, always, love and companionship. All humanity required them in varying degrees for successful fulfilment of themselves.

She stirred within his arms, her body unconsciously making its silent demands of him. Very tenderly and lovingly, he placated them, and wordless and open-eyed, they lay together for a magical non-physical instant of time never to be lost.

'I love you, Carlo,' she said, breathing the words into his lips. He lifted a light wisp of her hair from across her eyes and kissed briefly her forehead. 'I know,' he replied simply. 'And I, you, young Nicola.'

There was an unspoken understanding between them that what had occurred was but a beginning and that it would be endless despite all the trials and tribulations that would undoubtedly follow their mutual decision to belong simply to each other. Already vaguely formulated plans were revolving within his mind and he knew he need not voice them for they were understood by Nicola. Their former life pattern, with its empty loneliness was behind them. There was a sharing and caring future to be considered. He knew the remainder of the war had to be endured and that he and his comrades were about to join in the very last battle of the Italian Campaign. He hoped desperately that he would survive the attacks yet to be made for he now had so much to live for.

They dressed and washed quickly and ate hurriedly the meagre breakfast Nicola's aunt had prepared for them. It was but coffee and bread, but it was their first breakfast together. He thanked her aunt for her kindness and received a warm embrace from her. She, too, knew that she need no longer fear for Nicola's future and that one day he would return. So little had been said, but so much had happened during the few brief hours following his arrival at the small bomb-scarred flat. Once outside, the cold early winds sought them and Nicola snuggled closer to the roughness of his greatcoat, her head against his shoulder. Since they were in good time to catch the train, Nicola took him to the Treviso Fountain where, as instructed by her, he tossed in a coin to ensure his return to the Eternal City. As the coin slid crab-wise through the water to the marbled bottom, she reached up and kissed him; just to make his, wish come true, as she explained.

Oblivious to the waking world around them, they sauntered slowly through the empty streets making plans. The beauty of Rome as a city was made more beautiful for him by his companion. The impressive squares, churches, statues and fountains seemed to have been built many years ago simply to make this particular morning with Nicola memorable. Her own beauty surpassed everything he saw. Perhaps one day, he thought, they might wander again through the city with time their ally instead of their enemy. As they walked he told her of the arrangements he would make to send to her his accredited army pay and a weekly amount to follow which she and her aunt were to use to augment their income and for any other purpose they chose.

Nicola, too, entered into the bargain by promising to put aside a little of the money she earned as a part-time helper in a local cafeteria. His remonstrance that such sacrifice was unnecessary failed to dissuade her and she remained adamant that it would help in starting their life together. She finally convinced him of the soundness of her decision by telling him that she could then afford the railway or bus fare to Florence or some other city or town behind the front line, where they might meet if he obtained local leave of absence from his unit. So intense became their mutual concern for each other during their discussion of the time they would be apart, that eventually they both laughed at the ridiculousness of the situation.

'Here we are,' he said finally, 'having met but yesterday arguing like a couple of long standing.'

She nodded excitedly in agreement. 'Yes,' she replied, 'isn't it wonderful. I'm sure we shall be like this for always, and very happy too.'

'You are incorrigible,' he spluttered, laughingly in English, and of course, had to translate the word to her as best he could.

The cavernous coldness of the station as they entered gripped him tightly within his body. The troop train, metallic and impersonal, stood alongside the platform with the usual military bustle and activity present. Officers were checking their drafts of men and non-commissioned officers allocating particular unit personnel to specific carriages. Seemingly aloof from it all were the military policemen controlling the troops boarding the train. He shrugged his army pack higher on his shoulders before taking Nicola suddenly into his arms and kissing her fiercely. She clung tightly to him, her smallness pressed close as if to defend him from whatever lay ahead. 'Goodbye, Carlo, my love,' she breathed as their lips parted and then clasped his cold hands within her own. He raised them and rested them gently against his cheek as their eyes met. 'Goodbye, Nicola,' he said quietly. 'I shall write to you every day in my best Italian.' She nodded in reply, her crooked little smile concealing the emotion within her. He swallowed hard as he turned away and handed his travelling documents to the transport staff before boarding the train.

CHAPTER FOUR

Quickly he thrust his equipment on the luggage rack and then stood by the carriage door looking at her distant, forlorn figure. Love and tenderness for her welled within him and momentarily he gave thought to leaving the train and rejoining her. At that moment he felt the train jerk suddenly, heard the sound of closing doors and with a convulsive series of tugs, the train slowly gathered motion. His eyes never left her figure and he remained looking in her direction even when the station walls and adjoining houses slid into his line of vision and she could no longer be seen.

Serious of face, he entered the crowded compartment, sorted his kit into a reasonably ordered state and then sat back in his seat. Gradually, the countryside came into view, farms tucked away in the hillsides, steep, snow-covered hills, rivers grey and brown in spate; and, everywhere in the background, the dreaded grey, snow-capped; mountainous chain. In every vista he saw the small, lovely childlike face of Nicola and he knew he loved her with every fibre of his being. The memory of their few hours together sent a joyous feeling surging through him – a sensuous, mentally satisfying mood of reflection settled upon him. Occasionally he would enter into conversation with the other troops in the carriage, most of whom were replacements and had never before been in the front line. Seeing the African Star ribbon on his battledress tunic and his corporal's chevrons, they sought his advice and opinion on various military matters to do with the campaign. All appeared a trifle apprehensive, but endeavoured to conceal their true thoughts by small acts of bravado. He warmed to them, but continually his thoughts returned to Nicola and his plans for their future together.

Although aware of the official line on non-fraternisation, he dismissed it with a mental shrug. He and Nicola would be married soon. Whether in Italy or elsewhere, did not really matter. His regular service engagement of seven years in the army had but a few months to run and, although he knew his services would be retained for the duration of the war, he knew he would be one of the first servicemen to be demobilised. With his experience of the years of travel and discomfort, there would prove to be very few difficulties he would not be able to overcome. He thought of his first letter to her and wished that his studies of Italian had not neglected the written word. His oral command of the language was such that he had been offered a post in the Battalion Intelligence Section, but he had declined the post in order to remain with his section with whom he had endured so much. His services as an interpreter had always been in demand, especially when his platoon had been resting out of the front line. With an ingenious use of local dialects, learnt by ear, he had obtained wine, eggs, fresh vegetables, even the odd chicken, from the intensely suspicious farming communities high up in the hills and mountainous area. His exchange of army rations had always been done on a fair basis and he had kept rigidly to bargains struck. He liked the hardy mountain people. He never knew that many of his 'parishioners', as he called them, often spoke of him with affection and wished that one day, 'Carlo' would return with his infectious brand of humour and flippant indifference to the difficulties of life.

From his battledress he removed his Italian notebook and a very dog-eared English/Italian dictionary and, with references to it, began to compose his very first letter to Nicola. 'Cara Mia' might be his first salutation, he thought, but then decided that 'My very own Nicola' would be much more acceptable.

As the day wore on, the scenery altered and soon the truly beautiful city of Florence came into view in its setting amidst the hills of Tuscany. But, ever deep in the background, was the grim-looking Apennine chain. The clouds obscured the peaks but he felt their cold hostility through his clothing. The train halted in some railway sidings where lines of drab-coloured vehicles were drawn up awaiting their arrival. In the half-light he and his colleagues were quickly marshalled into unit replacement formations and allotted transport. With several others, he clambered over the tailboard of a three-ton truck, helped stack their army equipment at the rear and along the sides of the truck's interior, caught the ration packs slung aboard each vehicle, and then settled down as comfortably as possible for the journey ahead. In each of the individual ration packs there was a small bar of chocolate and he removed his bar and placed it in his small haversack. It was for Nicola and he reflected that he might have amassed a small store of such bars by the time they met again.

Later, as the trucks ground in slow gear up the twisting Borgo San Lorenzo road, he saw everywhere on the roadsides the devastation caused by the recent shelling. Whole forests of once beautiful trees stood splintered and dead in shell-pocked desolation. Everywhere lay black and orange fire-gutted tanks and half-tracked vehicles. Tank turrets, once used by the enemy as strongpoints, and now blasted from the tenacious earth and concrete by shellfire, pointed in crazy angles towards the darkening sky. Cruel barbs of rusty wire, packs, letters, shell-cases, ammunition boxes, helmets, rifles – the entire flotsam and jetsam of modern war was present, except the dead. They had been removed by War Graves Commission personnel, ostensibly for moral and ethical purposes, but he could not escape the thought that the speedy removal of the dead had morale-boosting implications.

The young soldiers with him, some but nineteen years of age, gaped open-mouthed and stared wide-eyed at the fought-over battlefield. This was war at its bitterest – a fierce, brave, stubborn enemy skilled in the so-called arts of war, but, although the German troops did not accept it, they were already beaten by their dogged adversaries. Then there were the elements – utterly indifferent to both sides. The frozen mountain winds, the snow, the steel-tipped lances of rain lashing all, quite indiscriminately.

Long before the others in the truck became aware of the sound, he heard the thudding of the artillery in the gun lines. The reports reverberated like thunder along the mountain ridges and he weakened momentarily in his bowels. It had always been this way, first a marked loosening of control and acute physical fear, and then, slowly, the disciplined tightening of nerve and sinew. Finally, but, gradually, the forced humorous cynicism born of experience and the need to hide one's innermost thoughts and feelings. This time, however, he wished not only to survive the coming battle, but also to remain unwounded and to return to Nicola and life itself. His introspective thoughts were intruded upon frequently by his companions and he found himself explaining the difference between the heavier 105mm guns and the medium 25-pounder guns in the artillery lines. He indicated to them the mule lines and camouflaged ammunition dumps in the rear areas and generally provided a sense of security for the younger soldiers. His companions became quiet as the military activity lessened and they approached the front-line area itself.

'It's a bit lonely up here, Corporal,' one youngster remarked, and the truth behind the lad's statement intrigued him.

'Well, we are a sort of select company up here,' he replied with an understanding grin. 'We call it the sharp end, but it has its compensations,' he added mysteriously.

'Such as what, Corporal?' queried another soldier, insistently.

'No drill parades, kit inspections, regimental guards and that sort of thing,' he replied. He left unsaid any mention of the discomfort, fatigues, night patrols and the ever present feeling of revealing one's fear. These things they would learn soon enough for themselves; why disillusion their youthful confidence and optimism, he reasoned. Perhaps in time they would acquire the knowledge that the way to survive both mentally and physically was to think of oneself as possessing a personal immunity; that others would be wounded or killed, but not oneself. It was a ridiculous assumption but, strangely enough, seemed to work in some cases. He had found that it was of paramount importance to avoid developing a moral insensibility amidst the brutality of modern war. The intense comradeship amongst those actually fighting helped considerably in this respect. He had witnessed the tender care given unstintingly to the wounded and the dying; had helped steady the stretchers harnessed to the mules as they made their stumbling way down the mountainside to the Regimental Aid Posts. He had seen the consideration given to the children, women, the old and infirm driven from their homes by the ravaging shellfire and bombing attacks. Altogether, he had seen too much of the stupidity of war and knew that in the end there were 'no winners'; all were losers in some way or another. What was it a Mr Jones, a Welshman once said? 'War is the sport of kings and the trade of hired assassins.'

His further reflections were cut short as the truck whined to a halt. Through the open canvas canopy of the vehicle he saw the deep layers of mud on the rutted road surface. The different tyre patterns of gun limbers and vehicles, hoof impressions of the mules, were all imprinted for an instant only before the bitterly cold winter rain washed them away.

The mist rolled down the mountainsides and added to the grey, discomforting picture, but within an hour he was with his former section billeted in a shell-battered farmhouse. He caught up with the various happenings in his absence, noted the new faces and made the necessary acquaintances. Satisfying himself that all his men had eaten and had adequate shelter, he turned to his own affairs. He found he had been allotted a bunk on a heaped stack of old sacks on which he spread his groundsheet and blankets and settled down.

Within the room it was tolerably comfortable, the boarded-up windows having been covered with blankets and old sandbags. A wood fire blazed in the large open hearth and light was provided by hurricane lamps hanging from the beams. Before commencing his letter to Nicola, he glanced quickly at the various weapons held by the section. Finding them all clean and serviceable, with a clear conscience, he began to write. With frequent references to his dictionary which tended to interrupt his train of thought, he soon completed the letter. He enclosed several lira notes in the envelope and knew that the eventual delivery of the letter and its contents posed no difficulty since he had previously made arrangements with his colleagues in the Divisional Transport Section whose duties frequently took them to Rome to collect mail, rations and other items of freight.

CHAPTER FIVE

A week before his section left reserve duties to return to the front line, he received Nicola's reply and his secret worries that all might not have been well with them were immediately dispelled when he read her opening lines. That she had couched them in simple Italian for his benefit was evident, as, too, was the love and affection she undoubtedly had for him. In every alternate paragraph she mentioned the fact that she longed for them to be together again with only her lucky rabbit for company. She gave him news of her aunt's welfare, her own busy activities, and mentioned that she would be able to get to Florence whenever he could manage to obtain some leave. Apparently, her aunt had arranged accommodation for them with relatives whose farm-cum-vineyard was but a short distance from Florence itself.

With this news warming him inside like a brazier, he returned, with his section, to the front line. For two whole weeks they endured the elements and spasmodic shellfire, but they were not called upon to mount any attacks. The bitter winter weather, with frequent heavy snowfalls simply did not permit a resumption of the offensive. Until well into late March it was a case of tours of duty in the line and then behind in support positions.

As winter slowly and reluctantly permitted the green fingers of spring to dress the land, he learnt of the moves preparatory to the huge Spring Offensive. That it was to be the final battle of the campaign was evidenced by the increased aerial activity, the accumulation of large stocks of ammunition, reinforcements of both men and armoured vehicles, flame-throwing equipment and amphibious vehicles for river crossings. He had seen too many similar battle preparations to be mistaken in his belief. Confirmation came when his division was warned to leave its mountain sector and move into its attack jumping-off positions near the bank of the River Senio to the south east of Bologna.

The brigade to which he belonged was withdrawn from the line to rest and plan for its part in the attack. Local leave was granted and he immediately wrote to Nicola and gave her the probable date of his arrival in Florence and suggested a meeting place near the Ponte Vecchio, the only bridge spanning the River Arno, left comparatively untouched by the German Army in 1944, the previous year. The days before their reunion sped by, bringing with them three further loving letters from her. These he read over and over again before adding them to the neat bundle of her letters in his haversack.

They eventually met when the buds of spring were just breaking. Although he had thought often of the moment of their meeting, he found he was strangely unprepared when he first saw her waiting for him. For a moment her loveliness blinded him and she seemed to be even younger than he remembered, even though but three months had passed since their first meeting. She stood still, awaiting his approach, her soft hazel eyes wide beneath her delicately arched brows. Her parted lips were cold for but an instant before his own melted into them and she was, where she always belonged, within the secure strength of his arms. Oblivious to everyone and everything, they stood, hands linked, committing each other to shuttered memory; then came a fractional sliver of shyness between them as if to permit a re-avowal of their mutual love.

Dreamlike, they walked through the major streets and squares, simply happy in each other's company. Great monuments, churches and public palaces conveyed a vivid sense of the past, but it was the present they shared most. Later, in the crowded, rattling bus they sat close and he smelled the beauty of her. Her brown curled hair intoxicated him with its myriad scents of fresh spring air and sunshine, the faint warm smell of her naturalness and even the well-remembered hints of Rome, their first meeting place. She, in turn, buried herself in his rough masculine tenderness, showing her need of him in her every look and with soft-gestured possessiveness. Endlessly, he repeated within himself, 'God, how I love you, Nicola.'

He knew himself to be reasonably competent and decisive in battle situations, well able to lead his men by example and self-denial, but here, with Nicola, he was a man so much in love that he was prepared to indulge her every whim if only their joyful happiness might continue indefinitely. This, she knew by intuition, but was also aware of the quiet strength his protective love gave to her and accepted this as a gift bestowed upon her especially.

They alighted from the bus some distance from the small stone farmhouse in which they were to stay during his brief leave period. Shouldering his army pack, he cradled Nicola with his other free arm and they walked along the track edged with the tender green blades of spring grasses and early flowers. Their pace was slow and deliberate as if they were determined to eke out their moments together. Nicola's relatives met them outside the farmhouse. Alberto, a tall, kindly man, whose hands bespoke a lifetime's work on the land and who had been a stalwart member of the local Partisan Group when the Germans occupied the area and then came his wife, Maria, a smile creasing her round nut-brown face; equally as hard-working as her husband. Their own children had grown up and had emigrated to America and he and Nicola found themselves accepted most readily as a part of a suddenly enlarged family. Nicola, who had arrived the previous day, led him to the small room provided for them. He noted her small suitcase on the bed, the toy cuddly rabbit with its one buttoned-eye look perched in the centre of the two pillows on the bed, and then saw a vase of small flowers on the top of the chest of drawers, their fresh colours reflecting narcissus-like in the polished surface of the wood. They exchanged amusing, caring glances simultaneously; their night together in Rome and her frequent references to their bedtime company – the rabbit – uppermost in their thoughts. He lowered his pack to the floor and slowly lifted her hands to his lips and pressed a kiss within each palm. Equally slowly and deliberately he replaced her arms by her sides.

Before the evening meal, they walked together in the surrounding countryside. With their arms linked they ambled along the lanes, talking and laughing the time away. Although utterly indifferent to time itself, they were captivated by their surroundings, the peace and tranquillity of which touched them mutually. He had realised that Italy in early spring was beautiful, but never quite like this. In these parts the callous scars of war were not readily seen, possibly because of the rapidity of the German withdrawal, and, in any event, the main defence line lay further to the north beyond the high mountain ridges.

As the evening shadows lengthened and placed their coolness upon the land, they retraced their steps. For both of them it had been an idyllic interlude in which their love had been reaffirmed beyond all doubt.

CHAPTER SIX

Immediately after their meal, they were ushered off to their room, their offers to help in the domestic chores kindly, but firmly rebuffed by Alberto and Maria. It was as if all present knew that each passing moment possessed its own precious charm and was vibrant with life and love. Nicola did not speak of the time when his short leave would end, nor of the last battle in which she knew he would be involved. It was enough simply to be with him and to know that she possessed his love entirely.

They lay close in the darkness of the room, her head upon his chest, his arms cradling her. Outside the uncurtained window, a light wind caressed the wooded hills and occasionally murmured against the windowpane as if seeking entry. His fingertips brushed her bare rounded shoulders as they talked quietly.

'Carlo,' she said, almost dreamily, 'do you think that love like ours is known to us in a moment?'

'Yes, I think I do,' he conceded, after a thoughtful pause. 'But what prompted you to ask?' he added, inquisitively.

'Well,' she replied, "we met so briefly and yet we both knew, didn't we?'

'Nicola, my love, if something so important is not known to us in an instant, it will never be known in a lifetime.'

'But we recognised it so suddenly,' she persisted, gently.

'Perhaps it was natural affinity,' he replied, drawing her warm young body closer to him.

"What's affinity, Carlo?' she enquired, her small slender finger tracing designs in the hollow of his neck.

He kissed her tenderly, before replying. 'I suppose,' he said creasing his forehead as if to seek the apt reply, 'it is like seeking treasure which only you know exists, but are unaware of what it looks like, and then actually finding it in a place where you least expect to find it.' His lips brushed her fluttering eyelids through which the faintest shadows of her eyes could be seen. 'Such as you, Nicola,' he said, finally.

Her eyes opened and she looked up at him. 'I like that, Carlo,' she said, smilingly, 'That's like poetry.'

'And so are you to me,' he replied. 'But you know that already, don't you?' he queried teasingly.

'Mmm,' she murmured archly, her soft hands exploring him. 'And I have affinity with you too,' and guided his hands in confirmation. Suddenly, her coral lips blossomed against him and he knew a world of untold delight as if he were being taken through passages hung with burgundy red tapestry, carpeted with softest fur. New vistas constantly unfolded before him until fevered ardour gave way to an exquisite languor and they both slept. She curled delicately against him, lest in the fluid, jewelled darkness, he slip away.

Later, in the night, he fought himself to the surface of wakefulness from a hazy nightmare in which he had been intensely alone. He remembered becoming colder and colder as his searches failed to find Nicola and his vision of her fading dully the longer the searches went on. Dimly, above his head, he saw the ceding, then his eye traversed the walls and, finally, he saw her warm still body beside him – faint blue shadows beneath her eyes. He lay motionless beside her and then, suddenly, with a sigh of relief that the nightmare had gone and he had found her, he clasped her sleepy body and held her desperately; desire and fear within his heart. The night was thereafter timeless and they saw it merge slowly and beautifully into breaking day. Maria brought them coffee and remained for a short time sitting at the foot of the bed discussing with them plans for the remainder of their stay. He expressed the hope that he and Nicola might be allowed to help about the farm and in the vineyards, for he wished to repay the many kindnesses and human understanding extended to them.

Maria was delighted at the suggestion and avowed that before his leave finished, Alberto would make a farmer of him and that Nicola would become a farmer's wife. It was said with such light-heartedness that, when Maria left them, they laughed at the notion, but, nevertheless, were pleased at the prospect of helping. She cupped his stubbly chin and the lean sides of his face in her small warm hands and gazed seriously at him. Her hazel eyes were wide with concern and tenderness and he knew he could never envisage life without her. Later, like a small child, she watched him shave and seemed so interested that he was compelled to ask if she had seen such activity before.

'Not someone I love so much,' she replied, bestowing a winsome smile upon him. She had told him previously of the loss of her parents during a bombing raid on Naples where they had once lived, and of the want and hardship she and her aunt had subsequently endured. It had been intended as a prelude to her explanation of the style of her life she had followed before their meeting, but he had kissed her explanations away. He had not wished to know of the other soldiers who had entered her life – it was not important to him. That they had found each other gave life its true meaning for him. It was enough. Apart from the comradeship he shared with his section, his life, too, had been comparatively empty and purposeless, before Nicola had entered it. He had always needed someone like her to provide his life with real meaning; to enable a natural expression of the love and affection within him and to return it in full. He finished shaving, dried his face and pulled her gently towards him. 'Do you know, young lady,' he said with a soft smile about his lips, "what Victor Hugo said about us?'

She shook her head negatively, querying the question with her eyes.

'He said that the supreme happiness in life is the conviction that we are loved.'

'Did he really say that?' she asked.

'Well, the saying is attributed to him and he was a great French writer, so I suppose he wrote it for a Nicola and a Charles who lived in France when he was alive.'

'I like him for that one saying alone,' she said, decidedly.

'Of course, he wrote many other things,' he explained.

'Have you read them, Carlo?'

'Not all of them – only *Notre Dame* and *Les Misérables*, but I hope to read his other books one day.'

'We'll read them together, Carlo? In our very own house one day when all work is done and the whole world and all time is ours.'

'I like you for that one saying alone,' he said, chidingly.

CHAPTER SEVEN

During the rest of the day he assisted Alberto whilst Nicola helped Maria. In the spring sunshine, he and Alberto worked hard and their conversation naturally turned to the bitter warfare being waged to the north. He learnt that his companion had been a member of the Committee of National Liberation and had taken part in many partisan battles against the Germans in and around Florence. Alberto told him of the reprisal action of the Germans in March of the previous year following a partisan attack on a detachment of fifty soldiers from South Tyrol. The Germans had taken 335 hostages to the Ardeatina Tunnels, outside Rome, where the SS troops had shot them and then mined the tunnels to bury the bodies. Alberto told the story in a matter-of-fact tone, but there was no mistaking the hatred he felt for the German troops concerned.

They spoke too, of the Italy of Dante and Michelangelo and of the First World War when Alberto fought high up in the cold passes of the Alps against the same enemy. Despite its misfortunes, Alberto obviously had a great love for his country and its music. In a rich baritone voice he would sing snatches from various operas as they worked together.

The two remaining days of his leave saw them both working busily about their respective chores inside and outside the farm, but, each afternoon, with the tacit consent of Alberto and Maria – their 'bosses' as they called them, feelingly – they wandered off into the adjacent countryside. Already the days were warmer and they soon found a space high on the hillside where, protected by the rocky outcrops, they would sit, talk and gaze at far-off Florence, spread out before them. Nicola would indicate the Duoma, the medieval towers and endeavour to tell him a little about the Florentines of the Renaissance period. Her schooling had been as scanty as his own, but she became beautifully articulate when conjuring up for him the inhabitants of the Florentine yesterworld.

She told him of the Tuscan spring following the damp bleak

winter, and of the visitors, pilgrims, merchants and other travellers who, like tourists, would reach their peak at Easter time. She regaled him with a long cycle of the religious festivals and the numerous holy holidays of the patron saint of Florence, John the Baptist, whose feast day began on the 24 June every year.

He listened attentively to all she told him, and wished all history could be made so real and true in descriptive terms.

'Perhaps,' he interjected, 'we might be here together on the 24th of June, if the war is over by then.'

She caught his mood and excitedly said, 'And you might be stationed in Florence and we could come up here in the hills and have our very own "picnic-feast".'

'Wherever we are on that day,' he said seriously, 'I shall always be thinking of you and loving you, Nicola, so don't mind too much if our wish doesn't come true.'

She sensed his thoughts had gone from the present to the days yet to come before the war was over. She drew him close to her, pressed his head lightly against her breasts and caressed his cheek. 'Don't worry, Carlo, my love,' she said softly. 'I know in my heart that one day we shall be together for always.' She held him tightly as if to shut out all the intervening coldness and loneliness of the war and its demands upon them.

He turned upwards in her arms, bent her lips to his own and kissed her lightly. Thereafter they spoke no more of the time of his leaving.

On the morning of his last day with them, Alberto told him of the arrangements made for Nicola to stay at the farm until the spring battles were over when effective plans could be made for their marriage and future. He and Alberto were of similar mind and outlook both regarding work matters and Nicola's welfare, and he knew she would be well cared for in his absence.

The vague, tenuous future held no terrors for him, for he knew in his innermost being that his actions were morally correct and that all would be well in the end. That night, with her soft innocent face close to his own, he felt himself to have been charged with the safekeeping of a very precious person. All previous events in his life appeared to have been intended that he might all the more appreciate the priceless love given to him so warmly and openly by the young girl who lay quietly beside him. Her face was serene and tranquil in sleep, her slightly parted lips revealing her small, white teeth. He lay awake for a while guarding her against the night, his arm beneath her shoulders growing gradually numb even with her light weight upon it. He thought of their tender love-making before she slid away to sleep when her eyes brimmed with both softness and a form of wanton passion, as if she wanted their last night together to be inscribed permanently in their hearts and minds.

Before dawn, a deep contented sleep claimed him and he awoke to find that Nicola had quietly left him and prepared their light breakfast. She had also packed his few items of kit and personal effects in his army pack on top of which she had placed her small Saint Christopher medallion on its thin filigree chain.

'But it's yours, Nicola,' he had protested, when endeavouring to return it to her. 'No, Carlo, it's ours and will bring you safely back to me,' she replied, with soft insistence.

They had discussed but briefly their respective religious views and beliefs and there was complete accord between them as to what constituted a good or bad life. As a young boy, he had had the teachings of the Church pumped into him, but had long ago learnt for himself the true meaning of Christianity – it was not always to be found in churches or stately cathedrals. For him, it was to be found in the eyes and in the hearts of mankind itself and manifested itself quite clearly when encountered.

In the vicious artillery bombardments below the heights of Cassino he had prayed often into the earthen walls of his dugout as the violence shattered the world immediately about him. Such prayers as he made now were always for the well-being of Nicola and a continuance of their mutual love. He asked for no more than that, and the more tangible, material things, did not interest him. He was certain that he would eventually find work of a suitable nature and with sufficient remuneration to enable him and Nicola to lead a useful life together. Perhaps, even, he mused, they might one day have a family and imagined most vividly a daughter as loveable and warm-hearted as Nicola herself. He smiled inwardly at the pleasing prospect, but that was for the future to decide. At present, there was the moment of farewell to consider – a thought he had purposely deferred ever since their meeting in Florence only a few days before.

He was aware that Nicola would show distress at his leaving, but it was shared in an equal degree by Alberto and Maria. Both hugged him close and kissed his cheeks in the true warm-hearted manner that Italians had with close friends.

"You have always a home here with us, Carlo,' Alberto said feelingly, and then added, almost gruffly, 'Don't forget us, *Amico*.'

'I'll never do that,' he replied, grasping Alberto's huge extended hand.

Nicola had his pack ready, but before leaving, he took Maria's hands within his own and kissed them lightly. He raised his eyes to hers, bent forward and then kissed her cheeks. 'Goodbye, Maria,' he said gently. 'Take care of Nicola for me.' Maria nodded dumbly and went to Alberto and clasped him protectively.

He turned away from them and saw Nicola, a sad, brave half-smile on her small face, ready to accompany him to the path leading to the distant roadway. His parting wave to Alberto and Maria returned and with Nicola at his side, he walked towards the road where he knew he would be able to obtain a lift on a passing military vehicle into Florence. Before reaching the road edge, he stopped and drew Nicola tenderly and finally towards him. 'Goodbye, my only love,' he almost whispered. Her lips sought his and she held him close until he felt her warm tears seal their farewell kiss – this saltiness a part of her inner self being entrusted to his care.

He withdrew slowly from her embrace and walked away. At the road verge, he glanced back, acknowledged her final wave, and then set out in the direction of Florence.

PART TWO

DEATH

CHAPTER EIGHT

His pace responded to his subdued mood. His boots on the metalled road surface beat out his thoughts. 'I love you, Nicola, I love you,' they echoed repeatedly. He looked back but a curve in the road concealed the farm and the small track where he had left his reason for living. Again, he entertained the same thought as he did when they parted in Rome, but a strong sense of duty prevented him from flying back to her. The sound of a truck behind him caught up with his thoughts and quickly he flagged down the driver and co-driver and obtained a lift in the vehicle. Flinging his pack over the tailboard, he clambered aboard and made himself secure on one of a number of wooden crates forming the vehicle's load.

He was oblivious to the passing scenery and let his thoughts travel down the paths of memory; of the days and nights with Nicola. Her image was ever before him and his heart went out to her for the tears she had shed for him. No one ever before had provided him with such unselfish love and sweet-scented warmth.

On arriving in Florence, he was singularly fortunate in securing further transport and, towards late afternoon, he alighted, somewhat stiffly, from a Jeep in which he had been taken to the headquarters of his brigade. Then followed the assembly of all leave personnel and within an hour he was again with his section. During the evening meal, they all discussed their various adventures and events during their brief leave period, but he kept his innermost thoughts locked within him when taking part in the discussion.

Three days of preparation, various inspections and explanations of the plans for the coming offensive followed, before his platoon left its rest area and, in a motorised convoy drove over the spine-ridged Apennines and entered Forli, a small town on the highway leading from Rimini through Bologna to Milan.

At first, he found the flat farmlands, banked rivers and the Adriatic Sea bordering the front line, very strange and oddly peaceful after the mountainous confines. Everywhere he saw the metalled sinews of modern war. Artillery, battery upon battery in sandbagged pits covered with blotched camouflage netting. Tanks, with lethally pointed 75mm guns, muzzles covered, squatting, squadron after squadron, beneath the trees. As they approached the front line beyond the flat skyline, he saw the usual shell craters mostly full of black, still water because of the low-lying land. On the rear of a flood bank of the River Senio, he and his section dug their trenches, put out barbed wire and a few protective anti-personnel mines. At intervals on the wire they hung old cans on a tripwire to ensure they had advance warning of approaching enemy patrols. Their activity was shielded by an artillery programme of harassing fire on the German troops dug in on the other side of the river. Smoke shells dropped regularly with the high-explosive shells and the usual acrid, bitter smell assailed his nostrils. How he loathed and detested the stench and smell of war and longed for the softness and warmth of Nicola and the sweet scent of her presence. She had added a new dimension to his world and had sharpened his natural soldierly self-preservation instincts, for, as the evening ribbons of half-light stretched into darkness, flashes in the northern sky triggered his senses. Quickly he ensured his men were in their dugouts under cover and, within seconds, a heavy German artillery bombardment began. The shells thudded thickly into the ground around them. Huge fountains of earth and smoke towered up as the vile coughing of the soft water-inundated earth began. Upheavals of sound and colour, black, yellow, orange bursts of fury and torn mud. Blasted earth was re-blasted within seconds as the shells followed each other, each seeming to vie with its forerunner in maliciousness and destruction. Saliva drooled down the side of his mouth as sickness gripped his bowels. Yet again, it was for him the moment of truth and the realisation of his mere mortality. He fought within himself to regain composure, licked his lips dry and gave a crooked grin to one of the younger members of his section.

'Only evening hate, young Ollie,' he said laconically. 'They do it to catch the ration parties coming up after dark.'

'Does it last long, Corp?' the lad enquired, nervously, his eyes wide in a white drawn face beneath his steel helmet.

'Not usually, they haven't got many shells left over there. They've nearly had it,' he replied deliberately, with the intention of instilling confidence in the lad.

Dusty Miller, another member of the section, who had seen his fair share of action, broke into the conversation. 'Yeah, they're getting rid of them to save lugging them back to Germany.' The newcomer brightened at the interjection, but Easton knew that there would be many more such bombardments to be endured before the final victory was won.

He felt concern for his section of fifteen men and knew what fatal results could be induced through an over-imaginative assessment. However, it was his job to nurse the newcomers through the first difficult stages and, if they lived, they themselves would soon become seasoned campaigners. The shelling ceased abruptly and he used the breathing space to check that no casualties had been incurred before attending to his own welfare.

Spreading his groundsheet three-quarters over the top of his dugout, he earthed down the sheet edges and dug a small drainage channel on each side with a downhill directional flow. It was an old infantryman's dodge to drain off rainwater or heavy dew in the night. He looked out into the darkness, pleased with the news he had received earlier from his platoon commander that another company was providing standing patrols during the night. They, themselves, would be on such patrols soon enough.

He never truly slept when in the line; the responsibility for his men precluded it. Inevitably it was a case of fitful dozes from time to time, then out to check that lookouts were awake and at their posts. A cigarette craftily cupped in hand, shared with a young lookout – a wisecrack or two, reassurance, brief talk of home and family, leave spells, after the war hopes and ambitions. Such confidence he gave to his men often left him drained, but now, with Nicola in his life, he found he had more to give of a source of confidence that had but been awakened. He longed to survive the coming battle for her sake, but he was resolved that it would not be at the expense of his men to whom he owed so much.

CHAPTER NINE

The previous rumours of the big attack proved correct when, in the first clean heart-lifting days of April, amphibious crablike vehicles crawled up close behind the front line. The weather remained clement and the torn shell-pocked trees in a nearby farm pushed forth faint spindly leaves of greenness. What he thought were swallows, curved through the gun-flecked evening sky, and in the grasses and reeds of the riverbank, nature's industrious citizens went about their affairs. Battalion orders were issued, company commanders held their conferences and, finally, his platoon commander briefed him and the other non-commissioned officers on the plan of attack and objectives to be taken.

His platoon commander, a likeable, uncomplicated man, courageous to a fault but a comparative newcomer, having been seconded from a heavy anti-aircraft battery of the Royal Artillery, gave them the divisional commander's plan of attack. Zero hour would be just before dawn when a heavy barrage would be laid down on the German gun and mortar positions and the front-line trenches. Flame-throwing vehicles would lead the infantry carrying vehicles which would then cross the river barrier. The attacking troops would be boxed within a creeping barrage with Royal Artillery officers and Royal Air Force liaison officers well to the fore. RAF Typhoon fighter planes would bomb and strafe the enemy immediately ahead to keep them engaged as the first wave of attackers crossed the river. The momentum of the assault was to continue non-stop; fresh divisions would leapfrog each other maintaining the attack that would go by both night and day. The American divisions of the 5th Army would also attack in the mountainous area to their left flank to give the Germans little opportunity to switch troops to the threatened fronts.

He passed on the orders to his section, arranged for them to get as much rest as possible before dawn the next day, and checked rations, water, first-aid field kits and that all weapons were serviceable. The waiting hours passed slowly and towards dawn, when birds and all living things were hushed, the darkness yielded to the first groping fingers of the coming day. Suddenly there was a shrill singing in the air, the light was broken by the ragged flashes of guns firing from the rear, their shells rending and tearing the air as they stabbed their hateful passage to the enemy lines. Sudden blossomings of yellow, black, orange and green erupted as they seeded the earth making man's inhumanity to man grotesquely manifest. Shell after shell fell to shake the bowels of the earth and earth, light and sound became inextricably mixed. Rivulets of earth fell down the quaking sides of his dugout as the ground rumbled and shook with hatred and fear. Shells drummed and drilled into the enemy positions, but gradually the German counter-battery fire began to take its human toll. Cries for stretcher-bearers became more frequent and he was relieved when the verbal order for the attack was given.

Clambering ungainly out of their dugouts he and his men moved forward in their set formation with about four yards between each man. Laden down with their weapons and equipment they entered the hellish inferno of dirt, dust and the demented sound of the cross-barrages. The fresh smell of living things was everywhere. Overhead, but unseen, they heard the Typhoon planes boring in, lethally low and then heard the sharp explosions of bombs and rockets discharged over the German front line. Placing himself centrally, he led his section up the flood bank keeping to the tape-marked paths through the minefields, partially marked by the Divisional Engineers.

Coloured rockets soared from the German infantry posts signalling to their own artillery for assistance to repel the attack, but to no avail. The offensive gradually gathered strength and could not be halted, however much the German guns were able to reply. Already the water-borne troops were being ferried across the river. The troop carriers lurched ungainly up the opposing bank, nosed through shell-blasted gaps in the wire, shook the water from their undercarriage and waddled irresistibly ever forward. Small groups of German prisoners, grey-faced, dirty and dust-covered, filtered wearily back to the rear areas. Some, badly wounded, were helped by their comrades walking slowly and considerately – others, still in death, lay in their gun positions. Everywhere lay the horrible, wasted litter of the battlefield. Helmets, wrecked guns, weapons, letters, ugly rust-brown stained field dressings, clothing, shell and bullet cases. Fire and smoke engulfed the entire area – tongues of flame from wrecked tanks and vehicles. The smoke obscured even the daylight itself.

Breathing became difficult as they groped blindly forward and he was relieved when it became the turn of his section to be ferried across the seething river, its surface whipped and lashed by invisible machine-gun fire from the German second defence lines. He took the opportunity in the carrier to check on his men and found no casualties had been incurred. Each earthen covered face, smoke-blackened rivulets of sweat etched into it. Knowing that it was but the beginning of a hard fight to clear the Germans from their defence lines, he displayed, as far as he was able, a confident air that infected his men. Cigarettes were distributed, grumbles aired, jokes exchanged wryly and morale boosted.

Suddenly, as the carrier mounted the far bank, a searing explosion shook its tracks and the vehicle reared up, its front clawing the sky like a terrified horse he had once seen being ill-treated. He heard the mine fragments hit and shatter the thin protective plates, saw the foul spumes of dirt and grey-black smoke, and heard the cries and moans of those of his men wounded by the lethal shards of steel. Apart from a dull headache and a feeling of light-headedness he had, as far as he could gather, escaped injury. Quickly he helped other survivors of the mine blast to free the wounded whose gaunt and bloodless faces showed the severity of their wounds. Without pausing, his head aching from the blast, his vision blurred, he tirelessly dressed the wounds of his companions, lit cigarettes for the less severely wounded and sent a runner to the rear for medical assistance.

CHAPTER TEN

The murderous machine-gun fire slackened and the sound of the barrage rumbled away in the distance – obvious signs that the attack had been successful. On the arrival of the stretcher-bearers and medical personnel, he reassured those of his men who remained alive and unwounded and led them forward once again to the attack. A huge dust cloud hung over the battlefield blotting out the daylight. He felt himself to be in an unknown world with unseen death and destruction on every side. Sounds were intense and unreal at the same time, and almost trance-like, he and his section trod the torn earth going ever forward to the still shell-shocked, red-rimmed horizon.

Towards noon, he met up with the rest of his platoon, reported to the commander and, after a hurried meal break, the advance was resumed. Throughout the long afternoon, strongpoints were overcome, their defenders forced out by bomb and bayonet but not without cost. From time to time high-explosive shells with hideous black air bursts fell away among the thin line of attacking troops.

He and his few remaining men were by now almost exhausted, and it was time for the reserve division to take over the momentum of the attack to exploit the breakthrough. Wearily he stumbled ahead of his section, his senses still alert despite his tiredness and throbbing temples. They had almost reached the German third defence line when beneath his feet he heard the deadly unmistakeable click of compression of a German Schu mine. He had seen many such anti-personnel mines detonated by unsuspecting infantry and knew the hideous wounds they inflicted on the human body from the waist downwards. Shouting at his men to remain where they were, he tried to control his trembling limbs. He knew that as long as he kept the mine mechanism compressed with his body weight, the mine would not throw its explosive charge above the surface and detonate viciously.

For what seemed an eternity he stood stock still as his mind wrestled with the problem of what action he should take. Ideas raced each other in his mind, each as useless as the one preceding it. He knew that his only salvation lay in his split second reaction, once he had removed his boot compressing the three prongs of the mine. With his other boot he awkwardly scraped a channel about four feet in length in the torn and trampled earth beside him. The deeper he could make it the greater his chances of survival, that he knew for certain. He refused to let his men assist him as there was always a cluster of such mines sown, never a single one.

From the distance they watched his despairing, desperate efforts, longing to help but were fully aware that their approach would surely detonate further mines. His legs ached and grew more visibly weary as the sweat dropped from him. He rested, regained a little of his strength and, with a convulsive jerking motion, lifted his foot and threw himself prone and sideways into the shallow excavation. The mine burst cruelly above the earth and lashed the air with its vile explosion. He felt the heat of its detonation, heard the shrill whine of its steel pellets in the air above him and sank unconscious into a morass of blood-red darkness.

Remote from his body, his mind remained suspended in a tightly wrapped cocoon of pain and darkness. He was momentarily outside of life itself and yet saw himself dragged out of the shallow grave by two of his section after three others had been killed in their attempts to pull him from the minefield. He heard dully the explosions that took their lives yet could do nothing to save them. Most disturbing of all, he found he did not recognise them nor could he rationalise his thought processes. Through the fog of pain he tried to speak but found his vocal chords muffled as strange sounds fought their way for utterance. Long, dark hours followed made up of jolting movement and ever consuming pain. Then a sudden peace after a further small injection of pain. He longed to be safe and had an anguished need for some particular person to comfort him but did not know who it was he was seeking. The name he sought in his mind forever eluded him, the face he tried to conjure up dissolved before his attempts at identification. He lived in one long nightmare of uncertainty, of never-ending corridors down which his poor, suffering shell-shocked thoughts raced in search of an essential part of his life, but never finding it.

PART THREE
RESURRECTION

CHAPTER ELEVEN

The coin he had once thrown in the Treviso Fountain brought him back to Rome in a hospital train, gently jolting through the night hours. But he neither knew it nor realised that the person he sought with all his heart and broken mind sat forlornly in the small flat but a short distance away. The cold, grey platform where they first met, slowly but surely receded into the distance as the train imperceptibly gathered speed.

Occasionally his mind verged on the borders of consciousness and he tried desperately to unscramble his ravelled thoughts. Something remained concealed and he fought to find it but in vain. After a brief stay in a base hospital, where the minor gunshot lacerations to his body healed, he was flown back to England where he was admitted to a military hospital located in the south of Hampshire. The pleasant warm days passed slowly for him, but the anguish he felt within him was ever present. Gradually, his powers of speech returned and he spent many sessions with a visiting doctor who specialised in neurology. He was always addressed by rank and name, but they were strange words to him. At night in the ward he repeated them over and over again, hoping they might unlock the gates of memory. The months passed and his visitors, few in number, dressed awkwardly in new civilian clothes, tried to get him to recognise them as members of his depleted section. They left, their efforts unsuccessful, helpless pity in their eyes.

In his empty, lonely purblind world, he found himself turning to nature as a means of relating himself to life that went on relentlessly. In the hedgerows, delicately he fingered aside the young green leaves to see the spring homes of the sparrows and the finches. Ribbons of green pastureland rising to the low hills were for him a source of constant delight. He leaned against the rough, gnarled trees in the spinney and forests and watched intently almost wistfully, the hesitant hoppity rabbits come out towards sunset in search of food. He stood as still as the trees themselves and like each of them he was alone – yet envied the mingling of their leaves rustling high overhead.

He grew rugged and strong as a result of the semi-outdoor life he led, but each morning and evening there was the loneliness of the hospital ward to be faced.

It was during one of his country walks that he found he was in a quiet country lane that led him to a farm tucked below softly protective hills. Haymaking had been in progress and he watched interestedly as the tractors deliberately circled at the end of each swathing run. He visited frequently and the genial farmer who owned the land let him assist in various ways about the farm. Vaguely, he knew that he had done such work before – somewhere, sometime – and that it had special and pleasurable associations for him. It was but a tenuous link with his past, but he held on to it resolutely in his mind. He now knew his own name and that he had once worked on a farm – there would be further links in the days ahead if he fought hard enough to regain his memory.

The months of summer and autumn passed and he obtained a job with the farmer who, unknown to him, had been approached by the medical authorities at the hospital who realised the beneficial effects of outdoor work for their patient. Shortly afterwards, he received his discharge from the army and was awarded a disablement pension which, although sufficient for his immediate needs, required the augmentation of his weekly salary at the farm to enable him to negotiate the purchase of a small cottage nearby. Although his shell-shocked condition had improved noticeably, the events in his life prior to his admission to hospital remained for him a completely blank page.

CHAPTER TWELVE

One day, when the first of the winter winds scythed the last of the russet leaves of autumn from the trees, he was sitting outside one of the barns in the bleak, watery sunshine. It was his midday meal break and, as he idly tossed breadcrumbs from his meal to the inquisitive but strangely timorous sparrows, his employer, accompanied by a stranger, a tall burly man, interrupted his meal.

The man was introduced to him as a Mr Logan, who possessed information regarding a former friend whom he had known in the past. His employer left them after giving him to understand that there was no need for his return to work during the afternoon. He took an instant liking to the stranger and, anxious though he was to learn of the reason for his visit, took him to his cottage before broaching the subject. Settled in old, but comfortable, armchairs in the low-ceilinged sitting room, they talked. The man opened their conversation by producing a photograph of a young girl and asked him if he recognised her. For an instant only his mind seemed to make a fractional recognition, but then the moment was gone and he had to acknowledge truthfully that he did not know the person depicted. He was asked if her name, Nicola, had any associations for him, and again, after the merest flicker of doubt he gave a negative reply. That he was intrigued was obvious and his questioner patiently explained that he was a private investigator acting on behalf of the young girl concerned who had made several enquiries to locate him. She was unable to visit the country herself and was still in Rome but had regularly forwarded money to facilitate the enquiries she wished to be made. Further talk followed but the discussion of the past and his former association with the girl jogged no chord of memory. Before leaving, his companion gave him the photograph and an address in Rome where the girl could be located and, finally, his own official card. After the man had gone, he looked at the card more closely and read:

Christopher Logan, Private Investigator
39 Wigmore Street, London W1.
Telephone Welbeck 4774.

Nervously he turned the card repeatedly between his fingers. Something stirred in his mind, but it was not the man's calling, the address or the telephone number, more the card itself. Suddenly he realised that it was the Christian name that had for him the faintest of recollections. He had known someone or something of that name in the past. During the night he lay awake trying to recall who or what it was and frequently looked at the photograph by the aid of his bedside lamp. The soft, tender look in her eyes had been captured to perfection by the photographer and he longed with all his soul to understand how she had belonged in his past life. He thought that perhaps a visit to Rome during his annual holiday due in the early part of the following year might enable him to regain his lost memories, and resolved to make the necessary arrangements without delay.

The cold, slow winter days followed one by one and now that the main farming work was over, he found himself with more time for leisure pursuits. He explored on foot all the surrounding countryside and one Sunday morning he heard the toll of church bells rolling towards him through the leafless trees. Drawn by their sound he found the entrance to a small stone church and, without really knowing why, joined the party of churchgoers as they entered the church porch. Inside, quiet organ music blended with the now muted peal of bells. He seated himself on a rose-coloured pew just inside the entrance and a peacefulness came upon him. The bells and music ceased and the morning service began.

Whenever the rest of the congregation knelt or rose he did likewise, but he was always wide-eyed and watchful during the moments of prayer. His visit to the church was, he thought, for some mysterious purpose and he was ever vigilant to discover it. He studied closely the tall, thin vicar whose kindly face was matched by an equally pleasant speaking voice. In turn, he looked at each member of the congregation but his inspection prompted no element of recognition. A hush descended as the young vicar climbed the few stairs to the pulpit. He watched the slender sensitive fingers open the Bible with practised skill and heard the modulated voice announce that the text for the sermon was taken from the 11th chapter of the Epistle according to Saint John in the New Testament. He listened at first with polite interest until the vicar referred to the waking of Lazarus and that when he heard of the circumstances of the death, Jesus wept. As if from a distance, he heard the vicar's voice continue and talk of the resurrection of the life of Lazarus. But the words that he heard stirred some small part of his memory. 'Jesus wept' ran continually through his brain. That they possessed a significance for him he knew, but the link would not fall into place. Leaving the church at the end of the service, he absent-mindedly shook the vicar's hand and walked quickly away, his thoughts churning endlessly over the words that he had heard. He felt as if he were nearing a gate of hope and realisation of a secret unknown longing. As he walked back to his cottage, he pondered on the things that he knew were important to him in his search to restore his shattered memory. Rabbits he had seen at sunset, the farm, Christopher Logan – there must be something else to close the chain and he thought hard and long on what it might be or what form it might take. Wakeful nights with their solemn paced hours of darkness became second nature to him and he grew thin of feature. Although he worked as hard as ever, labour appeared to be a kind of anodyne, as if it would tire him so physically that his miserable tortured mind might then find rest.

As Christmas approached, his appearance caused his employer's wife reason for concern, and she reacted by inviting him to the farm on Christmas Eve, when a small party for the farm workers was to take place. Appreciating her kindness, he accepted the invitation although he would have preferred the quietness of his own cottage. Contrary to his expectations, he enjoyed the warmth and companionship of those who attended and, when the party ended, he helped his hostess clear the tables. Whilst moving a half-empty wine bottle from the kitchen sideboard she dropped the bottle on the stone floor. The shattering of the glass particles as the bottle smashed to the floor awoke a memory deep within him. He watched its red contents spread across the floor and knelt immediately to assist her gather the fragments of broken glass. As he did so he noticed the creased label adhering to one of the larger fragments. Carefully, almost tenderly, he picked it up and read 'Lachryma Christi' and in a blinding instant of eternal time he knew it to be the Italian for 'tears of Christ'. Almost feverishly, he laced together the pieces of his broken memory. Like pearls strung on a gossamer thread, he related a rabbit toy with a Christopher medallion. He stood, white-faced, breathing deeply, willing his mind to respond to the promptings of his very soul. An interminable pause, then a farm with grapes and sunshine, love and warmth of belonging. Then, finally, a cascade of golden memory overwhelmed him and his tears fell unchecked and unashamedly when the lovely childlike face of Nicola came to him clearly from the wreaths of forgetfulness and tortured longing.

CHAPTER THIRTEEN

The same chilly wind of January, now over a year old, sent its exploratory fingers along the cold snow-covered platform of Rome railway station as the train bearing Charles Easton slowly drew to a halt. He had written to Nicola of his probable time of arrival and, long before the train stopped, he had moved down its corridors to the place opposite the platform where he knew she would be waiting. The snow fell steadily from the dark sky and emphasised the vaulted arches of the station itself. His pulses beat feverishly and he was half sick with fear lest she was not there and that something dire had happened to her. His anxiety increased moment by moment until he finally beheld her small figure in the distance. As the train neared her he saw her wearing the same fur coat she once wore long, long ago. She stood in the soft feathery snow, her young thin face wearing a smile of welcome and such delight that he leapt from the still slow-moving train. Slamming the carriage door behind him he ran along the platform towards her.

With the coat flared wing-like behind her, she ran into his outstretched arms, her beauty was ever fresh for him and he felt a wild joy surge within him. Their hearts and bodies met as his lips sought hers and, as the soft snowflakes fell wetly, he knew that never again would there be a parting between them. And, possibly, high above in the winter sky, in a place where peace is alleged to pass all understanding, there may well have been a person called Jesus who wept for them and their future happiness.

THE END

DAS BILD (THE PHOTOGRAPH)

For almost twenty-three years, Martin Hansen had kept the photograph, his reason for doing so becoming clearer to him as time went by. On many occasions he had vowed that he would one day make enquiries as to the identities of the soldier and his family, whom he presumed to be wife and daughter, depicted in the photograph, but had never taken positive action since he was convinced he had been responsible for the death of the soldier concerned.

Now, however, his resolve could become a possibility. He had that morning received a letter from his solicitor informing him of a substantial legacy left to him by an aunt who had recently died. He had met his aunt but infrequently and had never been aware that any close bond existed between them. However, her generosity precluded further prevarication on his part regarding his quest.

He reflected on his course of action. First to ascertain the unit or regiment to which the dead man belonged and next to make enquiries of former comrades or friends to establish his name and residence. Perhaps the insertion of advertisements in newspapers in the locality once it was established, might be of help. Also ex-servicemen journals or magazines might offer a useful line of enquiry. Next he thought of the dead man's family – the wife might not still be living, or, if she were, might have remarried, consequently these changes of name might hinder his search. He realised that all possibilities existed since he had left his decision so late. So allowances had to be made and he would tackle first things first.

In furtherance of this reasoning, he closely examined the photograph which he removed from his wallet. It measured five inches by three inches and three of its corners were missing. Its edges and surface were cracked and the print had a yellowish, almost decaying, tint. It was a balanced pose with the three figures centrally placed. The man was wearing the uniform of a private soldier and a forage cap with some form of army insignia at its front. The man had a fresh, clean appearance, no doubt heightened by his close-cropped hairstyle. His right hand clasped the small trusting fingers of a girl, aged about eight years, dressed in a short-sleeved cotton dress with a sash around the waist. Her fair and curly hair was bound with bows at either side above the ears, and a half-smile on her face showed the obvious pride in her father whose hand she clasped. To the child's left stood her mother in casual pose. She, too, wore a short-sleeved printed cotton dress, with stockings and open-type sandal shoes. Her hair was dark and wavy and she was sturdily built even though she was at least a foot shorter than her husband. Her tanned face suggested she was of the country rather than town-bred. Indeed, the background to the three figures showed a grass path bordering a small stream with several chickens on the far bank. The trees depicted were mainly coniferous and the snap appeared to have been taken in early summer. He turned the photograph over and saw, in his own handwriting . . . 'Taken from a dead soldier at Horns, Tripolitania, January 20th 1943.'

The occasion on which he had written the words he did not recall but knew it could not have been very long after he had buried the soldier concerned. The scene came back to him, not so readily or clear-cut nowadays, but fairly detailed, nevertheless. The night previously he had carried his machine gun along a winding track to the right of the Homs–Miserata road, just outside Tripoli. For most of that night the advanced armoured contingent and the infantry regiment to which he belonged had endeavoured to hold an attack by the opposing infantry.

The enemy had not been dislodged and, following a change of plan, he and his gun team had climbed to the summit of a rocky outcrop where, just as the first streaks of dawn lightened the night sky, he brought his gun into action again. He found he was overlooking the flank of the advancing enemy infantry. He opened fire, switching from target to target and saw the troops fall as the belt of fire covered them. He was not, by nature, an aggressive person and throughout the various actions in the Western Desert had experienced his full share of fear and trepidation. It was the sight of the small groups of dead infantry from his regiment lying in front of the enemy positions that incensed him and made him uncaring on this particular morning. Belt after belt of ammunition was fed into the gun and immediately beneath its muzzle the earth was scorched with the rate of fire he had maintained despite the stoppages he had quickly rectified. Suddenly, the battle area quietened as the attacking infantry began to scramble from their positions to avoid his line of fire. Although it was never a clear-cut victory, it was evident that the enemy would pause before continuing the attack.

A sense of weariness overcame him and he numbly obeyed the order to cease fire and to dismantle the gun. He heard vaguely his company commander pass on the thanks of the commanding officer of the infantry for the close, accurate supporting fire given to his men. He descended the hill, removed the cordite deposits from the gun and thought of a meal. It was already late morning and from the insulated food containers sent up from his Company Headquarters, he and his gun team breakfasted on hard bread and hot coffee. He had little appetite and smoked a cigarette as he drank his coffee. Looking about him he saw the lines of tanks and vehicles on the road ready to depart in the direction of Tripoli. Burnt wrecks of tanks and trucks had been pushed from the road and only scorched marks on its surface bore witness to the severity of the action fought.

It was then he had noticed the dead enemy soldier lying a short distance from the edge of the road. The thin drab uniform was torn in several places and the blood from the gunshot wounds had caked black around each laceration. The face was white, its features calm and silent; death had come instantly and a rifle was still clutched in the lifeless hands. Other dead were much in evidence, but not in his immediate vicinity, and Hansen felt uneasy in the presence of this particular body.

The sun had climbed higher in the cloudless sky, and he felt its heat through his tunic. With the increased warmth and stillness, masses of black flies had started to crawl heavily over the face of the dead man. It was the time during the aftermath of a battle, when rage subsides and those actually fighting become momentarily vulnerable. Sick inwardly at the carnage and yet pleased to be still alive, and well aware that other battles had to be endured, he never liked this moment.

Although he knew that the War Graves Commission personnel would eventually reach the battlefield and bury the dead, he had a sudden desire to atone for his part in causing this man's death by burying him quietly and decently away from the sun's glare and quick decomposition. Perhaps a peaceful spot, where neither flies nor the sounds of further battle would trouble him.

Acting on his resolve, with a spade taken from his equipment, he dug a shallow grave. Removing the identification tags and personal papers from the body, he rolled it gently into the grave and covered it as soundly as possible with earth. He placed the man's rifle with the helmet draped over it at the head of the grave and then glanced at the papers he had removed. Not wishing to know the name of the man he presumed he had killed, he did not read the particulars in the identity documents, but did extract the photograph from between its pages.

It was the simplicity of the face of the child depicted that intrigued him to place the photograph in his tunic pocket. He then gave the other documents to his section commander and received mild censure for his actions. Nearly three months later, during, another battle at the Mareth Line in Tunisia, he was wounded. Sent to a base hospital, he took no further part in the North African Campaign.

Now, twenty-three years later, at the age of forty-two, he intended to find, if possible, the family of the dead soldier and assist them in any way he could. He readily conceded that curiosity as to the kind of family they were played an important part as to his motive. Also pleasing, was the prospect of travelling abroad again and the fact that his passport requirements were quickly dealt with. The following morning he wrote to the War Graves Commission for assistance in locating the official war cemetery in which the soldier had been eventually buried. A few days later the commission replied that the former enemy country had moved many of their dead to cemeteries in Libya, but provided the names and particulars of ten former soldiers whose bodies had been recovered from the battlefield in question. Exact details of the next of kin were not immediately available, but further searches in records could be made if desired.

Encouraged by this prompt reply, he crossed the English Channel the next day, visited the commission's premises, where having explained the reason for his enquiries, he was given the names and addresses of the nearest next of kin of the ten soldiers concerned. Having secured accommodation at a modest hotel, he travelled by road and rail during the next six weeks visiting nine of the ten addresses. His enquiries were thorough but the end of the period saw him no further forward in his search. However, he ruefully admitted that his command of the language had improved and that he liked the country.

Somewhat tired and dispirited even though it was midsummer and the weather was superb, he set out in a hired car, to visit the last address of those given to him. Its location was deep in the countryside close to the edge of a slow-running river. His enquiries disclosed that the cottage he sought was situated on the outskirts of a small village surrounded by woodland. The village had two hotels and in one he found accommodation. It was late afternoon and, after a meal, he rested and decided to leave his final search until the next day.

The next afternoon, feeling confident that his search would have a successful outcome, he drove to the outskirts of the village. The cottage had trees bordering it and their heavy branches shaded it from the sun's glare. He edged the car off the road into a dusty grey track, parking it close to a hedgerow. Keeping to the edge of the wood, he walked slowly towards the cottage, thinking of the manner he would broach the subject of his unannounced visit.

His approach was seen by a young girl about eight years of age, standing on an upturned bucket in the rear garden, pegging out clothes on a line running from one of the corner eaves of the cottage to a low branch of a fruit tree in the far corner of the garden. Her fair hair tumbled about her shoulders as she stretched on tiptoe to peg the last of what appeared to be dolls' clothes to the line. She smiled, as if she had been expecting him, and her light-blue eyes sparkled in the sunshine. His intention had been to go to the front door of the cottage, but the girl invited him to enter the garden through a side gate.

'Have you come to see Mummy? She's upstairs,' she said.

He was about to reply to her easy acceptance of him when, from an upstairs window, he heard a woman's voice call, 'Kathi, where are you? Come inside quickly.'

'Your mother?' he queried.

'Yes, she wants me – would you like to come and meet her?' the girl asked innocently.

'Yes, I'd like that very much, but I'll wait here, in the meantime.'

He heard her confide excitedly to her mother as she entered the cottage, and the whispered enquiry as to the visitor and the reason for his visit. He anticipated the child's negative reply by taking a further interest in the bright colourful confusion of the flower beds bordering the small garden lawn.

On hearing their approaching footsteps, he turned, bowing slightly, as they met.

'This is the gentleman, mummy,' the girl said, introducing him.

He clasped the extended hand of the mother and said immediately, 'My name is Martin Hansen. Please forgive me for calling unannounced.'

'Yes, it is a surprise,' she answered and continued, 'Would you care to come into the cottage?'

He did so and seated himself where shown on a low chintz-covered settee in the pleasantly furnished sitting room. He looked at the girl's mother before continuing. She was, as he expected, about thirty years of age with the face of the young girl in the photograph still much in evidence. She was slightly over five feet tall and finely built. She wore a plain skirt and a white cotton blouse, the silver buttons on which sparkled in the sunshine filling the room. Her eyes, like her daughter's, were light blue and her hair almost a wheat-coloured fairness. The features were fine and even, with the briefest of smiles at the corners of her small, full lips. Her manner, both courteous and pleasant, seemed to indicate that although she had known difficult times, she was of a good nature and kindly disposition. He knew instinctively that she would make it all the easier for him to explain his presence if it were in her power to do so. Thus reassured, he continued.

'I am right in assuming that you are Mrs Karen Meyer, and that before, your former surname was Frank?'

'Yes,' she replied quietly, 'I am still called Mrs Meyer.'

His previous enquiries had disclosed that her husband had died several years before when her daughter was very young, thus he understood her qualified reply.

'Mrs Meyer,' he began hesitantly, "you may think it rather foolish of me to have come here today, but the truth is, I believe I once met your father many years ago in the Libyan Desert. That is,' he said quickly, 'if he were a soldier serving in North Africa?'

His enquiries had been as detailed as possible and he was certain that her answer would confirm them, but it did not.

'No, Mr Hansen,' she replied. 'My father died in the East in 1941 when I was about seven years old, so it would appear that I am not the person you are seeking.'

Although momentarily nonplussed by her reply, her likeness to the girl in the photograph was beyond doubt and he felt certain he was not mistaken in his belief. He remained silent meeting her gaze and then removed the photograph from his wallet. He passed it to her and gently said, 'But, surely, Mrs Meyer, this is a photograph of you as a young girl with your parents?'

She looked at the picture intently, then raised her eyes to his enquiring gaze. 'Yes, Mr Hansen,' she said slowly. 'I am the girl in the picture, but perhaps now I might ask you a question?'

'Please do,' he replied hastily. It was this moment he had thought about so often in the past, never finding a suitable reply to the question he was now required to answer.

'How did you get this photograph?' she asked directly.

Slowly and carefully, he explained the circumstances regarding his possession of the picture and of his long-held intention of finding the family of the dead soldier to try in some small way to assist them if it were possible. She followed his story silently, her arm about the shoulder of her daughter, as if in a protective way.

Softly, she spoke again. 'It is very kind of you to take so much trouble to right what appears to your eyes, a wrong. Very few people would have thought of doing what you have done for it was the war, after all, and you had to fight and our people had to do the same.'

'Yes, I suppose so,' he conceded, and added flatly, 'I wasn't a particularly efficient soldier, possibly just as well in the long run.' He felt suddenly weary and she came to him and placed a hand lightly on his shoulders.

'Stay there, Mr Hansen,' she said quietly, almost reprovingly. 'It is very remiss of me, I shall make some coffee and then we can talk some more.'

Her daughter, following her mother from the room, shyly gave him a smile of encouragement as she left. He sat still taking in his surroundings. The furniture, mainly of wood was old-looking and highly polished, and the floor carpet, although worn, was clean and brightly patterned.

Several photographs and pictures were on the walls. It was a tranquil house, reflecting the apparent closeness of mother and daughter, both of whom, as if echoing his thoughts, re-entered the room. They bore, between them, trays heaped with cups and saucers, milk jug, sugar bowl and a plate of small cakes. They smiled as they set out the meal on a small table, and beckoned him to join them.

The question uppermost in his mind was answered when next she spoke.

'I expect you are wondering who the people were with me in the photograph?'

He admitted quickly that this was so.

'They were my uncle – my father's brother – and his wife. They took care of me after my father was killed and my mother went into hospital shortly after his death. Both were very good to me and I remember so well how unhappy I was when I heard he had been killed in Africa.'

She seemed to sense that her remark, innocently frank in intention, distressed him, and looked at him intently as if to convey that it was needless to castigate himself for an act committed so long ago.

He knew that she, too, had known much of loss and unhappiness, yet was not embittered and was so obviously trying to alleviate his feelings of guilt. Life could not have been all that easy for them, and tentative arrangements to help them suggested themselves to him with her next question to him.

'And now that you have found us, Mr Hansen, will you be returning to your country, or will you stay here on holiday?' she enquired easily.

He had given little actual thought to his future intentions, beyond making financial provision for them, so he replied truthfully. 'I had not really decided what I was going to do, Mrs Meyer. I suppose I had intended to return to the local hotel where I have accommodation booked, and, after that, an eventual flight back home.'

Her daughter interposed excitingly, 'Couldn't Mr Hansen stay with us, Mummy, and not go back to his hotel?'

Her mother, obviously not expecting her daughter's interjection, quickly supported her however. "You are more than welcome to stay with us. We have a spare bedroom in which we have accommodated guests on holiday here. Mostly bed and breakfast stays, as I have a part-time job in the village and I am away from morning until early afternoon nearly every weekday. So, if you stayed, it would be a case of fending for yourself during my absence. Most of our other guests have gone touring or on day trips during their stay, so we have usually coped quite well.'

'And your daughter?' he asked solicitously. 'How does she manage?'

'Oh, Kathi comes with me in the morning, and I take her to school. She is usually home by 4 p.m. each afternoon, so we do have a successful family life in spite of everything.'

'In that case, I shall be most happy to accept your kind offer and would, of course, meet your usual terms.'

She smiled. 'That would depend on the length of your stay with us.'

'Well, say three weeks, if that would not inconvenience you?'

'Oh no,' she replied quickly. 'That would be fine, and at weekends we could show you some of our beautiful countryside,' she hesitated – 'that is, of course, if you would like that?'

'I'd like nothing better, Mrs Meyer.'

'Please call me Karen, Mr Hansen, after all, we are now friends, aren't we? so perhaps we may call you Martin.'

'Please do, and I shall try to be a model guest.'

'We think you are already, don't we, Kathi?' She turned to her daughter who gave her a hug of affirmation.

After explaining that he would attend to his affairs in the village, he left, promising to return the following evening. Early next day, he arranged with his bank by letter and with a local solicitor who found time in a busy day to attend to his request, to make an annuity of a reasonable sum to be paid monthly to her daughter. To be held in trust if necessary, until her majority was reached.

That evening, he was taken to his room in the cottage. Small, but extremely comfortable, its wardrobe was ample for his few clothes. Gaily coloured curtains draped the window overlooking the rear garden, and the last rays of sunshine lanced through the window and bronzed all they touched. Utterly content, he turned to see Karen looking at him.

"You are happy here, aren't you?"

A reply was unnecessary and he merely smiled and nodded in agreement.

The next two weeks passed most pleasantly for, having extended the hire period of the car, he was able to take mother and daughter to the various places of interest and especial beauty spots they wanted him to see and share with them. They returned to the cottage each evening happy in each other's company, recounting the events of their day.

One evening, when in his room, Karen knocked and asked to enter. He was brushing his hair and in the dressing table mirror, he saw her smiling reflection as she came into the room and sought out his eyes with hers. She wore a simple white blouse, a skirt and a blue stone at her throat. Approaching him, she removed the brush from his hands and placed it on the dressing table. She held his hands within her own soft, cool ones. As if by instinct, he raised her slender pointed fingers and kissed them lightly. As he did so, he pressed himself close to her. A mutual need of affection seemed to underlie their actions as he felt her body arch within his embrace.

'Thank you for being here with us, Martin,' she said warmly. 'Kathi has been especially pleased because of your many kindnesses towards her. When her father died in a road accident all those years ago, she had scarcely known him, so you've become a father figure almost to her.'

They had already spoken about their mutual backgrounds to some extent, and he was aware that the insurance paid resultant upon her husband's death had enabled the purchase of the cottage and a certain freedom from immediate financial problems. It was the fact that she was so lovely a person in all respects, kind almost beyond belief, and yet very much alone, that had caused him somewhat awkwardly, to ask her if she had ever considered remarrying. Her reply was that she would have liked to have done so if only for the sake of her daughter, but did not expect to find a person prepared to take on a ready-made family.

He had quietly conceded that possibility. 'There had been a few in whom I became interested, but they were not particularly keen on marriage. So,' she had sighed, 'the years just went by and I became older and less of an attraction, I suppose.'

He still recalled his instant reply, 'Never, to me, Karen,' and her shy acceptance of his unselfconscious compliment. It seemed as if from that point onwards, they willingly allowed their closeness to, develop in its own almost predetermined way. And now, at this moment, in the comfort of their embrace, he felt a surge of desire that he had once been willing to forget. He was not sure whether he should go further, and felt a slight relief when she drew slowly away from his arms and left the room.

He stood by the open window when she had gone, and felt again within him, the soft warmth of her body. He, too, had been alone for many years since his young wife had died shortly after their marriage at the end of the war. 'Acute Myeloid Leukaemia,' the death certificate had baldly stated, and it seemed then so unfair particularly since he had lost his entire family during a heavy bombing raid. Over the years, he had wondered why such things had to be and experience had slowly taught him that life had to go on and he lived according to its own fateful rules. No one appeared to miss out in any special way. All had their trials and tribulations and high spots of happiness to make up a kind of balance sheet. But he did admit that he did so miss the supreme happiness of the short time spent with his wife. With Karen and her daughter, he had found it was possible to let long-lost feelings once again emerge. Love and affection had every right to manifest themselves – they appeared to be the ultimate gifts freely given to those in need.

Kathi had already broken up from her school for the summer holidays, and it was arranged that same evening that within the final week of his stay, they would visit a nearby lake and, since the weather was fine, perhaps swim there. He didn't have a costume, he said, but was prepared to watch, sunbathe and be utterly content to do so. These days spent with them had revealed to him the barrenness of his life during the preceding years. He supposed that he possessed basically a friendly nature, but had lacked a reason for making an effort to slough off the strongly held mistrust in his capabilities. Set in his ways, loath to bring about a radical change, he had let his conscientious attention to his work as a minor civil servant become a form of refuge. Clerical trivia demanded little true initiative or responsibility.

That night he lay awake as his mind ranged over the events of the day, especially Karen's demonstration of affection earlier. He knew he had longed for the closeness they had briefly shared, and yet had not wanted to initiate anything of a nature likely to mar their companionship. He lay, wide-eyed, partially dreaming of the days yet to pass before his eventual return to his home country.

He sensed, rather than heard, Karen quietly enter the room and close the door behind her. A blue dressing gown covered her long white nightdress, her bare small feet silent upon the carpet. 'I couldn't sleep, either, Martin,' she said shyly, by way of explanation for her presence.

Emotionally aware of her warmth and tenderness, with his arm he made a cavern of the bedclothes and drew her close to him. All tension and shyness between them vanished as her soft lips met his own. An unspoken need, urgent and brooking no denial overwhelmed them. Days and nights of loneliness vanished as their hands ran over each other seeking that in the other they did not in themselves possess. A warm glow suffused them as they lay still and silent listening to each other's swollen breaths. He smiled at her as she lay within his arms and her physical reply compelled again a fusing of their bodies. He felt as though he had been enclosed between the folded wings of a beautiful butterfly as he slipped away into the quiet depths of a dreamless sleep. When he awoke, he was alone and he lay for a while uncertain as to whether or not it had been real. But his body provided him with the reality of the night. It was not a dream and it would always remain that way. An intense feeling of gratitude, affection, love, need, desire, excitement – all these feelings mingled inside him and he knew that simply basking in them would not bring her return.

He was not quite certain how to meet her gaze at breakfast. She had a warm, knowing look and bestowed a smile upon everything she looked at or touched. Their faces lit up automatically whenever their eyes met. Even Kathi, he thought, must be aware of his love for her mother. He was so blatant in expressing it. All he knew for a fact was that he did not intend to leave their lives – they were a necessary part of him and seemed to have been so since time was but a word. Later, as he drove them to the selected lake, the car packed with all the requirements, including a picnic basket, he thought long and hard as to ways and means he could remain with them.

There were many possibilities, and he would give attention to them all later. Meanwhile, there was the long, sunny day ahead to be enjoyed in their company.

The locality they chose was some distance from a group of summer villas built close to the edge of the lake. Both mother and daughter changed into their costumes in the car as he set out the picnic items on a rug near the water's edge. They then ran laughing to the lake. 'It looks a bit chilly to me,' he said.

'Not once you are in the water, Martin,' she sang out as they slowly waded into the lake. Leisurely, they swam out into the deeper water and he heard their mutual laughter rippling across the lake's surface.

It was warm, almost close and humid, with a suspicion of rain building up in the clouds forming over the distant hills. The grass was fresh and cool to his touch, and the nearby willow trees were reflected in the shallower edge. Concentric ripples in the shaded water showed from time to time as small fish lazily broke the surface in search of insects hovering beneath the arched lower branches of the trees.

Time seemed motionless with the sun shining fiercely from the unrelieved blueness of the sky immediately above. It was the insistent barking of a dog in a party of holidaymakers nearby that brought his reverie to an end. Some fifty yards from the lake edge he saw Karen supporting her daughter. Her shout for help was simultaneous with his action in kicking off his shoes and speeding into the lake. He swam urgently towards them. There was no time for fear or further thought and the initial coolness of the water was imperceptible as he drove his arms deep into the water, furiously impelling himself forward.

On reaching them, he quickly relieved Karen of the task of supporting her daughter and, in fiercely gasped orders, told her to make for the shore alone. This she refused to do and remained treading water trying to assist him. Kathi, seemingly, had been attacked by cramp and was panicking as he endeavoured to support her above the surface. Several times her flaying limbs struck him as he tried to turn her on her back with the intention of pulling her to the shallower water. Repeatedly, during their slow progress he took quantities of water into his lungs and noticeably felt his strength ebbing as a result of his exertions.

Aware that Karen was close at hand, he pushed Kathi towards her as he realised that his strength alone was insufficient to save the child. Suddenly, all was blueness, the sky, the lake surface, the water's depth, the very inner retina of his eyes. Then, just as quickly, the blueness changed to fragments of air and light inextricably mixed so that he knew not one from the other. Above him was life and the green loveliness of earth, but, strong as his desire was to grasp them, an engulfing blackness steadily loosened his resolve.

His outstretched fingers tore weakly at the waters which imprisoned him and their flurried surface became slowly still as Martin Hansen, former *Unteroffizier*, 125 Regiment, German Afrika Korps, sank forever downwards in the dark depths – his self-imposed debt repaid.

'ADESTE FIDELIS'

The Commando Memorial near Spean Bridge,
at the foot of Glen Spean, Inverness-shire.

ENTRY

Ship's Log, Norwegian Fishing Vessel *KRISTIAN* 29 December, 1973, 1700 hours outward bound from BERGEN destination fishing grounds N.W. of TRONDHEIM. Drifting 17 feet LAPWING Sailing Sloop *NONA*, 2.6 tons Thames Measurement, located position Lat. 62° 45' North: Long. 4° 30' East – No one aboard sloop which had storm jib and reefed mainsail set. Navigation lights on. Sail Number 18. Clean, neat interior and last recorded entry in log referred to position Lat. 62° North: Long. 3° 45' East. Port of departure not shown. No indication as to identity of crew thought to be but one person. Articles found aboard include:–

1 Sleeping Bag; calor gas container empty; 12 volt battery ¼ charged; 2 gallons water; depleted food stocks; eight lines of verse headed 'V' 28.12.41. attached to last entry in logbook; one empty drug bottle labelled 250 mgm tabs. Morphia, Lot no. MB 14756-1. Expiry date March 1974; empty half-bottle of brandy and usual adjuncts, flares, grapnel anchor, warps, plastic sextant, compass etc. Boat taken in tow to FLORO at mouth of FORDEFJORD and left in keeping of Harbour Master with report on attendant circumstances of recovery.

REPORT

Acting British Consul, British Embassy, Oslo, to Foreign Office "Re details as shown above, enquiries requested regarding abandoned sloop and origin of drugs Lot number as quoted."

CORRESPONDENCE

Inspector UV to C/Supt. TJ' Division – Ref 1'046/1735/73 "Lapwing Marine Limited; records show Sail Number 18 allotted to one of first craft manufactured and purchased in January 1969 by Mr. R. Greenway, 'Top Trees', Rainham, Essex, who still owns vessel and possesses original sails with figure 18 preceded by letter 'L'. All other enquiries negative."

ENQUIRY

of British Register of Shipping *NONA* – no record for vessel of this name of the specification shown.

REGISTER CHECK

CID Essex County Police Force – Re Schedule Dangerous Drugs Pharmaceutical Manufacturer confirms Batch 42/4 containing L MB 14756-1 as part of consignment despatched for distribution S. Essex area. Detailed enquiries proceeding regarding pharmacists receiving individual lots and subsequent prescription of same. Further report will follow.

VERSE

found aboard abandoned sloop *NONA*

SEA BURIAL 'V' 28.12.41

Let Death's anchor take me down
Fluked fathoms deep
Leaving the daylight trapped above
The running tides where mermaids weep

Where wavering tendrils soft entomb
Amidst the sea-green maze
Forever in the darkened womb
Skull-eyed the watered gaze

EXTRACT

From official WAR HISTORY, VOL 1 . . . In the gathering darkness as the Norwegian coastline receded from view a burial service was quietly read aboard the troopship *Prince Harold* and the bodies of three members of 18 Commando – Captain David, whose grieving troops had refused to leave him to be buried by the Germans, and two badly wounded men who had died while undergoing treatment in the ship's sickbay were committed to the deep.

INQUIRY REPORT

Register Births and Deaths (Foreign Section) – Recorded Burials at, sea in Norwegian territorial waters include those of

Captain J. David, Troop Commander	18 Commando
Sergeant T. Halloway	18 Commando
Trooper L. Bryant	18 Commando

. . . on 28.12.41 following Commando raid on the offshore islands; of VIGSO and MELLOS.

FURTHER REPORT

CID Essex County Police. Drugs in question related to prescription issued to a Mr. C. Johns, by Dr. J. Willcox, MB who, on 8 October 1973, forwarded a blood specimen of his patient for pathological tests – acute Myeloid Leukaemia diagnosed – limited life expectancy. Mr. Johns a widower, aged 54, no living relatives, absent from his home since mid-November 1973. Present whereabouts unknown.

OBITUARY

Commando Newsletter – Spring 1974 – Trooper Johns Charles (18 Commando) formerly batman to late Troop Commander, passed away 28.12.73. More detailed information of the above may be obtained on application to the General Secretary.

IN MEMORIAM

(A short tale of 'If Only's)

'You have two new messages – Message 1'

'Hi, Mum, Caroline here ("I know, dear," murmured her mother into the answerphone) – Good news, I've been accepted for the drama course at the academy and I'm coping well with all of its demands, so you've no worries about me on that score. Will call in to see you at the usual time on Saturday evening and we can have a tea and buns chat. I've lots to tell you. See you soon. All my love and do ease up on the work, Mum. Bye.'

'Message 2'

'Good evening, Mrs Taylor. Thank you for your letter regarding my father who died recently. There are no formal funeral arrangements made, but, since you expressed a wish to know more about his life, I should be pleased to meet you at a time and place suitable to yourself, preferably, not too distant a location from our mutual addresses. Do please let me know if this suggestion meets with your approval. Thank you again for your kind letter – Oh, and my telephone number is 0827 98451, under Charles Dennis in the book.'

Margaret Taylor wrote the number on a notepad beside the phone and deleted both messages.

It had been a busy time at the Obituary Department at the *Daily Recorder* newspaper where she was employed as a research assistant. The journey back to her small flat had been a nightmare in the wet December weather and the two windscreen wipers on her car had had an occasional altercation, getting momentarily stuck together when clear vision was needed most.

She prepared a quick snack for herself, accompanied by a small glass of wine. During the meal she thought of the reason for her

131

recent letter to Charles Dennis. Her duties as an obituary research assistant had, over the years, occasioned the receipt of three obituary notices from the father, Peter Dennis. They had arrived regularly in May, October and December of each year, well before publication date and never a quibble regarding the cost of insertion. Her earlier duties had entailed a detailed reading over the wording to ensure accuracy, obtaining address, telephone number of caller and details of choice of payment.

All the items related to former army comrades killed in action during the Second World War. One, a lieutenant colonel killed at Monte Cassino, Italy, in May 1944, another to a non-commissioned officer dying in battle at El Alamein, Egypt, in late October 1942, and the third to a well-liked and brave captain killed during a commando raid in Norway on 27 December 1941.

These regular, loyal remembrances of his friends intrigued her – particularly as her own father had been killed in the same commando raid referred to. She had never known her father, having been born a few months after his death. The numerous enquiries of official sources to establish his grave, or last known whereabouts, had been unsuccessful. She was quite young when her mother had later died and never had the opportunity of asking her about the matter.

Often she had intended to contact Peter Dennis and, when she had finally made up her mind to do so, it was too late. An obituary notice regarding his recent death had been inserted by his son, Charles, to whom she had written her letter of enquiry.

No stranger to losses herself, her much-loved husband dying at a comparatively young age, but two years previously, she considered herself fortunate having such a fine daughter in Caroline, now doing so well in her career studies. No doubt, in the course of time there would be the usual "nest-leaving", as it was currently called, but, for the present, hers was a happy, settled life.

After considering a place suitable for a meeting with Charles Dennis, she decided that the cafeteria in a local department store would be appropriate perhaps, a reasonably early hour at the weekend, before the store was too crowded. The cafeteria was spacious, service was quick and efficient and the menu, if a snack or meal was deemed necessary, enticing enough.

It was not too late to dial the number Peter Dennis had provided, but she wondered if her call might be inconvenient and intrude on a family matter. She made the connection notwithstanding and heard the reply 'Dennis'. She was tempted to reply in a similar business manner, 'Taylor here' – but the voice was pleasant and not at all intimidating. He agreed immediately with her suggested weekend meeting and the location chosen; a place he had often frequented and, he added, provided superb cakes – cream and non-cream ones, suitable for all comers, especially those but recently introduced.

The time, place and date settled, she bid him goodnight and expressed the hope that her call had not been inconvenient.

'Not at all,' was his humorous reply, 'just me and the cat at home.'

Thoughtfully, she replaced the receiver. "What kind of person was this pleasant-sounding man on the telephone? A sense of humour of sorts, no quibbles as to chosen venue, date, time, etc., and as a bonus, was kind to animals, a cat.'

And, presumably, no immediate family ties – at home, at least.

Charles Dennis, although not exactly the same thoughts in mind, liked her soft Scottish brogue – as quiet as a butterfly's wing in flight – and endeavoured to conjure up the kind of person she was. No clues given in her letter to him apart from it being well written and courteously phrased. And, of course, both losing a father, albeit at different times.

Eventually they met at the place chosen after loitering suspiciously trying to identify each other. He held the daily newspaper he had suggested as a recognition object, but there had been one or two other men also with newspapers, some already seated reading them.

They saw each other almost simultaneously – liking immediately what they saw in each other and the pleasant way the introduction occurred.

'Mrs Taylor, I do so hope?'

'And, Mr Dennis, I sincerely hope?'

'Indeed it is and it is a great pleasure to meet you, Mrs Taylor. Most of the tables are occupied, but I do see a vacant one over by the counter. Shall we investigate its having us?'

She liked his easy, uncomplicated introduction and, when seated, looked at him more closely. He was in his early forties, but a few years older than herself and, height-wise, there was very little difference between them. Clean-shaven, brown hair slightly receding at the temples, a neat blue suit, white shirt, suitably coloured tie, fair-complexioned and a warm, slow smile of welcome when introducing himself. She found him instantly likeable – no negative points whatsoever.

The choice of snack agreed upon, he bore the tray from the counter to the table and invited her to be in charge of the distribution process, as he called it.

He watched her and wondered how effortlessly she and countless women and girls dealt with the teatime activities; her delicate, slim fingers most certainly helped.

He looked at her appraisingly as he sipped his coffee. Fair, almost wheat-coloured hair, grey-blue eyes, well-dressed in a simple grey two-piece outfit, appropriate accessories and a small black handbag to match. Her manner, cool and possessed, yet no evidence of distancing herself.

During their 'coffee break' as she styled it, she broached the question as to whether he (now accepted as Charles, less formal?) could assist her in establishing the manner and circumstances relating to her father's death all those years ago.

What information he had gleaned from his father's written; account of his war experiences, especially the commando raid, he recounted to her. It added little, however, to what she knew already.

'Perhaps, if I have another look around in my father's possessions, I might discover something more of use to you. It is but an idea, but it might prove useful.'

'Thank you, but no doubt you have more personal matters to attend to first?'

'No, there is to be no funeral as such, since my father previously donated his body to the local hospital, in the pursuance of medical science, as he worded it. I understand. I shall later receive his ashes to be disposed of according to his specific wishes.'

'And where might that take place?' she queried gently.

'In the North Sea, close to the coast of Vaagso, Norway. This is his expressed wish as his much respected and extremely brave troop captain and, I believe, although I'm not certain, your father and other troop members were buried at sea. It was a simple ceremony late on the night of the 27th of December 1941 as the survivors were returning to their home base in Scotland.'

'Might I, eventually, accompany you when you decide to do this kind act?' she asked, her eyes gazing intently into his own.

He made no immediate reply, simply stretching his hand across the table to cover one of her own. She recognised it at once as sign of acceptance of her offer, letting him remove his hand slowly from her own.

He left to settle the bill at the counter whilst in his absence she prepared to leave. Returning, he asked if he might offer her a lift in his car, but she declined the offer as her own car was parked in the adjacent car park. When reaching the particular parking area, they found they had their respective vehicles, both of the same make and colour, but a short distance apart. Simultaneously, they both laughed and said, 'Snap.'

'It must be an omen,' she said.

'A favourable one, surely?' he queried.

'Why not?' she replied, a little uncertain as to whether it was an apt or suitable reply.

Before they left, he arranged to telephone her should he discover anything useful in his rummaging on her behalf.

'Preferably at the weekend?' aware of her employment requirements, 'and a time suitable to us both?'

'As before, would be fine.'

During her journey home she reflected on their meeting and their all too brief conversation. She would have liked to have spent more time in his company, discovering his interests, family connections and ties, if any. Especially the latter, she thought teasingly – after all, he was a decent, seemingly reliable and competent person. Helpful and generous, as he did meet the bill and waved away her reimbursement efforts. So different from many of the men she worked with in her daily research tasks. Since the loss of her husband, her social life had become restricted and most of her time spent caring and sharing with her daughter.

It was nice though, to have a male friend with whom to have mutual interests – and he does seem to fit the bill perfectly. 'Shouldn't think this way,' she lectured herself. 'Have only just met him. What next, indeed?'

'And?' stressed Caroline when they were together that evening.

'And what?' she replied, knowing full well the reason for the enquiry.

'You know very well what. What's he like, and so forth?'

'Well, he's a little older than I am, well dressed, polite and generous and drives the same make and colour car as our own. How's that for starters, Caroline?'

'Not enough, Mum. Does he like you? Do you like him? Do you like each other and so forth?'

"Yes, to all those questions, if you insist. We took to each other instantly and I hope to accompany him to Norway one day, perhaps soon.'

'Well, that is fast work. I suppose it is connected with Grandfather's death all those years ago, isn't it?'

"Yes, dear.'

'And what does he do, apart from meeting you and being charming?'

'I believe he was a former regular soldier and recently completed his service. I don't know what rank he held, his regiment or unit details. In fact very little about his personal life, except for the fact that he is polite, considerate and not bad-looking. Question answered, dear?'

'Not completely, Mum. When may I be introduced?'

'All in good time, my angel. Now, what news of the thespian career?'

'I love it, Mum, I really do. We beginners are treated so well. The teaching staff are effortlessly polite and helpful to us, one and all, no exceptions. I am to assist in the staging of Anton Chekhov's play *Uncle Vanya*. When the play's put on, couldn't you invite Charles as a guest to see it and, later, to meet your great actress-to-be daughter? I'll get the tickets for decent seats, close to the stage.'

'Not too close, dear. I remember all too well the cricked neck I had at your last school performance of *A Christmas Carol*. We were so close to the stage that we could have joined you in the cast. You made an excellent wife to Bob Cratchit, though. It is, of course, up to him whether he accepts the offer – but I shall be there in any event.'

'Oh, he'll come, Mum, just to accompany you. Don't be too negative. He doesn't get a good-looker like you to escort every day of the week!'

'Ach, Caroline, you sonsy lass, you're incorrigible.'

'Well, at least I'm honest – not using those euphemisms so often seen in your obituary columns, such as "doesn't suffer fools gladly" – equivalent "a miserable old so-and-so" – "He never married" – equivalent "couldn't commit or take on real responsibility for a family".'

'Oh, Caroline, you do talk nonsense at times.'

"Yes, admittedly, but with a bit of truth ensconced occasionally. At least I don't go hunting wearing a silk top hat, or clean my teeth in Champagne, as I read once.'

"You don't even have a horse and you've never hunted in your life, dear!'

'Oh, yes I have – "the thimble" and even fishing for compliments. I have other accomplishments also.'

In the way of a reply, her mother said, 'We'd better tuck in now, dear, don't want to see you underweight in your first performance.'

'Yes, Mum, let's fall to with relish, as Charles Dickens once said.'

'I believe he wrote "with appetite", Caroline, so you got close, dear.'

'Mmm, but I've got the appetite already,' she conceded.

After clearing the meal table, they sat together on a settee before the electric fire in the sitting room. Caroline loved the room, reflecting all her mother's interest in home-making design and colour compatibility – the room an undeniable example of loving cosiness. Family photos in simple silver frames and, always to the fore, that of her late father. She missed him so much, particularly his wonderful sense of humour. Always being available to discuss anything. Problems and worries, etc., ceased to be, once she received his always helpful advice: Never, "If I were you" had been his opening remark, but instead, "I wonder, Caroline, if you might have considered so and so." So genial, so loving and a truly splendid father who openly showed his great love for her at all times. She felt his loss constantly – cancer of the pancreas took him from them far too early in his life. She hoped, one day to find a permanent partner with even a few of his loving traits.

Charles Dennis, in the meantime, had completed his rummaging, but found nothing of further use to those facts already known and subject of official reports. He felt an overwhelming sense of failing Margaret (a nomenclature less formal she had insisted). He had already attended to the details of his father's simply expressed will. As executor, very little remained to be done. Probate, settlement of expenses and other matters would be dealt with in due course. He was the sole beneficiary, his mother having died several years ago and his father had never remarried. 'One true love is enough in a lifetime; with you as our son, I had more than most' was one of his many so apposite remarks to life's events. He had been a good father, seldom sitting in judgement on the character of others, having a kind of empathy with his fellows. 'François Villon (the French poet for Tramps) got it right,' he said and quoted, "There's good in the worst of us, and bad in the best, that it ill-behoves any of us to find fault with the rest. But," he had added, "perhaps it was another French poet, the one who wrote the lines I once promised your dear mother – the richest treasures I would bring to you if I were King. She liked that, bless her."

A former captain in the army – had obtained a regular commission and seen active service as an infantryman, a commando and, finally, the officer in charge of a small Special Investigation Branch section at home stations and abroad. Awarded the usual campaign medals, a mention in despatches, and twice wounded. 'No gallantry decorations,' he would say 'didn't try hard enough.' But, of course, he did as many service recommendations proved. Altogether, a loyal, well-rounded personality and a good friend to many. Towards the end of his life, he seemed content to let his heart condition run its final course.

Charles had been able to visit him in his small bungalow from time to time, when they chatted about old times, in their respective service careers. He knew his decision to follow his father into the army gave him much pleasure. Those last years were spent pleasantly reading the many books he had vowed one day to read, tending his small garden and painting small canvasses he would give away to friends. He looked the real artist in his paint-covered cooking-cum-painter's apron, its pockets stuffed always with pieces of cloth – referred to as his cleaning, daubing and dabbing items.

Above all, he was a helpful friend to many of his old colleagues and his local neighbours.

'Nothing old master-ish, Slade or Royal Academy about my art,' he'd say, then add 'but I hope to do better next term' – the term that never came, unfortunately.

Charles, himself, had but recently returned to 'Civilian Life' and had secured employment as an executive officer in the civil service. Pleasant working conditions, decent fellow workers both men and women, reasonable remuneration and a future pension to add to that relating to his former military service. Another plus being the work itself – worthwhile on behalf of others. A childless widower of several years, his wife dying suddenly during one of his tours of duty in the Far East, he retained an optimistic outlook on life, and hoped to use the years ahead to good effect.

His thoughts returned, swiftly, to Margaret. How kind and sympathetic she was to offer to accompany him in his last family duty. His father had known hers when they served together in the same troop with the commando. Then, he a trooper and her father, a well-liked sergeant, training hard under the superb command of a splendid troop commander, a Captain Frazer – the troop welded together and the raid on 27 December 1941 on the Norwegian coast was the first real action taken by the commando against the German occupation forces. Sgt Taylor had been shot when endeavouring to give aid to two wounded members of his section and was seen to fall when carrying one of them across his shoulder out of the line of fire of the sniper in a German strongpoint. How poignant it was to die far from home, a snow-covered, bloodstained patch of ground your final glimpse of life on earth. But, at least, with good, loyal comrades close by to grieve your passing, and, far away, a pregnant young wife to do the same. Not that the dead know these things, only those dying know; those whose last words seeking a comfort of a sort, are often, 'Mother', 'Mama', or 'Mutter'; cries often heard by his own father when fighting in the Desert Campaign was at its fiercest. Even their enemy commander at that time owned to the innate stupidity of war.

Charles' own research had established that following the raid, the German authorities had placed the town under martial law and imposed a curfew. On 30 December the bodies of eleven commandos were laid to rest in the churchyard at South Vaagso with full military honours. A service was read by a German chaplain and three volleys from a rifle squad as an honour to the dead. It was odd how correct the German military authorities could be at that time, when their so many terrible actions were taking place elsewhere. The identities of those killed did not, seemingly, include that of Sgt Taylor, whose last resting place, once thought to have been when buried at sea, had never been clearly established.

It was possible, since all the commandos killed had only their identity tags as identification, that such an item worn by Sgt Taylor, could have been lost during the fighting, or overlooked in their late burial.

Possibly, Margaret had researched these possibilities herself and, when they next met at their chosen venue, he was impressed by all the enquiries she had made but, unfortunately, without success. She thanked him for his help and asked if their friendship might continue nevertheless. He agreed immediately. If it were at all possible, he had no intention of losing her valued companionship. He had grown to like her warm smile, her soft Scottish brogue, in fact everything about her, always showing appreciation of his concern for her and her daughter. He remembered her laughter when he once told her, 'I like intelligent women like you, Margaret – they educate me and teach me more about myself.'

'Nothing there about male domination, then?' she had replied archly.

'No, I try to avoid it, if possible,' was his reply.

The arranged visit to the theatre was a great success with a small get-together in the flat afterwards equally so. Slowly and gently their friendship grew – an understanding one with small gifts occasionally, humorous exchanges, and always he was kind and considerate to Caroline. The warm closeness developed in its own way and at its own pace. In so many ways he reminded her of the father she had never known, but knew so much of, thanks to her maternal grandmother's tales about how her mother and father had met all those long years ago in 1940.

Her father had arrived in Largs, Ayrshire, seeking accommodation as the commando he had joined stationed its officers and men in civilian billets with a daily subsistence allowance, thus rendering barrack life unnecessary. Her mother, then but nineteen years of age, was employed as a 'land girl' on a local farm, when he visited the farm, found favour with its owners and was accepted as a lodger.

They met frequently whenever his hard training periods allowed. Often he was absent for days on end, sometimes at sea in Royal Navy vessels on gunnery courses, on schemes; cliff-climbing courses, long distance marches, speed marches – 'You name it, and we did it,' he informed her.

She liked this slim, fit young sergeant from North London. Quietly spoken, sincere, a well-liked troop sergeant who made no secret of his intense liking of the Scottish people, especially his 'very own land girl, Mary Rose Campbell'.

'Your mother used to call him her "very own Sassenach Bonnie Charlie" shortened to OSBC. They were ever destined to meet and marry. It was a small wedding in the local church – many of his troop were present, her older sister and younger brother. Your mother was truly beautiful and your father so smart and erect in his uniform. A wee get-together in a local hotel – their honeymoon billet – after the ceremony – and no need for him to return to the farm, as we had ample room in the house for the newly-weds. It was all too brief a time he had with us – but they were wonderful days. He was a good man, your father. He had had an institutionalised upbringing in his first sixteen years. He never knew his parents and had joined the army after six years spent in a military school of sorts. He made the army his career and hoped, eventually, to secure a regular commission as an officer in his regiment, if possible. He would have made a fine officer for he was, already, a gentleman.

'He did so like the books written by his favourite author, Charles Dickens. Instead of a field marshal's baton in his army small pack, he carried, instead, the book *David Copperfield* – an autobiographical fragment, he called it. Of an evening he would occasionally read extracts to your mother, telling her that, like Mr Micawber, he had been in constant expectation of her turning up in his life, and then bestow a kiss on her forehead in emphasis. Their uncomplicated and open love for each other was a joy and pleasure to see.

'Then, but three months later, before Christmas, almost overnight, the commando vanished completely. We never knew their destination and it was shortly before the New Year that the soldiers returned. Not all, for some had been killed and many others wounded. One of the former was your father. Your mother (who was expecting you at the time) never really recovered from her loss. They had been so close. "But a blink of an eyelash width away from each other's love," as your father often said.

'We all missed him greatly and were so happy when you were born safe and well in the spring of 1942. It was caring for you in your early years that kept the deep sorrow within your mother, from revealing itself. But it was always there and hard as we tried to encourage her interest in the outside world, it never left her.

'She had occasion to visit Glasgow when you were quite small, and was killed in an air raid on that city. You became everything to us, a bonnie wee Margaret, who grew up and, eventually brought that wonderfully kind new Mr Taylor to visit us, after your marriage.'

Her thoughts returned to the present. How fortunate she and Caroline were in having such a loyal, considerate friend in Charles. It's too good to last, she thought, and so it proved to be. She inserted the obituary notice herself in the newspaper.

Dennis – Charles – killed following a road traffic accident on Wednesday 21st January. Greatly missed by those who truly loved him. Private funeral already held. Donations, if desired, to Royal British Legion. Online Ref: 6208407.

He had endeavoured to prevent an inebriated person from crossing the road in the path of an oncoming heavy goods vehicle. The driver had braked suddenly to avoid them and the vehicle skidded on black ice, crashing into them.

She remembered his almost inaudible remark to the doctor in the hospital to which he had been admitted. "When one has had a good innings, Doc, I don't think disgrace can be attached to marking the score sheet 'Retired, Hurt'."

She and her daughter later flew to Bergen, Norway, and thence by boat to the mouth of the Nordfjord. At a quiet moment, and unseen by others aboard, they gently added the ashes of both Charles and his father Peter, to the unfathomable waters of the North Sea. The empty urns were then dropped into the sea – in one of them Margaret had written the last words Charles had spoken to her before his death, "If one doesn't love someone or something during their lifetime, it's a pretty poor way of living, Margaret. I am one of the lucky ones, for I love you."

She found comfort in the present tense phrasing he used – but no future progressive, alas.

On the return flight, her daughter commented on the family history and that it seemed to repeat itself with its repeated losses of good decent folk, who had harmed no one and helped many.

'Yes, darling, but there were also gains and you, my dear, are but one of many others. The world was a different place all those years ago. Violence and uncertainty abounded. It seems that there are people who always become the victims of history. The so-called little people, miners, bakers, builders, nurses, policemen, even the rank and file in the services, their wives and children, victims all, irrespective of their country. They have passed into history but will never be forgotten. You help to live their short lives for them, dear. Those who are no longer with us live on, on the lips of those living and in their kind and loving acts.'

THE END

APPENDIX B

MARIANNE PEYINGHAUS

QUIET YEARS IN GERTLAUKEN

REMINISCENCES OF EAST PRUSSIA

 **Charles Stacey** was born in 1920 and served in HM Forces throughout World War II, finishing his regular service as a soldier in late 1962. He lives in Bristol and particularly enjoys reading German history, and painting.

MARIANNE PEYINGHAUS

In 1941, a teacher, just 20 years of age from Cologne, came to the Village School in Gertlauken which she found to be a very small community in North East Prussia.

She wrote regularly to her parents in Cologne and, in her letters, told them about her life in the countryside that seemed so peaceful and so far away from the war.

At the begining of 1945, the advance of the Red Army commenced and brought to a brutal end the supposed idyllic Gertlauken, and, Marianne Peyingaus returned to Cologne.

"What a book" – Marianne Peryinghaus has succeded as a novelist and, perhaps, she was not aware of it."
Frankfurter Rundshau

QUIET YEARS IN GERTLAUKEN

Reminiscences of East Prussia

by

Marianne Peyinghaus

INTRODUCTION

Many years ago, when General Dwight Eisenhower was Supreme Commander of the Allied Forces in Europe, he was asked to make a speech to a small civic audience in the United Kingdom. As he rose to make the speech, in an aside to his aide, he asked, 'What shall I talk about?' The aide replied, 'About two minutes, then sit down.'

Such wise advice I shall follow, so as not to distract the reader from this charming, homely, but also sad, story by Marianne Peyinghaus.

I read her book in early 2000, and on 17 April of that year wrote to her, care of the publisher Wolf Jobst Siedler Verlag GmbH Berlin, and asked if I might translate the book into English to enable non-German-speaking friends to enjoy the book as much as I had.

On 31 August 2000 she replied to my letter informing me that she had no objection to her story being translated into English, a language she enjoyed but found easier to read than to write.

Since that date we have exchanged seasonal greetings over the years, together with correspondence and family photographs. It has become a friendship I greatly value. At last, through the good services of UPSO I am able to repay a little of the many kindnesses shown to me, not only by Marianne Peyinghaus, but by many other German friends.

The book and its postscript by editor Günther Elbin are deserving of a better translation than that I have given them, but an equivalent English wording of the day-to-day German colloquial expressions is not always to be found in my small German/English dictionary.

I hope that both the author and the editor can overlook any errors I have made, purely unintentionally.

This brief introduction is dedicated to the memory of Fritz Peyinghaus, a brave and loyal servant of his country and much-loved husband of the author – who died in September 2002 aged ninety-two.

Charles Stacey – February 2006, Bristol

THE BOOK

In 1941 a teacher just twenty years old from Köln came to the village school in Gertlauken, which she found to be a very small community in North East Prussia, half way between Königsberg and Tilsit.

She wrote regularly to her parents in Köln and told them of her life in the countryside that appeared so peaceful and so far from the war. The charm of her letters lies in her ability to illustrate fully the spontaneous daily events, from the small cares and worries and joys and delights with the schoolchildren, the village festivities, the cycle rides on muddy paths, walks in the woods and the trips to Königsberg where she could indulge in her interest in the cinema.

At the beginning of 1945 the advance of the Red Army commenced on the supposedly idyllic Gertlauken, and at the end of the year Marianne Peyinghaus went back to Köln.

AUTHORESS

Over a period of more than three years, Marianne Peyinghaus, then as Marianne Günther, wrote her letters from the remote agricultural part of East Prussia to her parents in the 1,000-kilometres-distant Köln.

'Publisher sought for letters from East Prussia 1941/45' – with this announcement in the *Zeit* newspaper she later found an editor and a publisher.

Edited and with a postscript provided by Günther Elbin.

THE JOURNEY

Instructions for the journey Köln–Gertlauken

1. Ticket from Köln to Labiau [East Prussia] written out, inclusive of extra charge – luggage sent to Labiau with 500 Reichsmarks insurance.

2. *Travel Day*
Köln–Berlin–Charlottenberg. Near to the station is NSV [National Socialist League for Public Welfare] a good homely hotel providing accommodation for young girls travelling alone.

3. *Travel Day*
The express train starts off from Berlin–Charlottenberg so that space aboard is available. The train travels over the Berlinerhofe: Zoo, Friedrichstrasse, Alexanderplatz and then on to Königsberg. Overnight accommodation is available in Königsberg as in Charlottenberg.

4. *Travel Day*
Königsberg to Labiau. Report to the district school inspector. To be dressed faultlessly. See re hairdo pp.

5. *And further journeys*
From Labiau to Gertlauken. Make enquiries in Labiau regarding possible journey arrangements, on foot or by other possible means of transport. Make enquiries actually on the spot.

6. *On arrival in Gertlauken*
Completion of the questionnaire about the salary for the post. Discussion with the head teacher about the political questionnaire which will be passed on by him to the district school inspector.
For the travelling costs incurred on the journey such as baggage costs, day and night accommodation, these to be refunded. Speak with the head teacher about the breakdown of such expenditure. He should prove very helpful in this respect. So ensure you make daily notes on your outlay.

Speak to the head teacher about full board, and eventually about the same matter with the district head master.

Your duty salary is to be paid through the district bank in Labiau. Eventually, as an economy measure, obtain a savings book and if Gertlauken has a savings bank the salary can be paid into that.

7. On the return journey you should be reserved with strangers as fellow-travellers.

8. Take along all identity documents and identity cards, etc.

9. *Reporting and Departure Procedure*

Police to be notified of your departure from the district of Köln and reporting in Gertlauken.

Notification to the Partei [National Socialist Party] in Köln-Deutz as to change of address and reporting to the Partei in Gertlauken on arrival.

German Civil Service Medical Office – carry on making payments until you have settled in and then you can change to whatever is required.

10. Sending back the advances as agreed. Take receipts with you.

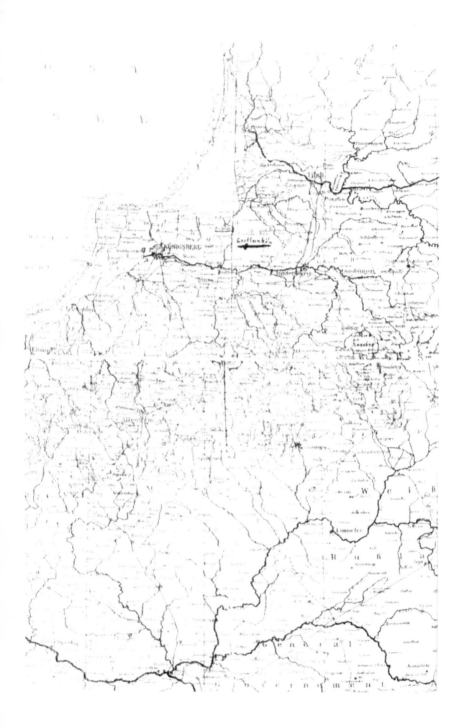

155

THE LETTERS

Dearest Parents

I've arrived at my first work destination. How will it end? But I will have to tell you the whole story.

In Labiau I had to seek out the deputy school officer. The chief school officer had been killed in action. The deputy is actually also a soldier but is on leave of absence. He is a head teacher, small, dainty, has black hair, is seemingly young-looking, speaks with a deep voice and rolls his Rs, like all the people here do. He helped me with the formalities, swore me in on solemn oath and introduced me to all the conditions relative to the Gertlauken school. My mouth went quite dry and it lasted for about five minutes, as I realised that I was the only teacher there.

Gertlauken has a three-class school. One of the teachers married shortly before the war and departed, and the other two teachers moved soon after the war began. The children, 115 in number, had no schooling for some time. Then instructions were issued for a temporary help teacher, who since 1 October 1941 has spent three days in the Gertlauken school and three days teaching in his own village of Nachbardorf nearby.

I stayed with the school official for so long that my train had left and of necessity I had to spend the night in Labiau. He recommended to me the Hotel Kronprinz and for eating purposes the Ratskeller, and thought I should have a look around Labiau. It is a place of 6,000 inhabitants and is an ambitious, small town. It is proud of a new sports centre and a small park at the railway station. I can honestly say that both appeared to me to be so tiny, like a little town at the end of the world. Perhaps this can only be seen as snootiness on the part of children from a large city such as Köln. The most impressive in any case is the town hall. It is newly built, whitewashed and over the entrance stand four wooden figures of religious knights. The town has been developed around a monastery which had a moat

157

[*Wassenburg*] and it is still in good condition, having survived the times.

Despite that, as a town Labiau does not appear to me to be quite as important as the head teacher thinks it to be. I saw nothing bigger than a fishing village, a main street with grey, low houses and off that a few lanes or alleys. Along the River Deime were a few fishermen's cottages. The river itself enters the Kurische Haff [lagoon] behind Labiau itself. Fishing plays the most important role and one notices the smell in the harbour. I stood on the Adler bridge that spans the river and I could sense the presence of the lagoon in the distance. But since it was cold and I felt frozen, I rushed back to the Ratskeller.

Later I had the hotel more or less to myself (it was a quiet day and only a couple of hotel guests were present) and I made friends with the waiter. He was scarcely eighteen years old, a chief officer in the Hitler Youth organisation in which he has to serve for a year. Here he is leading an idle life and is quite a show-off. He boasted of his many connections from which I profited a little by us stuffing ourselves with a quarter-pound bar of delicious chocolate.

This morning for my sake he got up extra-early and had my suitcases lugged to the station. Perhaps he will visit me this coming weekend with his car!

My train goes at 7.31 a.m. the next morning. I must travel three stations beyond Labiau, these being Deimetal, Scheleken and then the train halts in Mauern. Ten metres from it runs a dead-straight road which loses itself after thirty metres into the forest. Three small farmhouses border the road, and near and far are only fields surrounded by forests stretching to the horizon to meet a wide, infinitely high sky with its racing clouds.

I saw the train depart and stood with my three suitcases and handbag, and felt very alone and lost. No people were present apart from one farmer about to get on his horse-drawn cart. Before he could leave, I rushed over to him and asked for directions to Gertlauken. He said he was going to Krakau which was halfway to Gertlauken, and I could get on the cart and could then make my way further from Krakau. He put my luggage on the cart, placed a warm blanket over my knees and handed me a sheepskin-lined coat to put on – seemingly the wind whistles quite strongly in these parts.

Soon we crossed the tarmac state road from Königsberg to Tilsit and came through a large village where on the right I saw the roof of a castle, formerly a hunting castle of the great electoral prince who liked to hunt there [*Auerhahnjagd*].

Behind the village were fields, a smallish forest and then more fields. A broad vista, a couple of bends in the road and finally a new village, Krakau. Uneven pavements, whitewashed houses with thatched roofs nestling against the dark earth.

The farmer meanwhile had learnt that I was the new lady teacher at Gertlauken and took me in his cart the last five kilometres to the Gertlauken school. What he had told me about on our journey I then saw for myself. In June of that year a huge fire occurred in Gertlauken and destroyed fifteen houses. Their bleak ruins stood there still. The fire was at Whitsun and strangely enough had originated in a coal store. Here and there between the ruined houses stood an untouched and intact house that the fire had simply bypassed. The people are working hard to rebuild their houses and in the meantime live in their stables or with neighbours. Gertlauken lies midway between Königsberg and Tilsit, both of these towns being about sixty kilometres distant from the village. Twenty kilometres in the southerly direction lies Wehlau and another twenty kilometres to the north-west is Labiau. In peacetime an omnibus travelled daily from Gertlauken to Wehlau but now in wartime one is dependent on a bicycle as the nearest railway station is at Mauern some ten kilometres distant.

I placed my suitcases in the hallway of the school which is itself a massive three-storey brick-built house that was spared by the fire. It was the opinion of the town mayor that I should find accommodation and board with Frau Stachel. She is the wife of the head teacher who has been called up by the army. She is a cheerful, dainty, dark, thirty-year-old with two charming children. She was not very pleased about my request and sent me to the Krug, the only Gasthaus in the village, at the crossroads. The landlady at the Krug who also had two children gave me a very negative 'No.' Her husband is a soldier and as she is alone she does only the things that are energetically necessary. So back I went to Frau Stachel and explained that I was running from here to there between the mayor, the Gasthaus Krug and herself. And that I would like someone to please tell me where I could obtain food before I died of hunger. Frau Stachel apologised and said that she had not known of all the circumstances and made me some sauté potatoes with fried eggs. It was a marvellous, tasty meal and thereafter I saw the world once again as a friendly place.

In a short time Frau Stachel and I were in agreement as to my accommodation. For five Reichsmarks a month she rented her attic to me and for an additional sum monthly of forty-five Reichsmarks she took me in for full board. The attic is small but simply furnished and has one large tiled stove with pipes which heats the place wonderfully. I don't need to pay for wood as the town mayor says that it comes under the school expenses.

At midday Frau Stachel took me with her to visit her friend Frau Kippar, a forestry woman, quite smart and very pretty. Her forest house is surrounded by tall old trees behind which is the meadow. Beyond that the forest itself begins. I was very quickly on the friendliest of terms with her. She has no children and her husband is serving on the Eastern Front, as, too, is her brother. Her younger brother was killed, and left behind a wife and four small children.

Gertlauken 3 November 1941

My dear Father

Your loving letter of 29 October reached me today. Seldom have I been so pleased over the receipt of a letter. I read of all your love and care expressed in it and all that the ones at home put up with in such an understanding manner.

Yesterday, Sunday, I was in the school and occupied myself at once with the schoolbooks. It is not too bad and not completely disordered. The small Helma Stachel came and told me that a visitor had come to see me. It seemed impossible that I had so early such a visitor but it was so, and there and then Paula Wegman stood before me. She had come twenty kilometres on foot from her place of duty at Weidlacken. In her school there she has exactly 100 children but she is one of the two teachers.

On her journey to East Prussia she could not obtain a hotel room in Königsberg and so had to spend the night in the waiting room. We spoke about many things, whether our money is sufficient and whether in the Christmas holidays we might be able to make a journey to the West. Frau Stachel and I had been invited by Frau Kippar for a meal and I was allowed to bring Paula along. The meal was roast goose and in the afternoon, cake. I then accompanied Paula for half of her return journey.

This morning I was to have gone to Herr Schulz in Krakau in

order to receive teaching instructions. But in the night it snowed and the snow lay ten centimetres deep. As the shoes I had were rubber-soled it was impossible to venture outside. Early today I attempted to disregard the weather, went outside and fell violently head over heels, and eventually landed ten metres away in the snow in front of a lady and a child. I was not the only one unable to stand up on the icy surface but it must have appeared so comical, especially happening to a so-called respectable lady teacher. Then the lady introduced me to the child, her daughter, as the Lady Teacher. Apparently she had been in telephonic communication with Herr Schulz to ascertain my identity.

The food here is excellent. In the morning Olga, Frau Stachel's maid, brings the coffee up to me. Midday, afternoon and evening meals I eat with Frau Stachel. She leads a marvellous life here, just as Frau Kippar does. Both do much handiwork, sit cosily together at coffee and converse.

Gertlauken 15 November 1941

Dear Father

I feel like a non-swimmer who has been thrown into deep water. I followed your piece of advice and gave my schoolchildren a day off and hiked over to Krakau to see Herr Schulz. He gave me a wonderfully instructive talk, with many good hints and lots of advice. Also I was received in a very friendly way. It was about 5 p.m. when I left and the five-kilometre journey back proved to be a wonderful walk.

Organising the work of many differently aged pupils in a single class makes many difficulties for me. Arithmetic and German are both reasonably straightforward for me, but with regard to local history, general history and geography, these subjects make more work for me. Whether my allotted school hours are enough to achieve a successful result, I don't as yet know.

Because I have so many pupils of different ages to occupy my services simultaneously, I have to speak for quite a lot of the time. A constant question of mine is what prevention to take to avoid a sore throat. Two much talking is a matter to be addressed seriously since for three or four days I was practically voiceless and merely whispered. But things now are improving, even with my cold.

We have quite new toilets, earth closets, six metres from the school and there is one expressly for the teacher, solely for me. That, for me, is very unusual and peculiar, having previously taken second place!

The children have nothing better to do at the start of the week in this wet weather than to run over the seats with their muddy wooden shoes. Whenever I enquire as to the culprit, the reply is always 'Nobody.' My answer was 'Good, then in the afternoon all children in the upper grade will clean the toilets.' At 3 o'clock they were there, coming from Frau Berkan, the wife of the second teacher, with bucket and brushes, water and scrubbers and did their domestic cleaning duties in the cold, just eight degrees. I hope I was also their sole topic of conversation. In all other respects the children are very good. I don't need to ask for the help of Herr Schulz or the school head. By no means would I like to say that I couldn't cope – that would finish me with them.

I have not as yet come into contact with the rest of the people in the village. I have always to work, stop for meals and spend time with Frau Stachel whose children are very nice. Both Frau Stachel and Frau Kippar are very kind to me. Frau Stachel has already given me a bowl of gingerbread. This afternoon in Frau Stachel's kitchen they both baked Christmas biscuits, three different kinds and all cooked with good butter. The food is especially unique. I wish you could come here for a little while, then I would be able to reciprocate your kindnesses. Perhaps you could send me a good book? And how could I manage without Olga who cleans my room and washes my clothing?

Mother writes so anxiously about the waiter in Labiau. He is a high official in the Hitler Youth, just eighteen years of age and a Strutzer with connections. I thought perhaps he could take Paula and myself in his car to the station, should the opportunity arise to enable us to travel home to you for Christmas. But you need not worry yourself on that score as on the Friday in question he is not coming this way. He sent a telegram that I should go to Labiau today, Sunday. Naturally, I have turned him down, so my love does not become part of his connections.

My accordion arrived here safely on Thursday and I must collect it from the post office. A forestry worker lent me a cycle and I took it with me to school. I was most grateful to him, for the post office is a fair distance from the school and right at the far end of the village.

Most of the people here in Gertlauken are forestry workers but there are also smallholding farmers with their ten to fifteen hectares. There are also leaseholders [leased farms] who in summer work on their farms and in winter the forest. They are known here as wood movers and the women and children help in the tree planting. There are a couple of labourers, an over worker, a site marker, a shoemaker, a baker, a butcher and so on, on occasion sometimes even one or two charcoal burners. Larger farms with 90 or 100 hectares are rare. For the most part the forestry workers are friendly and live here in a housing estate. They own at the most about two hectares of land on which each has his pig, his goose, ducks and sometimes also a cow, and keeps chickens. A pleasant occupation is that of the beekeeper. One such owner has 100 beehives but most have each between two and ten hives.

Gertlauken itself lies on a long drawn-out village street but the houses with their barns and stables are a fair distance from each other. In the centre of the village two roads cross. On one side of the crossing is the Gasthaus Krug and on the other side a solitary shop. The country road comes from the direction of Laukischken and Krakau and then a road junction leads to Wehlau, where in peacetime a bus connection existed.

It is a little way further on across a stream, Nehne, that Frau Kippar lives. A little further at the edge of the forest stands the house of the forestry higher officials, and still deeper in the forest is hidden the small village cemetery.

If one goes in the direction of Laukischken along the road passing the Gasthaus Krug, the road itself narrows as it goes through Kuckers and Damerau towards Weidlacken. The Wehlauer street leads to the post office, beyond which a short way lie the woods.

Lauken is by the way Lithuanian in origin and called Feld. Actually the village itself lies in the middle of brushwood woods, through which runs the Nehne stream, the village being hemmed by its banks.

Send me please as soon as possible my cycle. Without it I am stuck here.

Gertlauken 26 November 1941

My dear Parents and Wolfgang
I've become quite settled here and the people are all friendly. Occasionally I feel quite strange and feel as if I am on but a temporary visit. But then again I feel as if I have been here in Gertlauken for

163

many months. The only thing missing is to have colleagues and their advice regarding the work to be done here in the school.

I have so many different and difficult pieces of work to do requiring knowledge and experience, all directed towards enabling the children to absorb the educational material, that I have scarcely any time to give though to anything else.

But what brings so much happiness to me, and I thank you wholeheartedly for them, are your loving letters. Especially the letter from Father that I received today. He is so well ordered and clear in his letters, so typical of Father.

Concerning my working methods, I try to do all I can and attempt to do my best, but it comes hard to me to do so. Women, at least myself, seem to possess but a little talent to shine. Besides, I work slowly.

My cold is better and that means I can again speak clearly and have only a strong sniff and something of a cough. I am pleased with my altered coat from Mother, for since yesterday it has again become considerably colder. Woollen gloves are wanted very much by me. I know Aunt Lies will knit me a hood and scarf and a woollen petticoat. Please also send me my tracksuit.

Getting to know trainee waiters and forestry helpers has little to do with happiness. Why should I not have a conversation with a waiter? Often they know a lot about human nature. But this one is a show-off.

I have just had the following exchange with a forestry helper.

'Fräulein, may I carry your packet on my bike to your house?' It was the accordion.

'No,' I replied, 'it would be too heavy and awkward for you.'

'No, just give it to me and I shall take it to the school and place it in the hall.'

'In that case thank you very much.'

Gertlauken 12 December 1941

My dear Parents and Wolfgang

For goodness' sake do not send me too many medicines and herbal teas. The water here is not easy to obtain and its supply is not very practical. The Stachels have a pump in their dwelling. The water comes from a well outside the house and one can only drink the water after boiling it. For the last two days Olga has brought me a

164

bucket of water for washing purposes but of course I cannot drink it.

In a moment I shall be clearing the teacher and training books out and have available the inventory and catalogues, of which many are missing. In addition, the complete numbered and registered circulars on science and education, and also the school records have to be put in order.

When the head teacher comes on leave at Christmas he must find no rubbish. Besides I stopped an extra afternoon's extra tuition for the 1st-year scholars. Therefore I must patiently and lovingly spend an extra hour for the whole year to make up for this. I calculate, for example, to spend from 1 p.m. to 5 p.m. with them in the arithmetic classroom. There one points to two benches and two benches, two windows and two windows, two ten-pfennig pieces and two ten-pfennig pieces, and so on. Then the question is 'How much is two and two?' Answer 'three'! Today I kept the 5th- and 6th-year pupils for an hour. I have taken them in history and spoke about Friedrich Barbarossa and Heinrich of the Lions, and before that I read them a saga and a poem. I believe they enjoyed it and before we knew it an entire hour had passed.

My salary for two months I received yesterday, 315.17 Reichsmarks. From the health insurance I received 7.50 marks. So it is all right. Father pays the bill and I pick up the money.

Laukischken with 1,200 inhabitants pays (Gertlauken has 800). It is about ten kilometres distant and reached only by bicycle. The nearest doctor lives there and it is a church village, and the children go on foot there to attend confirmation instruction.

Gertlauken 15 December 1941

My dear Kölners

It is now 5 o'clock and outside complete darkness. That's why I must get to the classes, clear away, tidy up and ensure the blackout measures obscure everything.

I have now received today information from Wehlau that I must pick up your parcel tomorrow. Your clever way of sending it express failed to take into account that there is no railway station in Gertlauken. The nearest station is ten kilometres distant. Because all the post goes to Wehlau and to the express goods office, all such packets naturally go there. That is twenty kilometres away from here.

So now I must see how I can get the parcel here. Tomorrow after school I will attempt to go to Wehlau on Frau Kippar's bicycle and that is an old, worn out, rattling bike without a luggage pannier and without lights. How I shall manage it is a puzzle to me. Additionally the paths are soft to such an extent that one could remain stuck there. Yesterday when I went to the toilet one of my shoes got stuck in the mud and as I made my way cautiously back, my other shoe also stuck and I stood in stockinged feet in the mud.

The holidays start on 20 December and on 18 December there is a meeting in Nautzken which is situated between Labiau and Königsberg. From there I shall travel home to Köln but the big question is, how do I get from Nautzken to Königsberg? In any case I want to get the train at 21.50 as it goes to Berlin. Paula also wants to catch this train. But it is holiday time and I am looking forward enormously to our reunion.

Gertlauken 14 January 1942

My dear Father and you lovely Kölners
I have been so pleased with Father's lovely letter, the first post again from home. Settling down here again is hard but still I will not complain. Instead I will tell you about my return journey. At Wuppertal, the small Ursula Lange got on the train and in Hagen I bellowed out on the station, 'Helga! Helga!' but no Helga was there, nor was she aboard the train despite my running up and down the carriages looking for her. We got out at Potsdam and the state railway connection for Berlin stood there already. In Charlottenberg we sat in the waiting room where a quarter of an hour later we saw Helga. You can imagine what a pleasure it was to meet her, especially after she had caught an earlier train.

Later in the train a young railway worker told us that in the vicinity of Konitz, Helga's destination, nearly all the residents were Poles who lived in very primitive conditions. I wished Helga all good fortune.

In the station at Mauern I met a lady from Gertlauken who was riding home on her bicycle and she loaned me her fur coat. Then I got in a sledge with a survey officer and his two assistants for the journey to Gertlauken. At first the sun shone but then it became extremely cold. The sledge was actually built to carry four persons but with the farmer driver we were five. I made myself as thin as

166

possible and squeezed myself in between the others. The seating was on straw sacks and as I sat in a squatting position I jumped about on the freeing sledge boards with every jerk and jolt. Difficult to keep one's balance, should the sledge start slipping over.

But all went well and in Gertlauken we first warmed ourselves with two hot drinks. Then I sunk into bed dead tired.

Gertlauken 16 January 1942

My dear Parents, Aunt Lies and Wolfgang
I will quickly write to each of you a couple of lines. The settling-down period still remains hard for me. But this afternoon Paula came and stays a week with me. The holiday period in Wehlau district is fifteen days longer in order to save on heating material. Paula found this out on her return. Frau Stachel is so good to us for without a murmur she took in Paula as a guest and put another bed in my room for her.

Gertlauken 18 January 1942

My dear Parents and Wolfgang
In my village of 800 inhabitants I still meet with kindness. It is most certainly a forest village [country village] with more people being foresters than any other calling. The king of all is the Head Forest Master. Many of the family names here end with 'at' like Dannat, Stuppat, or with 'eit' as in Schusereit, Nikoleit, but also with 'ke' such as Lemke, Liedtke, Of course there are also common names like Schwarz, Beckmann and Neumann, while the ending 'etter' occurs as in Scharfetter for instance (the Head Forest Master is so named). Austrian origins are few. The people with such names come from being refugees, on each exodus of such from Salzburger Land in about 1732, because of their religious beliefs being different from those of their bishops. Also, following the wars of Frederick the Great, these refugees settled in sparsely populated areas of East Prussia because of the big plague from 1709–1711. At the church at Laukischken the pastor has to give his sermons also in the Lithuanian language. By the way, the famous parish minister Annchen von Tharau has also been there.

In summer Paula and I intend to make a thorough exploration of our immediate surroundings. We are also glad we have electric light as this is not the case everywhere.

Compared with Helga's circumstances we have things exceptionally good here and yesterday I received the first letter from her. She is in an eight-class people's school in Konitz where in addition to her, there is the schoolmaster and one young trainee schoolmistress. The people are exclusively Kaschuben and speak scarcely any German. Now the head teacher has thirty German children to teach whereas at the beginning he had 171 children who could speak hardly any German. In addition there is a weekly afternoon vocational school with thirty pupils.

On Saturday was the village community evening. Hitler Youth and Bundes Deutsche Madchen gave a lot of trouble. The local branch leader first spoke, then followed organised dancing and a sing-song. The youths all had a marvellous time until the meeting closed at midnight. Frau Stachel and I had left earlier. As a BD Madchen myself I should have confirmed the speeches, but I wish I could only find the time to do so.

Now I am deeply into a fairy tale about which I must write a report. We have now about an average of twenty-five degrees of frost. On Sunday it was even thirty-five degrees of frost. The poor soldiers at the front in Russia.

Gertlauken 5 February 1942

Dear All of You

I now thank you most gratefully for your dear letters and especially for the two packets. From Heinrich Kuhn from Köln came the following books: *Geography and Local History as People's Cultural Heritage, National Heritage and School, School Physics and Their Application as a Learning Process, Life Experiences and People's School Days*, and *Musical Appreciation and Application in People's Schools*.

The concerns of the school are gradually giving me pleasure and I hope that all my greatest difficulties are now behind me. I understand my duties inside out and know what I may show confidence in and in what subjects I may not have such confidence. In the beginning always I had too much to take in, like how to go back to my goal and limit myself to what was really necessary. Sometimes now I do only repetition work and then I am underemployed and notice how little responsibility attaches to the task in hand.

Here it snows on and off but it is not quite so cold, only just minus twenty degrees, and in the sunshine it is almost warm.

Monday evening Frau Berkan and I went to a small hill near the frozen River Nehne and attempted to discover how the children slide downwards in a crouching position. They go quite naturally almost on their trouser bottoms. Then we skated backwards and forwards and lay on our stomachs and tobogganed. We spent two hours outside and it was wonderful and it was almost midnight before we left for home. We had a full moon and it had two large auras, such as I had never seen before. The sky in East Prussia is exceptionally wonderful.

Gertlauken 13 February 1942

My dear Parents and Wolfgang
Is it always not so cold in Köln? Does not so much snow lie there? It has blown a terrible storm for two days here and the wind howls and whines round the house. For the 7th and 8th school year pupils I have set an essay that I must soon check. It is about the First and Second World Wars. After Hitler's speech on 31 January. I was horrified about myself for each excerpt is obvious. Foreign words and names I have to write on the blackboard and such names have to be written in German-sounding equivalents – Tschordschell for Churchill! I have to push myself but it is the only way I shall learn all the same. The resulting image is that my pupils and I have a good understanding. In the opinion of the old East Prussian teacher the best way of learning was by using the cane. That, for me, is not a pleasant way and the cane should only be used in the worst case. The children of course have long ago got wise to this fact.

Quite often when teaching, something laughable happens or occurs but I must put on a stern face, which again I find amusing. But if I look into their eyes it is my own reflection I see. Often my sternness collapses and goes entirely, such as when a girl, a 7th-year pupil, held her finger up to answer a question, and at that moment I was distracted elsewhere, and when after two minutes I returned, she still held her finger up. She looked at me so innocently and wondered what was to happen, but I praised her very much.

I could write and talk about the children for hours on end but this letter has to go to the postbox to ensure it leaves tomorrow morning.

My dear Parents and Wolfgang

As I posted my letter at 9.30 p.m. the previous week it suddenly became eerie outside. The storm howled and the clouds raced across the sky, no stars were to be seen and the only light came from the snow. In the evening large numbers of dogs in the village and its environs ran around and howled. Suddenly I noticed something crawling behind me, it was something dark creeping towards me or it could be motionless. Then there was howling on one side of the road and then on the other side. Also the trees in the wood rustled violently. No wonder one gets frightening thoughts and anxieties. As I got to the school I said to Frau Berkan 'It is really quite frightening outside and the weather is really nasty to go out in. At first we told each other crime or ghost stories but after an hour we donned our coats and went outside. Before we reached the woods there was a housing estate and Frau Berkan said that it was her opinion we should proceed no further. Although we were not completely frightened, our hearts did beat furiously and our mouths were dry. Suddenly she sank up to her knees in the snow and I likewise. Further stumbles in the snow followed and our mutual laughter at our wallowing in the snow drove all our fear away and we lived to tell the tale. Then the sky suddenly became clear and one star after another appeared to light us on our way.

My dear Parents and Wolfgang

Today there was a young teachers' conference in Labiau. I should have held a lecture on arithmetic and volumes but I know I still find difficulty in subjects. I read a page three times and still do not know what I have read. Such is the work I have here before me all day long. (Father, don't grumble!) So as a result I work late hours and before I know it I hear the cry 'Morning up!' and at 6 a.m. I must get out of bed. Then at 6.30 a.m. at the latest I must be on my bike and the day begins at 9 a.m. And it is to Labiau I must cycle – twenty kilometres!

Yesterday evening a strong storm arose and Frau Berkan suggested that I should not travel. However, at 7 a.m. I got on my bicycle. I was dressed in woollen stockings, socks over them, boots, tracksuit, over which I had a black jacket, pullover, cardigan, a tracksuit blouse, coat, Mother's woolly hat over my head and the brown hood. In addition to all that, a long woollen scarf from Frau Berkan and three pairs of woollen gloves. The morning was wonderful, the sun came out and gleamed brighter in the snow, the birches bent in the wind and the fir trees rattled noisily. Because I had the wind at the back of me it was a glorious journey and I reached Labiau at twenty minutes before 9 a.m.

Those attending the conference had decreased in number but as usual we had to submit our travel expenses. I didn't have any and only received two marks subsistence allowance for the day. But the district head teaching official couldn't get over my cycling efforts.

'How could you cycle in this weather?' he said. But the farmers have always ridden so, when the sledge is broken or the horse is sick. Therefore one does not loiter but just takes the easiest way to go on. 'But can't you travel on the train from Laukischken?' he continued.

'But that way I would have had ten kilometres of bad roads to content with and this also applies to the next ten kilometres. So better to travel on the country road.'

Then, a shaking of the head and he paid me my daily expenses and also five more marks for excellent sporting activity, and I can most certainly use the money. I have had to pay out this month twelve marks for a bookcase, twelve marks for four strong, solid wood pieces for the coming winter, with the cost of carriage and delivery of same between eight and ten marks. On top of that I have the opportunity to buy a couple of hundredweights of coal at five marks per hundredweight.

I like visiting the conference, as one becomes stimulated by something new and also sometimes how one should not do things. I really earned my five marks on the return journey for it was indeed cold, even though only minus six degrees. The east wind was so cutting that it penetrated all my clothing and blew consistently into my face. After Laukischken my cycle chain came off and I had to push the bike three kilometres to Krakau, where I was helped by teacher Schulz who made my cycle roadworthy again. I like going to him as he is such a confident teacher and has a little agricultural land with beehives. I like especially his wife, who is expecting a child. Naturally they didn't let me leave without coffee and cakes. After our cosy chat I set off to cycle the remaining five kilometres.

Meanwhile the strong wind had turned into a snowstorm and

covered the path in an instant. On the way I met the father of one of my pupils. He was a soldier stationed in the district. We journeyed on together but he set a terribly fast pace, that I kept up with as I didn't wish to be left behind. Because of the freezing cold little was said, but as we said our goodbyes, I remarked, 'Normally I don't travel so fast, but you set such a terrific pace that I had to do the same.'

1 March

Today is Sunday and I have used five hours to darn my stockings and put clean collars on my clothes and pullovers, as this chore was plainly necessary. Whilst so employed I listened to the radio and heard a wonderful hour of ballads.

On the Sunday previously I travelled to Paula – it was a terrible bicycle journey. In the morning an awful amount of military traffic had used the whole road. So for the first eight kilometres I had to tread in the snow and push my cycle and the cycle I had from Frau Kippar is now worn out as a result of going across fields. Please send me my own cycle as soon as possible.

Paula came part of the way to Schirrau to meet me and bought something from the butcher. I could have fallen asleep in the snow while waiting and had the nonsensical thought 'Beforehand you must empty the butcher's shop,' so long was my wait!

But on the next day I found the return journey not half as difficult. It made one think whether it was best to encounter and overcome difficulties at the beginning or at the end. As I reached the outskirts of South Gertlauken I compared it with Rome and the seven roads all leading there, as my path lay all white and shining before me.

Gertlauken 2 March 1942

My dear Parents and Wolfgang

Once again, wonderful post. Naturally you will say 'Yes' even if I would like a lot of things. First, for once a bit of advice, and please give a really quick answer.

You know well that Frau Stachel is very nice and kind to me. Despite this I would like to leave her attic and find a single apartment. The 3rd teacher apartment stands empty and for three to five marks I could rent it. Above all things, furniture I can borrow or you may remark that you can send my room's furnishings to me. I hope that

Frau Stachel will loan me her bed but some bed linen Mother must send to me. Thankfully there is a wire connection for a portable immersion heater or cooker or an electric hotplate. What should you think best?

The apartment lies on the 2nd floor opposite the floor of the house of Frau Stachel, through which now I have to pass to get to my attic. The apartment has a large room (with smart wallpaper) through which one comes to a small, dark kitchen, which is windowless but with a cooker. This kitchen leads to a further room with a broad view of the garden, the long village street and the meadows and the River Nehne, leading to the forest. These two rooms possess a typically lovely East Prussian tiled oven with pipes. Write at once and tell me what you think of this idea?

For the teaching lessons I need material about wood, wood extraction and processing. Which trades use wood?

Also a shoe purchasing coupon for Olga. There are no shoes to purchase here. Dear Mother, do please do me these favours. Olga has shoe size 37 and she would like a sports shoe with flat heels.

Gertlauken 13 March 1942

My dear Parents and Wolfgang

You are completely against my apartment plan. Mother was so disturbed that she wrote to me forcefully by immediate return of post. I looked at all the difficulties relating to this idea beforehand. Only I must have this chance as by the time you receive this letter I shall be living alone. Frau Stachel travels shortly, within the next week, with her children and Olga to stay with her parents for three weeks. I know that this is the best opportunity I shall have to cope on my own. But what shall I eat, as the Gasthaus food supply is out?

This morning in school I asked who has furniture to spare, above all a bed, table and chair. I have but only one request and that is Mother to send me as quickly as possible a tablecloth and sufficient bed linen for changing. Perhaps she also has a couple of lengths of cloth from which I can sew drapes, or perhaps something for small curtains. Wants, nothing but wants has the child!

I must now cook only for myself, at least that so far is known. If you should visit me in Gertlauken you must not go hungry. I may obtain potatoes from Frau Stachel, also daily a litre of full cream milk. In spring we shall plant a seed bed in the school garden

173

producing vegetables and potatoes for the next winter. This will be an amateurish effort on my part, first the theoretical part and then the coping with the physical part, also much work.

Anyway, now on to another topic. The meadow next to the River Nehne was flooded in autumn and now there is an enormous stretch of mirror-smooth ice. Each afternoon the village children hurry there with their skates. Often they join hands and make a huge chain or they use a large piece of cloth as a sail and with a wind blowing strongly, glide over the ice. They always urge me to take part in the fun. As I do not possess a pair of skates, I borrow a pair from one of the pupils. That is why, really, I have been able to skate with Frau Berkan by moonlight, when it is utterly heavenly to go on the ice. It goes much better than we thought it would and we have had much fun. We had on two occasions skated almost until midnight and very romantic it was in the bright stillness of the night.

By the way, it is again very cold, minus thirty degrees. The pump does not work any more and we must fetch the water from the well.

There the surface was frozen and I had to get a ladder and then climb down with an axe to smash a hole in the ice. That was exciting!

Has Father heard anything about his discharge or Wolfgang about his call-up to the military? I did not know that Hans Klefisch had been killed. The poor parents, the only child, and they had not begrudged it, only that he had to leave his studies.

Gertlauken 18 March 1942

You dear Parents

My plan gives you all great excitement but there is not much more to change. Today I got a table, a chair and a mattress. The bed is following on. Please send all that you can spare. A small frying pan would be splendid.

On Sunday I was in Laukischken for the Heroes' Remembrance; Ceremony. One has yet again a duty to do but I have sufficient energy to do it. On Monday a telegram came from Paula and I wanted at once to go to her. My holiday request for Tuesday was granted and I cycled to her. The journey was a cruel strain to me and many times during it I thought it would be better to just lie down in the snow and sleep. It was dark when I arrived in Weidlacken and Paula was not in her room. I waited with the very kind lady teacher who told me that Paula had gone for a walk in the woods. She did not come home and we experienced many worries on her behalf. But where should we go to find her? By 10 o'clock we were all dead tired and the lady teacher offered me a free double bed – her husband is away as a soldier – in which to sleep. It was a real bedroom in which all her six children slept. Despite my cares and worries I went off to sleep at once and when I awoke next morning, Paula was there.

Her brother was killed near Stalingrad. She was especially close to him and she was greatly disturbed. For hours on end she had wandered through the woods in desperation. Those were such sorrowful hours we spent together and one felt helpless in the presence of her pain. It made me think all the time about Wolfgang – but no, I cannot even imagine it.

Gertlauken 25 March 1942

My dear Parents and Wolfgang

A thousand thanks for your letters. I can see that my resettlement plan gave rise to much excitement for you. When I am in Köln during my Easter holidays I shall answer all your questions.

This afternoon is for the trainee teachers' conference and tomorrow afternoon I teach the smaller children. After that, the next morning, there is another conference. Additionally there are still reports due to be sent to the head teacher. In the past week there were several school-leaving certificates to write – and how many times have I thought pleasurably – ten children less to teach. But when it came time for them to leave I nearly cried with the children. What must this feeling be like if one had a class of children for eight years!

I have heard about the attacks on Köln. That must, once again, have been terrible and I worry about you constantly. If Father is not discharged then in any case Mother should come here to me and she can cook for both of us. In haste.

Gertlauken 16 April 1942

My dear Parents and Wolfgang

It was lovely that I was able to travel to Köln and to be with you all again. My return journey was without incident and in Berlin I caught the 8.16 train at Charlottenberg for Königsberg and what a rush that was! On another track there was a train going to Krakau and a few minutes later one to Wien and then yet another going to

Warschau. Beyond Dirschau our train became empty. One noticed that as once again the colder zones were entered, the dirty, brown-coloured snow vanished. In Warthebruch and even here there are wide stretches of land underwater.

My room was nicely clean and warm and that was Frau Berkan's doing. She had also sent a cart to the station. At midnight, dead tired I sank into bed and felt very lonely after those days spent with you all.

At midweek the teaching begins and when I entered the classroom all was quiet as a mouse. The desk was covered with garlands of green fir, cones and birch branches. On the desk stood a vase of white snowdrops and purple woodland flowers, and in between, placed most artistically, built up so beautifully wrapped, were tissue-papered packages and bags tied with coloured ribbons.

What should I do? I was so surprised and simply speechless and then in came the small ones and it was really moving. Each wanted to shake my hand and congratulate me on my birthday. Most of them held very tightly in their other hand a bouquet of snowdrops and woodland flowers. One even had a piece of cactus with three red blossoms, another child gave me a picture card and yet another child gave me a photo of his mother. On top of the tremendous number of flowers I was given a hefty sack containing 109 eggs, 3 lb of ham and pork, ½ lb of sausages, 1 lb of butter, two small vases and a box containing home-baked biscuits. Frau Stachel baked a cake and Frau Birkau invited me for a meal.

The flowers have pleased me so much but as to the other presents I don't quite know how to go about things. I thought of Father – 'Only not acceptable'. I spoke with both the lady teachers about my problem and both said I must keep the presents otherwise the people would be offended.

Gertlauken 25 April 1942

My dear Parents and Wolfgang

I can see clearly that you are in a state of annoyance. But please, dear Father, being cross is useless in the end and you make it unnecessarily difficult for both yourself and Wolfgang, also for Mother. He didn't dare admit to you that he had enlisted voluntarily in the Waffen SS. First of all he has to do his basic training. Be patient with him and show your love and concern for him, and not your annoyance and anger.

My cycle arrived unbroken in Labiau and I am very happy that finally I have got it and many thanks for sending it. I rode on it at once from Labiau and on the way saw the first storks. One sees them here locally and here alone in our village there are twenty-six nests. The spring is uniquely beautiful here. In the woods, in the meadows and on the River Nehne, life is stirring everywhere. Cooking is fun for me. Daily I fetch half a litre of full cream milk. Delicious whipped cream one can prepare in the following way: one teaspoon wheat flour, two teaspoons sugar with a quarter of a litre of skimmed milk, all mixed together; leave standing for twenty-four hours and then whip. Have you got potatoes? How is it going with the air raids? Write to me, above all, about Wolfgang!

Gertlauken 1 May 1942

My dear Mother

How are you feeling? I find myself always thinking about you and you will probably be depressed following Wolfgang's departure. But first comes his basic training and fancy he being stationed in Berlin, where he will most certainly become enlightened. Don't let yourself get depressed, my dear Mother, I think so much of you and Wolfgang and I am eager to get first news of him.

Today is a free school day, and Paula and I are going very early by train to Memel. Now Father must think, 'Such a flitting-around person I have as a daughter, she should be studying, that is more important to her.' But still, it is through our travels that we are learning more about the country and its people than books could convey.

On Saturday last I was with Paula and on Sunday we set off early at 5 a.m. on our cycles. Our destination was Gumbinnen where Paula's sister is in hospital. Which particular hospital she did not know, but we packed a lovely parcel for her. Such an early morning is wonderful. No people were on the street and the woods were so fragrant. We travelled in a circular route, over the River Pregel to Norkitten where we took the main road to Gumbinnen. Not far beyond lay Gross-Jagersdorf where in 1757 the Russians and the Prussians fought. First we came through Insterburg, a friendly, lively place that made quite an impression on us. Many troops, a large market square with a couple of beautiful gabled houses, a church and also a castle. We didn't stay all that long and travelled smartly on further. By the way, the River Pregel flows first to Insterburg then the Inster flows from the north, the Angerapp to the south and the Pissa from the east. All these rivers join together. Gumbinnen lies on the River Pissa. Unfortunately we did not see much of the town. We went to one hospital and then went on to another but neither had the name of Paula's sister in their registers. Finally we went to another hospital where we learnt that the Friday previously she had been transported to the west. For us a disappointment, but for her most certainly a blessing.

Gertlauken 7 May 1942

My dear Parents

Father's account of the destruction of Köln is dreadful. I am with you experiencing all through the wreckage. Karthauser Church intact, the Finance Office burnt out, Maria im Frieden and Sankt Pantaleon destroyed. I am so happy that all is still standing in the Cimbernstrasse. Luckily the chest from Kaufhof arrived here safely and I had to collect it at once from the station. It contained that beautiful crockery in which I delight so much, my heartfelt thanks. I took the chest immediately to the carpenter to enable him to put in a shelf so that I can use the chest as a crockery cupboard and a food pantry.

The weekend in Memel was heavenly. Paula and I took the first train on Saturday and went from Mauern to Tilsit, which we wanted to see first. Tilsit – Queen Louise, Napoleon. The Queen Louise Bridge must be the most beautiful bridge known in Germany. Tilsit is a small town with many memories of Max von Schenkendors of the Freedom Writers ('Freedom – that is me') and a lovely Jakobsruh park. Here I would like to live, I thought, and would have liked to have stayed a little longer. Naturally we also visited the Luisenhaus where the Prussian queen met Napoleon.

In Memel we found a good hotel room opposite the theatre and felt quite princely. In the square stands the Simon-Dach Fountain you will know, the writer of the songs of Annchen von Tharau. Memel lies at the exit of the Kurische Lagoon. The Kurische Nehrung, a narrow sand-dune piece of land dividing the lagoon and the east sea [Baltic] ends here. A track connects the town with Sandkrug on the spit of land itself. We travelled along it and so I have for the first time seen the sea in endless water that meets the horizon. I was overcome by the experience and could scarcely leave.

I like the country here and particularly the people who are so friendly. Literature plays a great part in the district. The life here is so calm as in the depths of peacetime, but then comes your account of another terrible world.

Gertlauken 16 May 1942

My dear Parents

It is 22.55 on a Saturday and although I am dead tired I must thank you for your loving letters. Are you now discharged, Father, and always at home? Have you news of Wolfgang? Write to me please at once. No, I can't go on, I am too tired and can scarcely keep my eyes open. I was house cleaning today, kitchen and room cleared out and wiped clean. What luck that tomorrow is Sunday.

Gertlauken 17 May 1942

My dear Parents

Naturally I woke up as always at 6 o'clock and couldn't sleep any more with the heavenly blue sky which I can see from my bed. Glorious sunshine and the noise of the birds twittering. Also yesterday evening for a quarter of an hour I sat at the open window and heard them. It sounded like a nightingale, but there is a variety of birds here. The people call them *Sprossers*.

At 8 o'clock Paula visited me and we cycled to Labiau but not on the main road, instead through the area of the River Deime. The, river itself flows north to the lagoon. In World War I, one spoke of the 'Miracle on the Deime' because here the Russian troops came to a standstill. The area of the river is wonderful. The land is somewhat hilly and between the hills flows the river itself with many meanders, hemmed in with such lush meadows in the brilliant sunshine. The fields and meadows are of bright green and on the street verges stand the light-coloured birch trees with their delicate green leaves, which came almost overnight.

In Labiau we visited the courthouse, the castle in which there is the town museum with a fisherman's room with colourful furniture and the coloured dresses of the fishing folk with its artistic handiwork. Labiau is an historical place. Twice the Lithuanians were beaten by the army of the Order of the Knights and in 1657 the Great Electoral Prince entered into a treaty with the Swedes which led to his becoming the head of East Prussia.

From Labiau we went along the Grosse Friedrichsgraben Canal to the lagoon via Haffenwerder. The canal was dug in the 17th century and on the dyke road there was first-class cycling to be had. The wooden houses of the fishermen lie directly behind the dyke and carry at their roofs gables a horse's head just like those on display in Lower Saxony. Each household owns a boat. Twice with our cycles we had to cross the River Deime in small swaying boats. Similarly crossed was the Friedrichs Canal and that was great. In order to call a ferryman one has to ring a large bell. The further one goes north of the lagoon in the direction of Memel, the better the life on the water. There are small villages, Gilge for example, which one can only reach by boat. The worst time of the year is the 'Schacktarp' in autumn and in spring when the ice is not strong enough to cross the river on foot, or is too thick for the passage of a barge. Then, it is, that the people are cut off from the outside world, often for weeks on end. A friend from Dortmund has landed up in such a village called Elchwerde, formerly called Nemonien.

My dear parents, it was a beautiful, unending, peaceful day that enabled one to forget the whole terrible war with all its misery. That such a contrast can exist in the same country at the same time! How we enjoyed sitting on the edge of the lagoon, eating our bread and butter, before us a Keitel barge with its characteristically coloured, handmade, wooden, triangular flag on its mast. And we lay long, looking at sky and water, quoting Waiter Flex.

Gertlauken 19 May 1942

My dear Parents

Aunt Lies' portable immersion heater came today and for the first time I made myself my own substitute coffee. In addition the large and small packages came from Colonia! You cannot imagine, all of you, how pleased I am. In fact, in such a good mood, I sang all day long. In the afternoon I had to cycle ten kilometres to Laukischken in the pouring rain in order to go to the butcher to draw our entitlement. On the return journey I called in to see Herr Schulz and spent two hours nattering with him. Frau Berkan got very worried. As I came home, utterly soaked, she said, 'And she is still singing!'

So, about the things I am especially pleased with. I now have some cups and plates, two dishes, and one large and one small jug.

I have on loan from Frau Birkau a pot but Aunt Lies will soon send me one. I have also cutlery, above all a wooden spoon and two pieces of old cloth for washing-up and cleaning purposes.

As for food, I have here more than you. Perhaps I can send you some sweets. I often cook semolina pudding and eat much sour milk. In order not to use too much current I cook once a day a large pot full of coffee – usually this is at midday. Then I keep some of it in a jug and drink the coffee when it is cold. The rest I pour into my Thermos flask, so that I always have warm coffee available. The sweets I keep for giving to the children whenever they have occasion to call to see me, to bring me something or help me, or have questions to ask.

I must relate something about Mother's Day to you. The youngsters learnt a poem and we acted it out as we recited it at school with curtsies and bows. Then I said to them, 'You should go to the woods and pick as many flowers as you can carry and decorate Mother's chair with them, but do it very prettily.'

As I went to the post office in the afternoon I met Gisela Schwarz and Waltraud Pahlke, each with a huge carton under their arms. Shortly afterwards I met four other children, also with boxes and baskets, and soon after that another ten children, all bound for the woods to pick flowers. Businessman Schustereit told me that his shop is constantly full of children looking for presents to buy for Mother's Day. Later still, I met Gunter Buttkus, a friendly well-mannered youth, who stopped me, looked around cautiously and showed me a biliously coloured green belt he had bought for his mother for, he said, '1 mark 40'. I had my doubts whether his mother would fit into it.

Gertlauken 21 May 1942

My dear Parents
Just a short, heartfelt wish to you all at Whitsun. May the English leave you in peace and you spend a beautiful lovely day. Not long ago a strong storm blew in. It rained steadily and then suddenly left as if it had never been heard of. I had thought previously that because of the weather I need not go that evening to Krakau to the athletics. But at once the storm overhead must have heard and the sky now is blue as silk. The woods glisten freshly, all the birds are singing and the air is wonderfully clear. Somebody has said that if in East Prussia one

dares to leave the house without a wardrobe, then one should adapt himself to quickly changing weather.

From my window I have a wonderful view. Through the richly green meadow the River Nehne meanders and on the horizon the woods are sharply outlined. For a couple of days now the meadows beside the river are covered everywhere with marsh flowers and, from a distance, seen like a yellow sea. And throughout the entire day the cry of 'Cuckoo! Cuckoo!' is heard in the woods. So at 22.15 I came back to the house. The storm had gone by, the moon was in its first quarter, so it was not too dark. The clouds dashed across the sky and very secretly lifted themselves over the dark woods. I have only a certain amount of work and don't know whether I should rightly tackle it. I would like to give more to the children but there remains little time for these afterthoughts. There is one thing I do know and that is I would rather be alone than in a crowd of people and that I am better being quiet and inconspicuous than in the public spotlight. In the Bundes Deutche Madchen group it is terrible – 'Stand on the spot!', 'Forward March!' No, that is not for me, not to be like sheep following each other in a herd. Of that I am critically contemptuous. One should let people exercise their freedom, like myself.

Gertlauken 31 May 1942

My dear Parents

It has become midsummer here and one cannot see anything but greenery and blossom. In the meadows the cows stand up to their bellies in the grass. It was at first the yellow marsh flowers, now it has become a red sea because the meadow is covered with pink brook carnations. But also in the gardens, in the woods and in the ditches, everything blooms in colours of red, blue, white and yellow.

I never go out without my flower identification regulation book.

We had our county athletics competition today and in the course of it acquired a suntan, but still it is bearable. Yesterday Paula helped me do a huge laundry. You must excuse me that I write so messily – it is because I am so tired, ready to fall down in fact. On other occasions though I am full of news about my daily life and I like to write for hours on end about these activities of mine.

After the sports meeting I went to the farmer who has lent me a bed. I asked if it were possible to purchase it but unfortunately the answer was 'No'. But I had to stay there and enjoy a midday meal. It was *Stintenflinsen* – that I had never heard of. Apparently *Stinte* are tiny fish about six centimetres long and eaten with head and tail. They come from the lagoon and the sea outside, and as *Flinsen* they are salted, mixed with flour and cooked in the frying pan.

Recently we had a teachers' conference day from the National Socialist Teachers Union in Labiau. It was all speeches in full swing about the meaning of the collection of old materials, the war against the Jews and the likes of which, anyway, no one much listened. At the end of the meeting the head teacher approached me. I was a glider pilot, he said, would I like to take part in a flying model building course? The course lasts from 26 July until 8 August and takes place in Ferndorf, Bahnstation Kreuztal, in Siegener Land. What do you say to that? Is that not charming of the school head? And, I told him so.

Gertlauken 1 June 1942

My dear, dear Parents

What is happening to you? I still have no radio and always each morning I read the Armed Forces Report in the newspaper. There I read of the huge attack on Köln. I am quite bewildered. That must have been terrible for you. Please give me a sign of life, for I must think of you always, so do please let me hear from you soon.

Gertlauken 5 June 1942

Dear Father and dear Mother

Today I received your telegram of 1 June. Is Köln still in being? It is horrifying and my thoughts are ever of you. When can you come here? Father's report made me quite tense and anxious. It can be only good for you both to be together now that Father is again home. And, dear Father, don't upset yourself over the insults from stupid people, stay above it. How is it with the food situation? I think all day long of items and would love to send them to you. Do come here when it is possible.

You know that at Easter I was in Danzig. The difference is not easy to understand and it is inconceivable that at the same time terror and fear abound, whereas on the other side there are people enjoying beauty, peace and quiet, and drinking. I scarcely like to describe the fabulous Whit Sunday I spent, one is almost ashamed of such enjoyment. Danzig is the most beautiful town I have seen up to date. I am still quite full of it. Helga's acquaintance in the town acquired a room in a plush hotel, with a bath and a telephone. As Helga and I walked through the narrow alleyways of the old town we saw the illuminated high red-brick spire of the Marienkirche. I was overwhelmed, I know well our own cathedral in Köln, but this brick one here is so different with its many pointed turrets and big windows. The Köln cathedral stands free but this Danzig one is in the centre of the old town surrounded by houses that seem so small in comparison. And this, despite the fact that such houses are of three to four storeys in height and have wonderful gables.

Inside the cathedral one wanders through a forest of pillars beneath a star-bedecked roof. The contrast of the towers embracing the Marienkirche and the dainty towers of the town hall is most marked. And in the Langen market are a row of the most beautifully gabled houses, both high and low ones with only two to three windows width, but so surprisingly deep. I visited one, the Uphagenhaus with its furnishings dated from the 18th century. In such circumstances indeed did the businessman of the day live like a prince.

Near the town hall stands the Artushof. It corresponds to our Gurzenich, a meeting house of the town's people in the late Middle Ages. The Langgasse is very romantic, each house having in front a stairway of four to five steps. Then there was the Zeughaus [court]. At first I thought it was a castle with its staircased towers and splendidly decorated gables, although nothing like our simple dark building in the Komodienstrasse in Köln, no comparison at all.

There are many gateways to the Mottlau. One is called the Milchkannenturm mit Sahnekannchen [Milk Tower with Cream Jug]. That it is the symbol of the archway is only natural. The view, when one stands by the water and looks at the many storehouses, at the many archways and all the houses surrounding the Marienkirche, the latter with its impressive angled towers, is such that you, Father, must see. It is a beautiful view and if compared to many others, only our beloved Köln of an evening, with its Sunnerterrasse with the kilometre-long Lichterkette am Rhein, the glorious cathedral, the piled-up houses and the towers of Sankt Martin, stands in comparison. But then I know absolutely nothing about whether anything in Köln is still standing. I wait on your report.

On Whit Sunday Helga's acquaintances, a pleasant, childless

couple, were introduced. We first travelled to Oliva and visited the church there. The entrance seemed odd – two enormous, narrow but nevertheless massive brick towers with loopholes like windows and with pointed roofs. And in between, similar high and narrow baroque frontages with magnificent doors and a high window. We travelled further to Zoppo and the sun shone and all the world was afoot. The band played music to open its season. A long bridge led from the concert hall to the Baltic Sea and the people were lolling about or sunning themselves in deckchairs. With an untrammelled sky, a blue sea, cheerful people, nothing warlike going on, just simply a beautiful day.

The next day Helga travelled to Konitz but I had a further day and wanted to stroll again through Danzig.

And now, listen to this! On the Mottlau near the archway were shops, one after another and in one of which one could buy quite easily marvellous amber necklaces. I bought myself one and a small attachment.

Helga also wanted to buy presents for her sister and her mother and after a brief consultation about the financial position, the unique opportunity of buying presents, etc., we decided as follows. Bearing in mind Father's discussion and instructions regarding sending money by telegraphic order, I let Helga have all my ready money and was willing to pay the whole of our joint hotel bill when I received it. Next morning Helga went off happily and I went to the main post office where it was terribly busy. There I learnt that an Armed Forces Announcement had priority and that I would have to reckon on waiting for about eight hours. I was anxious and already saw myself locked up in prison for not paying my bill. Then I had a lucky break. The acquaintance of Helga was by chance in the post office. She saw me and my anxious face and loaned me 100 marks. I was so happy and immediately bought her a bouquet of roses, and as a result enjoyed even more my stroll through the town.

Gertlauken 8 June 1942

My dear, dear Parents
I have just received your letters of 2 and 4 June. It is dreadful that you had to endure so much. I howled when reading them. Nothing but destruction, smashed things, burnt-out buildings, annihilation in a scene of devastation and death. And what is there yet to

185

happen? One finally gets some news, only for it to be overtaken by more events. You are probably at the end of your tether with the nervousness of it all. How is the situation as far as food is concerned and those many without homes? And then the indescribable sorrow of so many families with all the valuables, etc. destroyed.

The Apostelkiche and Gross-Sankt-Martin were my favourite churches and in the Antoniterkirche I was confirmed. And Deutz has also suffered badly and the area surrounding you must have been burned. Isn't it possible that you both could come here for rest and relaxation? I have this awfully bad feeling if I so much as think of the danger you are in and the security such as I have here. I spend my time here in unbelievably peaceful, quiet days in Gertlauken and I am ashamed to tell you how pleasant a time it was for me on the previous Sunday. On Saturday Paula visited me and we got up at 5 a.m. and cycled to Labiau. There we boarded a boat and went on the lagoon past Rossitten and Pillkoppen to Nidden, an extremely picturesque village. It is a favourite drinking place of artists and a very pleasant swimming location where there is very fine sand on the beach. Also we visited the sail gliding school and to end we climbed the high dunes and had an especially good view of the still, blue lagoon and the broad green Baltic Sea. It was a wonderful pleasure to run through the enormous expanse of the dunes and sink into the deep sand.

I can't send my laundry out to be done – the wives of the forestry workers have their cattle, agricultural land and many children to look after and don't wish to collect my laundry or my money. But then again they earn enough, especially if their men have been called up.

And how is our garden doing? On Saturday I picked the first lettuce and had it with sugar and sour cream.

Gertlauken 17 June 1942

My dear Parents

Just a short letter today. In Hindenburg am Haff we had a young teachers' conference. The first instruction regarding our duties was given by a grey-haired lady teacher. But the head teacher was not very happy with it and his surly face showed it. Then came a pretty, blonde, young teacher whose delivery I didn't find especially good, but the head teacher was quite charming to her, which I thought was very nice of him, as she certainly was very nervous. But it seems to me that young, pretty women have all going for them over the men. The voice to me is seemingly passive, but on the other hand the male colleagues have it much easier. Their voices carry without any assistance. But if a woman speaks loudly, it sounds like a scream or a shout. The men, too, have their individual ways when teaching – the pulling of the hair, a pinch of the cheek and thirdly a flap of the hand – all fairly successful mannerisms that I have observed.

Can you conceive the extent of East Prussian hospitality? No, it is inconceivable. I had cycled here, had a long return journey ahead of me and felt hungry after the conference. A young lady teacher who resides in lodgings in town took me with her. Her landlady said that she had very little to offer but when we said we would make do with whatever there was, she placed a washbasin containing eels and gravy on the table and with it potatoes and pudding in bulk. We couldn't eat it all and I wasn't allowed to pay for anything, for I was the guest of their young lady.

Gertlauken 29 June 1942

My dear, dear Parents
There are loads of wood berries here, small but delicious and so aromatic. From the garden I have picked the first spinach. The growth is wonderful, all over growing up very well are peas, beans, beetroot, and in time before the rain we have small cabbage plants growing up. The head teacher has said that we should help with the harvest in a suitable village and so thereby 'We are noticed'. As if one is only known in such a way! Many times I have asked the children whether I can help with the haymaking somewhere. I was out a couple of times, on the first occasion in a convenient meadow in the middle of the woods. On the day following I had a hundred gnat bites on my legs, arms, neck and shoulders. Just for the fun of it, so to speak, I had numerous stings on one thigh – there were over fifty of them. I know of a fabulous way to train yourself – don't scratch, and when you think of doing so, go out into the fresh air. I get on well with the people in the village. I certainly don't know whether my severe father with all his understanding knows what his daughter gets up to. There in the village I get cake, milk, some cream, eggs, some butter, cheese (cooked cheese with caraway seeds – delicious!) or pork. At the beginning I had thoughts as to whether or not I should accept such things. Because

the parents would not accept money, I stuck savings stamps in the children's exercise books.

Recently one evening I attended a birthday party with the shopkeeper, Frau Schustereit, whose only daughter has left school. Frau Schustereit is such a lovely, homely lady but unfortunately is ill. She has unfortunately high blood pressure. Once I saw her doctor place leeches which, when completely full after sucking, fall off. This procedure must be repeated from time to time.

At the birthday party there was an evening meal about which unfortunately I was not enthusiastic, and naturally a quantity of strong things to drink. But no one was drunk. It was an enormous party and the people here are exceptional singers. Each party ends in an hour-long sing-song – hikers' songs, musical hits, folk songs – one 'When I Ask the Wanderer' – all sung with great enthusiasm. The people here are surly and a little disappointed with me as a Kölner, because I am no soul of the party and not much of a singer.

Joniec 14 July 1942

My dear Parents

We have come here for the harvesting, but I will tell you of that later.

On the Wednesday before the school holidays I arranged a school outing and the children were out of their minds with excitement. For the small ones I had engaged a horse and cart and the rest travelled on their cycles. It was through Lautischken to the lagoon, which they saw for the first time. What a tale it was to tell, and the chattering whilst eating! We sat at the water's edge and played games and I was most certainly happy when we all got home, safe and sound, in one piece. The entire school was very considerate and made many brief stops so that the youngsters could recover themselves. For all of them the outing was a great experience.

On 10 July the holidays started and in the morning I had the certificates distributed, and about midday I left Gertlauken straight away. My cases I gave to the milkman to take to the station. In Königsberg we were received at the HJ district leader's private quarters. My fellow guests were very caring. Of an evening we three young lady teachers from the Labiau district would go to the cinema and if that were full we would land up in the Café

Alhambra, a musical café, full to bursting point with officers and elegant women. The following morning the journey took us further through Allenstein to Hohenstein. There we were taken to the youth hostel. We were, altogether, 200 Bundes Deutche Madchen teacher trainees from East Prussia. Here we were located in an area that had, until 1939, belonged to Poland. Dirt, laziness, primitiveness, fleas, lice and scabies were everywhere and we were told we should bring out culture here. I found it very amusing to be known as a 'culture bearer'.

On Sunday we visited the National War Museum at Tannenberg. It appeared to be like a holy place to which people make pilgrimage. With its mighty towers and the sentries on guard in front of the graves it made a huge impression on us.

On Monday I set off and I belonged to the group going to Joniec. The journey took us through Zichenau to Nasielsk. From the houses and fields one can see at once where the earlier German–Polish border was. Nasielsk is a miserable dump with small, dirty, decaying houses with flat roofs, many carts drawn by small tough horses, many herds of sheep, a decent German café and a striking, practical building – the synagogue. Of the 7,000 inhabitants, there are supposed to be 4–5,000 Jews. Everywhere one meets the people of the East one knows from picture books – the women with their heads covered by large head cloths and mostly barefooted.

From Nasielsk a slow train took us further and in Wkra we got out and marched on foot the two or three kilometres to Joniec. Our accommodation pleased us tremendously and we were brought to the school, a stone brick building where we had brand-new beds and straw sacks as mattresses. Also a kitchen, washroom, gymnasium and so on, all spotlessly clean. In the village live about fifty Polish and four German families and a similar situation exists in the surrounding area. The houses of the Poles are of simple wood and loam construction.

Today was our first day of work and I worked with German people from Bug, a family named Restau, fabulously clean and very nice. Their fifteen-year-old daughter lives here and their son is serving in the forces. They didn't know at the beginning how we should be treated and did so as if we were summer visitors.

My dear Parents

I am treated like a child in the house of the family Restau. I am not allowed to work. Their constant wish is that we should tell them of our way of life, to which they listen intensely until the end of each story. So I told them the entire story of the *Nibelungensage* and was thanked profusely by our listeners. Then there was the *Volkerwanderung*, and parts from *Karl dem Grossen* – a typical cross-section of the stories told. It is most encouraging, all the same, that they had never before heard them.

Whenever, quite suddenly, I want to do something, or when the cleaning has to be done, it is quickly said 'Oh no, it is much better to tell us stories.' Sometimes I include a song in the story, for example the 'Nibelurgen' from *Agnes Miegel*, but above all I tell the stories I know by heart, such as Eichendorff, Mörike, Fontane, Storm. I believe the people like the stories so much, as they distract them from their cares and worries, or if they feel unwell. They had left their homeland in Upper Bug, thinking that they would be settled in a German village. Instead now they live among the Poles. The Poles must hand over their farms to the Germans. However, the Restaus were not prepared to evict the married occupants of the farm. Now he, the Pole, works as a farmhand on the farm that once belonged to him. The Restaus have a most profound feeling of unfairness towards the Pole. I find the situation for them both to be terrible. The Restaus cannot return to Bug and the Pole obviously hates the present situation. The Pole once took me to the school in his horse and cart. Without speaking he harnessed the horse, and in silence helped me to my seat in the cart. We went through the village, where the men, women and children standing in front of the houses looked at me intently and silently. I had real fear and also felt ashamed.

Tomorrow we go to our families and at 5 a.m. are back in our camp again. Breakfast is in the school but before that we have the morning games, then washing and flag raising. We are ten girls and each day one of us hoists the flag, a second girl announces the daily text, then altogether we sing a song. I don't know why, but this ceremony seems so strange since we are on our own in the morning, almost lost and forgotten in fact. It was quite different in the sail gliding camp – there we were full of life and much happier.

After finishing work we went a couple of times on the river on which Joniec lies, a rather wide and clear river with a simple wooden bridge with railings crossing it. Its banks are really lovely. A little way from the village we found an isolated place and went swimming naked. Never before have I found water so soft and smooth. It was a joy to swim there.

On the train 26 July 1942

My dear Parents

You'll be amazed and I don't quite know how to begin. Well, on Thursday I received post from Wolfgang in Doberitz vom Truppenubungsplatz with the news that he is soon having leave. That gave me the thought that on the journey to the west I should find time to visit him.

The employment in Joniec finishes on Sunday so I asked if I might travel early on Saturday and that was granted. The train rocks so pleasantly and I have plenty of time ahead of me. Before I satisfy you with the curious news about Wolfgang I must first tell you of a journey to Plohnen (in Polish times it was called something else) and it is in the district town area of Joniec.

Our lady camp leader had something to do there and thought the two of us should go there and collect a skirt left at the tailor. When we got there the skirt was not finished, so that for two hours we had the opportunity to stroll through the town. Just imagine going through a town wherein the houses, the windows and doors are nailed up with thick planks, and coming from behind there are incessant sounds of murmuring and movements. Then, in between the houses there is a longer wooden fence that comes almost to ground level and beneath it one sees feet, numerous feet, some bare feet, others in slippers, in sandals or in shoes. The babble of voices comes from many people and when you stand on tiptoe and look over the fence you see bald heads. Then you are suddenly aware that this is a ghetto and the people crammed therein must be Jews. We returned quickly to our tailor and he told us that he too is a Jew and is allowed out of the ghetto each day so that he can work. Straight away he ironed a pair of trousers with a red-hot glowing iron. He spat on the back of the iron and ironed as fast as lightning – spitting – ironing – spitting – ironing. We praised his workmanship and he smiled in a sad way. But I was very pleased when we left Plohnen behind us.

Now to Wolfgang – I sent him a telegram to Doberitz detailing my arrival time in Berlin. My train arrived, a crowd of people getting off, but no Wolfgang. I remained on the platform, no persons present except a soldier who looked in each compartment window. I thought to myself, 'He is like me and looking for someone.' Then we recognised each other. It was Wolfgang. I wouldn't have recognised him from the former narrow-chested, tall youth, for he has become a man with broad shoulders. He thought I looked really well. It was simply a case of sending a telegram to the effect 'Will arrive there and then.' His sergeant had laughed and had given him a leave pass marked 'To the orthopaedist, Berlin' – such a nice sergeant.

We then sought the possibility of overnight lodging for me, but it was far from simple. Quite often they thought we were not brother and sister, instead took us for a pair of lovers. We went from hotel to hotel, with aching feet and hunger. Finally we found one with a huge attic piled up with chairs, tables, boxes, cushions and, in the extreme corner, a bed. 'If you want it?' was the question posed. Well, what was there left for me to say? Wolfgang and I ate in a local inn and after a while I went back to the attic, during which time Wolfgang made his way back to the barracks. On the following day, Wolfgang had a free half-day, so that we were able to spend the entire afternoon together. We had much to talk about and we found a tiny café in which we sat undisturbed.

It was really lovely and what we spoke about I will tell you at length at home. The parting was so hard but now I will seek a little sleep. Tomorrow the flying model course in Ferndorf.

Ferndorf 29 July 1942

You dear Kölner

Soon I shall be with you and then will be able to tell you everything, especially about Wolfgang. I would have liked to have taken him with me, for I loved him so much. Your ears must have been red, for we spoke so much about you. Your letters and the cake arrived on Sunday and I am writing this during the midday break, which is soon over. Paula is also here and that is so nice. In the mornings and afternoons we saw and glue, but whether or not these things may fly . . . we are making bets on the eventual outcome.

The countryside here is very pleasant and our journey from

Hagen went through Huhenlimburg, Finnentrop and Altenhundem to Kreuztal. Today, Wednesday, we are free at 4 p.m. and journey together to Siegen. On Saturday afternoon there is an outing to Hilchenbach, and finally on Wednesday 5 August the course finishes.

Osnabrück 22 August 1942

My dear, dear Parents

I surprised Aunt Lies here. The street tram in Richtung Lotterstrasse is running again but not to Iburger Strasse. Here in Osnabrück one sees how bad the attacks have been. Only a couple of houses stand, near the railway station, and the post office is completely destroyed. All of the Herrenteichstrasse and all the houses are either collapsed or burnt out and the Grosse Strasse looks terrible. A part of the cathedral, the theatre, the church on Hermannsbrunnen, the hospital, Hebammen-Lehranstalt are damaged or burnt out completely.

The entire corner of the Wischmeyer bread factory is missing and near Kriegerwaisenhaus, forty houses are missing. In the Meller Strasse near the Police Department on the Petersburgerwall and in the Schepplerstrasse, all is complete destruction. All the houses have been destroyed and burnt out. Three terrace houses near the Meyer pharmacy and the people's school are also destroyed. There, thirteen people died and only the daughter of the pharmacist was rescued. The town smells of burning, and I will save you any further description of the scene of destruction.

Aunt Lies is always the senior of us and she does pamper me. When I arrived she was on the point of preparing her evening meal – simply dry bread and beetroot. Immediately she brought out cake and the best from the cellar. Young peas – my favourite – grown by her in her garden. Also meats, and I could not prevent her from doing this. Yesterday I was at first with Aunt Lina. She also brought out all sorts of things – such a dear soul. There, the upper wall has been knocked down and on the 4th floor the ceilings are all loose, and all the windows on the four storeys, together with the doors, are damaged. Much work will be needed to repair the damage. And the dirt!

Dear Father and dear Mother

Despite everything the days spent in Osnabrück were lovely. On Saturday afternoon Hildegard and I visited Bosmanns in Kloster Ohrbeck and even there the conversation relates solely to the awful attacks.

Gertrude and her parents grieve still so very much over the death of Hans-Hermann and Karl-Heinz. Theirs is such deep sorrow. The small Karl-Heinz looks like his father and Aunt Lina. He is a delightful boy and brings them great relief.

My train left on Saturday at midday. Aunt Lies took me to the station and cried when my train left. Aunt Lies cares always for others and does not think of herself. It is horrible when one must be so alone – you alone in Köln and Aunt Lies in Osnabrück, Wolfgang in Berlin and I here in East Prussia. Now that I am no longer with you my sadness feels twice as bad.

Wolfgang was not at the station in Berlin. So after lots of running about and asking questions and driving around (there are two Lichterfeldes apparently), I marched through endless streets to the famous Kadettenanstalten. Aunt Lies had given me cakes, bread and butter, cigarettes, sweets, apples and pears to give to Wolfgang. At the guardroom the evening duty guard called Wolfgang out. After waiting seemingly a long time, Wolfgang emerged. I knew his walk out of hundreds. He was taken aback a little and although our joy was great, our time together was short. We both didn't know where to begin. He had undergone a night route march and only just returned to barracks at midday on Sunday. He was sitting in the camp cinema and when called, was in his gym kit, and first of all had to dress himself. Unfortunately, after a little while he had to go into the barracks. At the railway station zoo in Berlin I freshened myself up in the washroom and spent a half-hour doing so, as it had been a hot day and a clean-up was necessary.

Shortly before midnight my train left and I had obtained a seat with two nice lady companions, one a genuine Kölner and the other from Hamburg. In Elbing an exceptionally nice railway official got into the compartment. The lady from Hamburg whispered to me in her old native dialect that only Low Germans understand, 'There's a man for you.' I had to laugh. 'But so handsome a man,' she said, quite enraptured by him.

At 8.14 a.m. we arrived safely at Königsberg. I washed myself in the washroom, drank coffee, made purchases in the town, ordered schoolbooks and so on. After such activity I became quite hot in my suit. In Mauern I saw a chimney sweep and I considered him to be a luck bringer. After that I collected my cycle which I always leave in one of the three sheds on the railway station, mounted it quickly and cycled first of all to see Schulz in Krakau. Unfortunately he was not there but his wife naturally insisted that I should have a good meal. So she gave me a few slices of bread with thick fingers of butter, and ham also. Her son is an intelligent student and can ask questions for hours on end, and the small baby girl is now five months old and a sweet child.

During my holiday, Herr Stachel, Herr Berkan and Herr Kippar had been on leave here and I was pleased to hear that. My lodgings looked grubby everywhere. Dust, dust and more dust, and fly dirt. On the windows swarms of small flies by the hundreds. Now it calls for a cleaning session. This morning the school beginners came. There are only eleven of them so I merely took their names and particulars, talked with them a little and sent them off again until tomorrow. Now I must go to the post office, several reports are due and my preparations for the new school year have to be made.

Our baker, Radtke, is very ill. He has inflammation of both lungs and now I must fetch the bread from Laukischken.

Do you know that despite my long absence away, as I rode my cycle through the fields and woods to Gertlauken, the people greeted me in a very friendly way. And when I saw my children again it made for great happiness in my heart.

Gertlauken 28 August 1942

My dear, dear Parents

I am feeling quite dreadful, in fact I could almost howl. The schoolwork grows over my head or I am not prepared. The cleaning is hard for me as I have no materials and this evening it is tragic, probably because everything lies only on my empty stomach. When it is full, the world looks a completely different place. Because I felt so depressed I went to the Schulz family and got physical and spiritual help. First I had to have a nourishing meal and then talked with Herr Schulz about the schoolwork. He advised me always to go over each subject again but quite quickly deal with only the important work with reference to only the important books. Additionally what I don't know, let it go by, otherwise I would never be prepared for the more serious subjects. Frau Schulz gave me bread, honey and eggs to take with me, and on the way home I met Frau Neumann from whom I received potatoes. What a day it was and now I am lying in bed.

29 August 1942

All went well with the children today. At midday I roasted some potatoes with ham and eggs and after that ate a carrot from the garden. Everything in the garden is growing up well but what shall I do with the many kohlrabi. Afterwards I took a firm grasp of the broom and cleaned the room thoroughly. Afterwards I shall do some schoolwork following the advice of Herr Schulz.

Gertlauken 14 September 1942

My dear Parents

I spent the weekend with Paula. It was really cosy and the conversation we had did us good. The weather was sunny and we walked for a few hours through the fields and woods, during which time we sang simple folk and hiking songs. Then I became a little more secure in myself and so many of the songs we sang in unison with two voices.

Such hours are carefree and make for much happiness and it is inconceivable that during the same time mankind is ruled by war and people must undergo indescribable sufferings. Naturally we eventually came to talk about the war, involving Paula's brother and cousin, and equally about Wolfgang and my cousin at the front or about to go there. Also we spoke about another of Paula's brothers who has been killed.

Paula does not feel at all well here. Her school superior does not concern himself very much with the young teachers. For example, therefore, she does not have a bed. Instead she sleeps in a hammock or on the floor. When she discusses such matters with the school official he spouts that she should not burden herself with such trifles and that is all the humanity offered. He is certainly in a position to help her but he shows little intelligence.

I have myself visited him for instruction but only on two occasions. The journey there is too long and I shall never forget the shock I had on the occasion of his first appearance. Classes 1 and 2 immediately sang really loud and quite out of tune the song 'Hansel and Gretel Lost Themselves in the Wood. It was so dark and bitterly cold.' A song that can move me so much. Probably he is very unmusical because he found the singing 'Not bad at all'. When it was the turn of the bigger pupils, the subject lesson was history – 'Bismarck and the Founding of the German Nation'. History is my favourite subject and obviously his as well. Finally he took over the lesson and I had only to listen. He expressed his satisfaction when he left and that made me feel extremely good. Now he has been called up again and is at the front. We have now a new head school official.

Gertlauken 17 September 1942

My dear Parents

You'll never guess who visited me on Tuesday afternoon. It was Dora Krell with a girlfriend from Linz. I think they found my lodgings very primitive and made off the next day to Nehrung where we shall meet in Pillkoppen. Hopefully the weather will improve as it is pouring in torrents.

By the way, the Russians have already flown to Königsberg and our village lies on the flight path of their planes.

Here it's darker a good hour before it is in the west and about 9 p.m. one hears the throbbing sound of the planes' engines. A strange feeling it gives if one doesn't hear the anti-aircraft fire first.

21 September

I wanted to go to meet Dora and her friend in Pillkoppen but since Wednesday of last week we've had some really 'so and so' weather. Stormy, raining and cold too. I'm hoping for sunshine on Sunday. At 4.30 a.m. the alarm clock rattled, while outside the storm howled round the house, the rain splashed against the windows and it was pitch-black outside. Just the sort of weather, in fact, where one likes to stretch and then turn over on one's other side, with a thought 'Shall I get up or not?' They can see whether or not you are on the steamboat. 'Yes, but I have promised.' So one gets up, has a cat's lick of a wash, and if shortly after 6 a.m. one sets out on a cycle journey, one is less likely to catch the 6.30 train to Königsberg. In Laukischken I asked whether the train to Königsberg had gone through already. Indeed it had. What bad luck. Rumble, rumble, rumble, there it goes along the track and sets itself in motion without me. What is there to be done? A further ten kilometres to travel and it is raining and I have the wind against me. In a waiting shelter on the street stand two stupid boys who watch with smirks my battle with the wind and my handbag constantly slipping from my cycle's handlebars. Angrily I toss it back, and back it comes again and the cycle slides in the sandy, earthen path, and I fall full-length in the street. The boys laugh loudly. A fist-sized hole has appeared in my stocking, the knee bloody, the coat muddy and the handlebars twisted. I cleaned myself up the best I could, bent the handlebars straight and travelled on with confidence and equanimity, certain that I would see only the stern of the steamboat in Labiau. But twelve minutes before 8 a.m. I reached Labiau, over the Adler bridge and then through the market, and the boat was still there. I parked my bike in the shed and went aboard the boat. On deck two ladies in addition to myself, and the rest all soldiers. The ship's captain sent us at once below deck in case the sea came over the side. Previously I had been on the lagoon in good weather, and I was nervous about a stormy passage.

With the soldiers we are having a high old time as it is the sergeant's birthday. He has nice eyes and I thought he could make a good travelling companion. His lovely, true brown eyes reflected his true character, as I later established. The soldiers had brought aboard at least ten litres of wine and soon the singing was under way. What do you think they sang? 'O du schones Sauerland' and 'Ich mot zu Foss noh Kolle jonn' – all Kölner and Westfalen songs! And in between the jokes of Tunnes and Schal, as the bottle made its frequent rounds. I didn't think the waves in the lagoon were too bad but one of the party of valiant warriors found they didn't agree with him. The cheerful sea journey finished in Nu but I had to disembark in Rossitten because the sea conditions did not permit the boat to dock in Pillkoppen.

Dora was, naturally, not to be seen. Therefore she and her friend must have looked for accommodation in Rossitten quarters. From one guest house to another I went without success. So she must have obtained private accommodation somewhere. Finally I had

had enough and decided to go to the Baltic, which I did. It was exactly as I had imagined it, but in fact so much nicer. A rush and a romp about and everywhere white wave caps. I was quite alone on the beach, solitary me, all alone. Then I visited the bird sanctuary, always interesting with its display of rare birds. A splendid sea eagle, singing its song in the cage, made a good impression on me.

Before the return journey I needed something to warm me up so I went into the guest house Zur Mole where there was a party of soldiers from the boat. With their malicious jokes they reduced the plump landlady to despair. She reacted crossly and although she apologised to me, I had to laugh, albeit cordially, for God should have mercy on one with such a crowd to handle and not able to appreciate a little fun. And further, does not have a ready wit.

On board I met Captain Larsen, an old Köln Deutzer whose wife is in the Fire Acknowledgement Insurance Association. Mother was also there for a time and Father had often seen him in Hohenlind. His only son had studied law and was always to be found with Hans Unterber in 'Jagerhof'. During the entire journey we sat together and he spoke, really whispered, non-stop, about his work, his home, his son, but especially about his son. He seems to keep himself to himself but was obviously pleased to be able to talk at length. But he only just moved his lips so, with the noise of the boat's engines, I could barely understand half of it and merely kept nodding my head in affirmation or otherwise.

I took my time on the return cycle journey home. It was splendid, the storm subsided, the moon and stars stood high and the world was still and quiet.

This afternoon Frau Strupat asked me to visit her. Her brother lives in Chicago and on 25 March she had received news of him through the Red Cross. The letter was in English and I was asked to translate it so that a speedy answer could be sent. Anyway it seems that there is scarcely one family in Gertlauken that does not have a relative living in America.

And so now I shall feast for I got 5 lb of apples and *Kruschken*. The latter are quite small pears. In addition I have myself some thick milk standing, the cream from which has been scooped and mixed with sugar – heavenly!

And again to reassure Father, I had a second pair of stockings with me and the hole in the knee I covered with sticking plaster, and just today on my travels I saw the famous fighter pilot Gallan in Gertlauken. He lives in Nachbarforst Sternberg.

My dear Parents and Wolfgang

The teaching course is over and the autumn holidays are here and I am on the great East Prussian journey.

The teaching course was nice and interesting and it went particularly well with at one time all the colleagues being present together. One gets not only jokes, good entertainment and good advice, but also the opportunity to observe many other types of people, many of whom are correct and honest, some stuffy and staid, with whom one can at best joke, but most have a sense of humour. Then there is another kind, for example Roddek from Mauern. Tall, slim, dirty-nosed, always with a pipe in his mouth, in unironed trousers, he has overall no comments to make, is nice to everyone, and can be childlike in himself. His characteristics – unshaven and long hair. I had already thought yesterday, 'Young lady, you have never seen your father with such stubble' and today, even more stubble, quite like an entire forest it was.

Then there is the teacher Bauer. Fat with a bald head, spectacles and a resounding laugh. He goes at people without inhibitions. And now the end. I will take the small railway line to Tapiau.

So, now it is 2015 hours and meanwhile I sit in the 'Schwarzen Adler' in Insterburg and have a double room for which I paid 4.90 Reichsmarks. In Labiau I nearly missed the little train for Tapiau. You know it is such a small railway track with a tiny train and two small carriages behind it. In such a train one sees more of the countryside and comes more in contact with the people aboard. Between Labiau and Tapiau the village of Goldbach lies in the middle. Once when I was travelling with Frau Neumann we came through this way and I felt immediately at home in this region The church is built on a tiny hill which in these parts is almost a mountain. It is surrounded by trees over which the church spire rises and through the foliage the white bricks of the tower shine. Our train went through the village with so much clashing and ringing and lay so steeply on its side as it went round the curves that it sounded like the straining and puffing of an asthmatic person. When passing through Nautzken the recollection of the previous journey there with Frau Neumann came to mind. It was where we rested in a ditch and Frau Neumann, as if by magic, produced from her bag legs of chicken, ham sandwiches, eggs and apples. However, my good mood became very subdued when we reached Tapiau, where I saw near the railway platform a hospital train full with white beds and their very still, wounded occupants. Standing on the platform were several other wounded, all bandaged. I am always gripped by the same question, "Why is one person so affected and another does all right?' It is the same question that I had discussed with my religion teacher and to which no answer could be given.

It was to Trakehnen I wished to go eventually but at Insterburg the train halted and we all had to get off. So I went to look for a hotel. I was rejected at my first port of call but accepted at the second. So I wish you a 'Goodnight'.

Trakehnen 26 September 1942

The journey is lovely, only I miss your letters so much. At the moment I am sitting on the railway station waiting for the postal van in which I shall travel to Hauptgestut. I have telephoned there and booked a room. The post office should open at 3 o'clock. Beside myself in the waiting room there is a youngster, very correct in short trousers, 'with it' hairstyle and lively flashing eyes.

He pointed to a button and said, 'Press it once.'

'But you also are able to do that,' I replied.

'No,' he said, 'I don't know what it is for.'

So I said, 'Do you want me to try it out for you?'

'Yes,' he replied, 'because I am not from here.'

'One can tell that. Surely you are from the Rheinland?' I said.

'Er, yes,' he said, 'from Köln.'

Then we chatted for a quarter of an hour until the counter official arrived and opened the post office.

27 September

I travelled in the postal van yesterday to Trakehnen and stayed in the Hotel Elch which I am well pleased with, since twice I have had an omelette with mushrooms to eat – quite outstanding! I am well provided for here with my food coupons. Today, Sunday, there is no visiting but perhaps tomorrow I can look at the grounds and the stables. But even so, I took a walk with a Wiener lady living here. Also two men live here, one of whom is supposed to be the son of Field Marshal Keital. Now it is raining so I am remaining in the hotel where it is warm and cosy, and of course I always have a book with me. When on holiday it is the usual case with me not to think of anything too seriously – no work, long sleeps and at table pamper myself – really heavenly!

Yesterday I had another look round Insterburg. It is a garrison town with municipal traffic, lovely old houses, a museum and a church that from the outside doesn't look much, but inside is very beautiful and has a rich history.

In olden times there was supposed to be a pagan font of the Lithuanians standing here but later the Order of the Knights occupied the district and founded the town. Still later, the Poles, Swedes, Russians and French made the district insecure. And worst of all was the plague of 1709. Then came King Frederick Wilhelm I of Prussian Protestantism from Switzerland, the Palatinate and particularly those Salzburgischen settlers. The memorial of the soldier king stands in front of the government building in Gumbinnen.

28 September

It is evening after a long day. Unfortunately I could not go to the station and also found no one who could give me information about horses and horse breeding. In fact if you ask anybody here about horses, and everybody knows something about them, they think you are stupid!

But despite that I simply took a stroll through the district, through broad meadows and enclosures, and saw many wonderful horses, all carrying the branding sign '7', elk horns. The state stable master resides in a so-called castle that is situated in a beautiful park with broad, tall trees. In front of the castle is a statue of a horse.

After the plague the district of Trakehnen was devoid of human beings. However, the king used his soldiers to drain the area, laid down pastureland and had stables built. And since 1732 a thousand horses have come from the line of the 'Royal Mares'.

My dear Parents and Wolfgang

Goldap makes absolutely no impression on me. Most noticeable is
the huge market square with relatively new houses. It has everything
necessary – a church, a post office, courthouse and hotels. In one
hotel I found accommodation and I had grey hairs almost, after
I took a look in the kitchen. So what had I not seen! The floor
was alive with noisy, black, large beasts crawling everywhere. They
were, I believe, cockroaches. And in front of my window on the
opposite side, stood a house like a horrible box. How much better
it was in Trakehnen where, when in bed, I could hear the sound of
rustling leaves in the park.

On Wednesday morning I travelled in the postal van to Rominten
and it was a twenty-four-kilometre journey. The road we took went
over hill and valley, through villages and past two lakes, until we
drove through a wooden archway made from heavy wooden logs.
On these were carved pagan rune signs in red. Also the swastika
and SS sign 'Rominten Nature Reserve'.

From here we went through ten kilometres of wonderful forest
of pine and fir trees and other heavy trees, all so wonderful and
so beautifully shaped they were. In the village of Rominten one's
first impression is of the various types of buildings, houses made
from dark red and brown pinewood. Their roofs are curved and
decorated with strange-looking dragon heads. I had seen pictures
of the Royal Hunting Castle in Rominten, so I knew that the style
emanated from Norway. Kaiser Wilhelm II had them built in
about 1890. The entire district takes its name from the small River
Rominte.

I saw first the hunting castle. It stands on a humble, average
section with two tall side wings, and has a lovely wooden veranda.
A friendly old gamekeeper guided me and told me much of interest.

By the way, there are many soldiers from the Hermann Göring
division, with their white collar tabs.

After that I wandered to the Marinowosee – small lake quite
surrounded by dark woods. There is also a *Kurhaus* [sanatorium]
built of wood on posts, also a large pavilion with a dance floor. In
peacetime it must have been very much in use. Now, however, the
soldiers are quartered here.

Finally I saw on the water three boats and when I asked if could hire one I was told, 'Yes, 1 mark an hour.' Suddenly behind me stood a young lieutenant who said, half in jest and half earnest, 'Wait a moment, I'll travel with you.' Naturally I declined his offer at once, but you know how it is if one is always alone and one has no one to talk to, an entertaining talk is perhaps acceptable. So I asked him, 'Do you really want to travel with me?'

To which he replied, 'Yes, I'd like to as I'm off duty.' He was slim and had nice blue eyes and long silky eyelashes. He was with his batman and his friend and so all four of us got into the boat and glided over the placid lake. The water was calm and deep black in colour, quite weird, and on the banks were dark fir trees.

At the so-called Tea House of the Kaiserin, we landed and strolled through the unspoiled countryside. Very solitary it was there. We made our way through the undergrowth to a small path leading to a small wood, where suddenly a deer sprang out.

But when we returned to the *Kurhaus* it was far too late for me to catch the bus back to Goldap. That meant I had to find a vacant room in the *Kurhaus*. All the others were occupied by soldiers. The housekeepers, Tetzlaff by name, were charming, the wife large strong with washed hair and he tall, gaunt, with spectacles and kind brown eyes. Both understood so well how to spread comfort with an inviting hand gesture and 'Please take a seat', and then led me to a small private room next to the guest room. There I sank into an armchair and they brought me biscuits and wine. I stayed there for six days and telephoned the Goldaper Hotel every evening to postpone my room stay each day.

But every morning at 6 a.m. the cry 'Company Attention!' and in the wooden house the thud of soldiers' heavy boots, quite like a small explosion. I then got up and acknowledged the wonderful morning with its sunrise and, from the balcony, my view of the lake. During the day I wandered about the countryside and in the afternoons even bathed in the lake with its very cold water. Of an evening I often sat with the Tetzlaffs who had their own car, and in peacetime earned good money and travelled throughout the whole of Germany. They can relate many wonderful experiences. We have often played cards of an evening, during which time biscuits and sweets went the rounds. At night one often hears the stag roar, as it is rutting time. Shortly it was daybreak and time to stretch. I am astonished how I lasted an entire week without recourse to all the things I brought in my suitcase. Soap and hand towels are in the room, but hair curlers I made from small twigs. When I returned to Goldap someone had placed my suitcase in a small chamber but I did not need to pay for it being there.

My dear Parents and Wolfgang

In Lyck the weather was so bleak and grey, cold and raining, that I felt so forlorn when I stood on the bridge and looked out on the broad, grey lake. It is the principal town in the Masuren lake region and in the last war suffered a great deal. Several times it was occupied by the Russians and after the war, the Poles wanted it. But after the voting in 1920 the Poles got only seven out of 8,000 votes.

Although Lyck is beautifully situated, it made me quite depressed, so I quickly journeyed on to Johannisburg. If I cannot spend the lovely time with you, at least for a little while it was lovely being with the Tetzlaffs in Rominten.

Your question on the telephone, 'Have you enough money?' I found touching, for this time I brought my post office savings book with me. I will now close and hopefully Tommy [the English] will not spoil the whole of Wolfgang's leave. I think much about you. And you, I hope, think also a little about me.

My dear Parents and Wolfgang

Excuse my writing but my hand is so cold that I can scarcely hold the pencil. I left Johannisburg early the next morning and then on to Rudczanny, always through marvellous spruce and pinewoods. It was awfully cold and I was frozen. Nothing came of my big hike round the Niedersee, in spite of the fact that a woman told me of the latest scare story about a murder, a robbery and a disappearing man. It made shivers run up and down my spine. But the mist disappeared and the sun broke through as I made my way to the *Kurhaus*. It lies directly on the Niedersee, is pleasantly situated, has fifty beds, is fairly busy and all its residents must be well-to-do. I had a large breakfast and my neighbour at the next table was a mayor from Platen who had a lady reading to him. Shades of peacetime!

As the sun climbed higher it became really warm, and the lake shone and glittered. I simply could not stay indoors but instead went out in a boat for twelve hours. The lake is quite magical, is enclosed by woods and has many islands. One circles one island and then sees more lovely islands to row around. Such peaceful, calm solitude – so enticing.

In the afternoon I made a small outing to Königseiche and to a lock. It was very interesting to observe how the many wooden rafts travelled because of the difference in height between the two lakes. At evening time, as a result of a lovely day, I journeyed quite happily back to Johannisburg, where I purchased a cinema ticket for the film *The Great Love*. On the following day when I continued my journey to Lötzen, the weather was dreadful. It rained the whole day long and it was so horribly cold that I took only a small walk to Lowentiensee. Despite the weather, however, I could visualise what a lovely picture the town would make in the sunshine.

Here in East Prussia I have the feeling that I can breathe freely, while at home one has the feeling of living in one's neighbour's back pocket. The land is wide, peaceful and utterly beautiful. The towns have large market squares and small houses, and most noteworthy are the old stone churches. In Masuren many towns have suffered as a result of the Russian incidents in World War I. As a result one sees so many new houses. Naturally, in Lötzen I visited also the Boyen Fortress, besieged by the Russians.

From Lötzen to Angerburg is thirty-five kilometres, so in the afternoon with my suitcases I boarded the late afternoon train to visit the Heroes Cemetery at Jagerhohe on Schwenzaitsee, and on the following morning travelled from Angerburg to Königsberg, and on the following afternoon returned once again to Gertlauken.

So good, the train set off and I soon had the feeling it was travelling backwards to its siding because of the storm and rain. At the same time, I had the feeling that it was a kind of goods train, because of its speed and frequent halts at stopping places. It was dark and grew even darker before I arrived in Angerburg. So dark, in fact, that the thought of going for a walk and sightseeing was out of the question.

At 6 a.m. I was ready to make tracks and strolled through the still sleeping town and the nearby barracks en route to Schwenzaitsee. It was horribly cold and I thought to myself that I would be so grateful to you if you could get me another pair of woollen gloves

– my clothing card is in Köln. Instead, here I bought myself a rain hat that really I can do without.

The Jagerhohe Heroes Cemetery lies on a hill overlooking the lake and the view covers a wide area of the land and water. One feels here how the lakes link together – a truly fine place for a soldiers' cemetery. From the main road one must turn off right and then go along a sandy pathway through a bare, hilly landscape. Such round, small hills, quite without woods, only overgrown with grass. A strangeness exists of waste and barrenness, desolation and abandonment.

In the middle of the cemetery a tall wooden cross rises upwards and on a plaque it says:

> They died – and they live still
> They slumber – and wake still
> They rest – to a new deed
> The future seed

All round the cross lie the dead – Germans and Russians. Again and again it is always shattering to read, 'Here rests an Unknown German soldier', '35 Unknown Russian Soldiers and an Equerry', '3 Unknown German Soldiers'. Many a mother would perhaps be a tiny bit comforted to know that the grave where her son lies is so well looked after. I stood there a long time, engrossed in the sight of the graves and the lakes at my feet, light misty clouds blotting them out. It was then I noticed, down on the bank of the lake, a fisherman with his boat. He waved at me and I waved back. As I turned, I chanced to see him approaching the cross. I did not know his motive for doing so, but mistrusted it and just ran. Once I reached the main road, I felt safe. I don't know whether the man had ulterior motives, but I know I suddenly experienced a great fear.

Then, enticingly, on the other side of the road I saw a small hill, barely a hillock, but wooded. I climbed to the top and found two graves of the fallen. On one of the crosses I made out the following inscription, 'Biermann, born 30 December 1794 . . .'

Königsberg 11 October 1942

My dear Parents and Wolfgang
I find this night particularly disturbing. I am in the waiting hall and in four hours' time the train leaves for Mauern. It was about 6 p.m.

yesterday evening I got to Königsberg, and to obtain a hotel room on a Saturday was impossible. So I went back to the waiting room for refreshment and to enquire about a cinema. The station was empty and with more luck than intelligence I got hold of a ticket.

It was an amusing film, *The Mixed-Up Grandfather*. Now I have been in the waiting room since 10.30 p.m. and it is my hope that you at home are not sitting in an air-raid shelter. The people waiting here sleep, doze, talk quietly, play cards or like I do, read. The air is dreadfully close, full of tobacco smoke.

Gertlauken 12 October 1942

My dear, dear Parents

During the entire journey I had been happily looking forward to collecting mail delivered here in my absence. I was not disappointed and thank you truly for the four lovely letters, Wolfgang's photograph, the lovely parcel and the clover leaf.

When they had the plum harvest here I would have liked to have helped. Here there is little fruit – most of it had been attacked by the frost.

It would have been nice for you to receive compensation for the bomb damage and you could have used the money to rebuild the garden house.

My cold has returned again. With your lovely parcel came another one from the Lowen chemist with lots of medicines of all kinds. Did Ursel Ristenpart pack it for me? Now I am my own chemist and have a reassuring feeling in consequence.

Naturally I have in the first place my other vocation. I even have a monthly plan in a large format, also my weekly plan set out in detail. The housework is quite an annoyance but on the other hand when it is done it is so nice to see the pleasing results.

What in peacetime would I not have tried out in cooking and baking? In the first instance I would have been at a loss.

Gertlauken 16 October 1942

My dear Parents

I have just returned from the Neumanns where I had to eat delicious waffles. I will now answer completely your letter. I have been indescribably happy with Wolfgang's picture and now have all my loved ones together. The photo is very good and he has not the slightest resemblance to a rough, unfeeling SS man (as one still imagines him). He seems more like a dreamy youth from the Eichendorff and Brentano beloved.

I cannot, above all, grasp that Franz Bucker is dead. I have to read it over and over again to convince myself that I am not going mad. It is so shattering and the poor parents! It is just as well we cannot see the future. In 1938 Franz and I celebrated the carnival together. Franz was at the front in Stalingrad. Is that where he was killed? No, I just cannot grasp it at all. The second son already lost, and Franz had just finished his studies. On his last leave he always sat in the kitchen and had no enthusiasm for going out. It is as if he had a premonition! Two sons lost inside a year!

I have read the copy of the letter to Cousin Martha and she will be very happy to know that her nephew has been awarded the Knight's Cross. Let us hope that at least a couple of men will return home from the terrible war.

Here we are well into autumn. It storms and rains terribly. I hear the especially strong winds howling round and over the house, for it is a detached one and the winds assail from all sides. But I am nicely warm. And I even got a letter from Wolfgang. The poor boy is still lying in military hospital with diphtheria.

Gertlauken 30 October 1942

My dear Parents and Wolfgang
I take it then that Wolfgang is now at home. You must tell me exactly how quickly you reacted and your surprise at finding him standing at the door. Hopefully you will have a peaceful night in Köln. It must again have been very bad in Osnabrück from what Aunt Lies writes.

The weather is wonderful – a gold autumn. Yet a year ago it snowed here at this time. On 28 October I had spent an entire year here in Gertlauken. After the lessons I was with the town mayor and then with the chief forestry officer. The conversation was about the raw fruit and vegetable breakfast that all schools have in the break. Seemingly, I shall have to see where I can get a hundredweight of cabbages, and when obtained, where can I store them in the cellar? Thereafter I tried for hours at the post office to contact the school official in Wehlau but without success and it was quite dark when I got home. I wanted to wash my coloured things at once but once again the electricity failed so that I nearly sat down in the soapsuds in the pitch-black darkness. Also I had no candles, so I fumbled and grappled and finally, with an armful of my clothes for mending, I stumbled down the stairs to Frau Berkan who had a paraffin lamp. We both chatted away there until midnight. About 11 p.m. the light came on again, so I fetched a bottle of red wine from my room and took it down to Frau Berkan. There Frau Kerwath filled a jug with lemonade and we made ourselves each two glasses of mulled wine and ate the gingerbreads Frau Berkan provided. So passed 'Year No. 1'. But what may happen in the next year?

All single women without children now have to be engaged in war employment. Frau Kippar fears that she may be obliged to go to Laukischken for her duty. Therefore we shall speak with the school official, whether she may instruct school years one and two. She is, after all, from an old school teacher's family and is very skilled. Perhaps then, in the circumstances, the school official might make an exception on her part. Sometimes I cannot imagine myself spending my entire life as a teacher.

Yesterday was the first party assembly in the year. It began at 8 o'clock and when I set out on my cycle the light was so dim that one did not know how to separate the path and the meadow. I travelled at a neck-breaking rate and the reason for that you know – my strong sense of being punctual. Suddenly I saw everything in a hazy way and more or less guessed where the huge heaps of stones were on the road verges in East Prussia. Many of the fields are full of such stones which, allegedly, fell out of the Devil's sack as he flew over East Prussia. The farmers collect such stones and stack them in layers at the road verges.

I sped towards one such heap, collided with it and saw myself flying into a tree with the angels stretching their arms out for me. But when I recovered, my knees and arms were in good order when I felt them and only the handlebars were a little twisted. A few moments later I was off again on my journey.

In the evening the moon came out and bathed everything in its silvery light. Such journeys are real experiences such as I will never forget. Only yesterday the thought struck me that the world would have been much better and above all much safer with a revolver in my bag! Because, after all, it was a journey of some ten kilometres through fields and woods – and entirely on my own!

Dear Parents and Wolfgang

Over 1,000 kilometres away from me you sit now cosily in the kitchen and have much to talk about. It is light and warm where you all are perhaps, the table is still covered with milk, coffee and cakes, which Wolfgang sitting nearby is causing to disappear piece by piece. I, on the other hand, sit with atlas before me and my finger tracing the route from Königsberg, Berlin to Köln.

I will quickly write the recipe for potato croissants for you: 200 g flour, 250 g boiled and grated potatoes, 1 baking powder, 1 egg, 50 g fat and 125 g sugar; all mixed together and rolled out into squares; a blob of jam also on top and smooth over. One can, of course, use less fat and sugar. And now a recipe recommended to me – it concerns something to spread on bread and I will try it out tomorrow: 2 onions and 1 tbsp. of clear fat, 8 tbsp. breadcrumbs into which crumble 20 pfennigs' worth of yeast, some salt, pepper and, if one has it, marjoram; all stirred with milk and bring to the boil; the result should taste like liver sausage and keep for a long time.

Gertlauken 6 November 1942

My dear Parents and Wolfgang

Here since yesterday one can sing 'O how it has become cold'. And how the wind howls.

Yesterday there were no lessons because a student teacher assembly was held in Liebenfelde. It began at 2 o'clock and two probationary teachers were required to speak and it was over by 5 o'clock. Fräulein Eggert from Laukischken organised a treat of especially delicious cakes for a few of us and all for the outlay of very little money. We all sat comfortably together until our train left at 8 o'clock. Such meetings are really nice. Although I have been here a year I am only slowly getting to know my colleagues. Many work in distant places, out-of-the-way solitary villages, and many have no electric light and receive just one litre of petrol per month.

The new school chief seems to be not too bad but knows little about the work we young teachers do, and that such work is far from simple to accomplish. That means he will probably wash his hands of any difficulties arising from our various tasks. In a novel about workers on the land in Bohmerwald which I have just read, it says: 'Life is not something thrown at you which you can just look at in amazement and then just turn aside from. It has to be earned afresh each hour and experienced to the full. How one leads one's life, so we become.' Another good saying is: 'In the hour of the boy's homecoming he sits with his elders and his soul has a day off, and he really enjoys that. But then everyone's soul needs a holiday and if all that is bright and pure does not come completely from within, then it has to be finished with.' And now I will finish for if I do not, Wolfgang won't read it all through.

This morning I had some trouble in the school, for from time to time I have to examine the children's hair for lice and nits. They are not all found and removed, but I must ensure they do not spread. The battle against them is always a tiringly long procedure. One must go about it cautiously. A sleep head got a slap and later I spoke with the mother about it and she explained that her youngster stays more at home than the others because he has to help with her other children. Therefore he may, on occasion, doze off in school. That really is a problem, especially when the fathers are soldiers, for then the elder children become the workforce and many parents place schooling very low on the list in relation to other things.

I was disappointed about three youngsters, the worst ones I have. They took a glass of cherries and a bottle of cherry juice from Frau Stachel's cellar without permission. A youthful prank, or the beginning of something worse? After the wintertime it is completely gloomy at 4 o'clock but the evening is accordingly splendidly long. The passing of the seasons gives rise to an activity that I experience intensely – that is, in all weather I cycle, come wind or rain, sunshine, snow or ice. Yesterday evening, for example, from Liebenfelde to Mauern by train, then ten kilometres with my cycle to Gertlauken in pitch-black darkness, so dark in fact that one could not see one's hand in front of one's face, and not a solitary star in the sky.

Gertlauken 10 November 1942

Dear Parents and Wolfgang

Boy, oh boy, I can just imagine Wolfgang's mood – if he was expecting fourteen days' leave and then this was increased to three weeks! Dearest, don't you connect this with going to the front in winter? Most of all I would like time to stand still, so that you don't have to go so quickly. Did you receive my parcel and were the contents quite satisfactory?

Father described it exceedingly well, how it was when Wolfgang suddenly came on leave. For me it is a case of 'If only I had been there'. Hopefully, Tommy will leave you in peace.

Paula visited me on Saturday and we had a good time, cooking and trying out a recipe we spread on bread – it tasted really good and needed just a little more milk. Then we baked curd cheese biscuits – there were some for Wolfgang.

On Sunday our first snow fell, and infernally cold it was. Paula cycled off about 3.30 p.m. and had an icy-cold wind against her, and it will be pitch-black by the time she reaches Weidlacken.

Now all is white outside and so cold that I should like to creep into the oven. I'm certain to get chilblains on my hands and feet again.

Gertlauken 16 November 1942

My dear Parents and Wolfgang

On Saturday I went straight to Paula's school, since the weather was somewhat reasonable, but I wore thick clothes nevertheless. The journey was lovely and all the colours stood out from one another in the clear, hard air. The blackness of the woods, the blueness of the sky and the whiteness of the fields, and where very little patches of snow lay, the exposed dark brown of the actual earth. In the night it thawed and on Sunday storm and rain until evening, and then it froze.

After the school yesterday I first cleaned my room and then washed my yellow pullover, the black jacket and two large woollen blankets. After that, what should happen but Reinhard Neumann came up and straight away took me to his mother's and wouldn't accept any excuses on my part. Of course I had a meal with them.

Now I have a request. At Christmas time I would like to organise a Christmas celebration. So please send me Christmas paper, glossy paper, coloured bunting and such other items as you can get hold of. But it must be soon.

Now don't be too sad if Wolfgang is away again. We all dearly hope that we all keep in good health, that we see each other again and that Wolfgang survives the war.

My dear Parents

When one is expecting the post, none comes and one becomes quite fidgety and uneasy. It is then that one turns into a little devil and this makes one unhappy and irritable. And when the post finally comes, as it did today, one is suddenly and completely another person and absolutely nothing can shake one. Now, for example, once again we have no light, so I write by candlelight. The storm that howls and hisses dreadfully had better take another direction.

Dear Father, as to what you say about democracy, I cannot really say as I have not as yet been so occupied by the subject. Perhaps I have a false idea about it and am a little immature or I am influenced by, or stand too much in, the National Socialist world theory of life. You speak of perfect democracy and at once I would counter with an attempt to ask, 'Have the people been made perfect? There are never perfect people, so can a perfect democracy exist?' Democracy, national people's power, many heads, many minds, good and bad, clever and stupid – who has the last word? Oh well, I talk too much for I have never really given democracy any thought.

As to your discussion with Wolfgang, I too hope that there is nothing serious about it and that the few days of his leave time were not ruined. I always read from your letters your worries about Wolfgang and his future. But your words, 'I have faith in him' ring out like a confession.

In two and a half weeks the Christmas holidays are here but I have more than enough work to occupy me. Tomorrow there is a diphtheria vaccination and this afternoon I have to deal with over 100 index cards regarding my pupils – their names, birthdays, place of health insurance and so on. To do this one has to make an early start and I've done two-thirds of it already. Tomorrow my older girl pupils may help me with the rest of the work.

My dear Parents

Only a brief greeting today. Yesterday I spent the entire day helping to count the cattle. It had snowed, and paths and road could not be distinguished from fields and meadows. Often I sank up to my knees in the snow and as to the actual counting of the cattle and the people doing so, I could write a novel. I may be so full of stories about it all, but not today as I still have reports to write and 80 exercise books to correct.

This afternoon I have to run through once again our Christmas play with the children, as in one week's time on 12 December it should be staged.

Since a couple of days ago, the 1st- and 2nd-year pupils are taught by Frau Kippar. As a result of this there is a considerable lightening of my workload and I am not so knocked out when school closes. Frau Kippar is knowledgeable and has a pleasant way when handling the children. But all beginnings are difficult.

Gertlauken 9 December 1942

Dear Parents

It is now 11 o'clock and I have two choices. The first is to go to bed for tomorrow I have a conference and must get up at 4.30 a.m., (especially as yesterday I went to bed at 3.30 a.m., or secondly to write to you. I have chosen the latter and will write to you, so do have sympathy for any mistakes and bad handwriting. Father would say something like, 'From Anne we are used to all sorts of things, but I wonder myself that one lets people with such miserable handwriting run around as teachers.'

Yesterday I received your loving letter of 4 December and it reached here especially quickly, as usually a letter takes five or six days. Also in the post a registered packet for 1,200 Reichsmarks. Frau Stachelowski was quite excited. 'What could be in such a packet? 1,200 marks!' We have never had anything like that in Gertlauken before.

But what a lot of work and effort you put into that package – all the lovely paper and the exercise books and the many coloured pencils! How did you manage to organise it all? It will all make such a surprise at Christmas. Please write to me and tell me how you are situated.

My children have collected acorns and chestnuts, for which we got 38.80 marks and that helps to defray our expenditure. And, to top it all, Herr Neumann brought my wardrobe trunk from the station. That was almost too much for one day. As for the wardrobe trunk, my eyes grew larger and larger, and you had cleaned everything. Everything arrived safely, even the lamp and the bottling jar. The candles are also wonderful, for I had no candle stubs left in the house and the electric current often remains off. I am in the best of health and still to come are the joys and delights of the holidays.

After the autumn holidays I had trouble with the blackout as it was difficult to get the black paper and even harder to get the rolls together, so as not to give even a glimmer of light to the outside. The people here take it that this is where little happens – much better and so different than in Köln. I was very annoyed that they had reported me and I received the very large warning – and that as a teacher too! I had a nasty feeling in my stomach about it and didn't want to see anyone especially not the Stachelowskis from the post office who had informed on me several times, and also Herr Naujok I do not wish to see. But, as my cycle pump was stolen, Frau Stachelowski said that her husband might be able to get me another one, and he did so. Afterwards Frau Stachelowski invited me to an evening meal and that was the burying of the hatchet.

But the fat Naujok, who I would rather avoid, wanted me to go to him regarding the cattle count. I did not encounter him when I got there, only his wife who is very friendly. She didn't exactly know the details about the count so I said, 'Nah, it doesn't matter, I'll just have to return again.'

'But,' she said, 'in this weather?'

'That doesn't matter,' I replied. On my second visit, he was again absent but he had written down exactly what was required. I complied with these instructions and then left.

The day before yesterday I went to the baker, Radke, as I wanted to exchange my old bread coupons for new ones. Radke himself is unwell again but I was greatly surprised to be told by his wife that I still had 3 lb of bread to come, and on top of that she told me that if I could do with another small loaf she would give it to me.

I am up to my neck at present in the preparations for the school's small Christmas celebrations. Complying with Father's instructions in his letter, I've sat down and put together a proper programme. It goes like this:

Song: 'Gently Falls the Snow' (all)
Poem: 'Before Christmas' (by an elder girl pupil)

Light Conversation (more boys and girls). At this stage the advent wreath will be lit (the candles naturally!).

Song: 'High in the Night Sky the Stars Are Clear' (upper school)
Poem: 'Winter' (girls of the middle school)
Song: 'Ah-ah-ah, the Winter Is There' (1st and 2nd year)
         'Goblin's Christmas Wish List Worries' (a short play of four minutes)
Poem: 'Santa Claus' (middle school)
Song: 'Let Us Be Happy and Lively' (all)
Play: 'Santa Claus Travels to Earth' (we have to do this together ourselves)

Father Christmas comes (Herr Neumann). As author, I am involved in this and a small rhyme by each child will be cobbled together.

Closing Song: '*O Du Frohliche*' [a well-known Christmas carol] (all)

Duration: two hours.

Originally I had thoughts only of the children attending, but now I would like the adults to come – cross my fingers! Friday afternoon is the dress rehearsal and at 5 p.m. on Saturday the celebration itself. Please direct your next letter to Wolfgang in Berlin, because in one week's time I shall be there with him, and in two weeks' time at home with you.

Gertlauken 13 December 1942

My dear Parents

Quite quickly – the Christmas celebrations were a success but for myself nothing good to report, for in the past few days I've endured a cold and a small fever. I just cannot tolerate fatty food, which everything will be loaded with in this festive period. I shall travel early on Wednesday and I am so very happy about seeing Wolfgang and you once again.

On the train to Königsberg 27 January 1943

My dear Parents

I have now got over the journey to Berlin but something dreadful pained me – the new suspender belt – it pinched and nipped me. The thing is a torture instrument from the Middle Ages.

At 5.30 p.m. I arrived in Berlin where it was raining and pitch-black. The moon only emerged later. Through puddles and rain I made my way to the hand-baggage payment unit, then to the Ribback family, the parents of a colleague. They said I could sleep there on a couch, so I moved quickly, took the house key and left. Without Mother's pocket torch, I would have been lost but by 7.30 p.m. I was at the barracks at Lichterfelde after a non-stop journey. The party took place in a large hall which was decorated with flags and almost full to bursting point. Hundreds of soldiers were present so it was impossible to find Wolfgang.

On the stage rolled the complete Wintergarden programme and at its end, the Joffner brothers and sisters danced the 'Kaiser Waltz'. As all of them streamed out, I looked for Wolfgang, but in vain for it was too large a crowd. Suddenly someone tapped me on the shoulder and Wolfgang stood before me. Two comrades, with the mother of Heinz Goldammer and the petite Sister Erna from the military hospital, were with him. The young soldiers had leave until 2 a.m. and wanted us all to keep together. First of all we remained in the barracks for a while. Sister Erna is on the whole well-known by everyone and was greeted by all present, and greeted by her as Kurtchen, Hanschen and Haschen, but Wolfgang especially holds a soft spot in her heart. Finally we decided first of all to take a trip on the train, then after a quarter of an hour's consultation to adjourn to the Alexanderplatz, which we reached at 11.30 p.m., but there was nothing else in which to take part.

On Sunday without fail I had to be at 7 a.m. at the Ribback family's for a meal, and got to Wolfgang at 2.30 p.m. He had a leave pass until midnight. He showed me the Reich Chancellery and talked about his duties. We waited for the changing of the guard at the Reich Chancellery and it is well worth seeing, especially if one's loved one is taking part. But it was dreadfully cold and we had icy hands and feet, particularly as we had been watching the ceremony for two hours. Now as we were famished we went to Haus Vaterland [restaurant]. We had a wait there in the queue as it was against police orders for the premises to be overfull. We therefore tried our luck in another locality, where the same crush was experienced. Finally we found two places in a large, pleasant restaurant on Bahnhof Friedrichstrasse. There we warmed ourselves and ate spinach or kale, in each case with a coupon-free sandwich in addition. With this we each had 3 jacket potatoes and we were both full. We were warm and cosy eating there and had much to tell each other.

On Monday we met once more in the canteen at the barracks, where we stayed from 6–8 o'clock, and on Tuesday afternoon I took my leave of him. Afterwards when I was alone, the leave-taking really affected me terribly. Now, I hope that once I visit the government offices in Königsberg I shall be able to get some answers to my questions.

Gertlauken 28 January 1943

My dear, dear Parents

Arrived safely! Herr Beckmann picked me up. His wife had sent him with a warm fur coat so that I didn't freeze. Here it is considerably colder than it is with you in the west. In my room the water and the ink were frozen, so at once I lit a fire and then went to Frau Stachel. She made me most welcome and at once I had to eat with her and also had coffee. Real coffee beans and strong mocha it was, and then at evening time bread and *Spirkel*, that is drained-off bacon fat on bread. It tasted excellent.

Now about my visit to the government office. A transfer to Köln is out of the question at the moment and as for studying there, there are no grounds for such a request being made. I simply raised the questions but I was still depressed about the manner in which the answers were given to me. 'Our soldiers battle in Stalingrad and you wish to desert!' What do you think of that? I was never before in such a homesick mood and felt such an after-effect. I didn't want to see anybody and lay in my bed for six hours, howling.

Gertlauken 31 January 1943

My dear Parents and Wolfgang

Please, Wolfgang, send this letter on quickly as Father and Mother are waiting on the post.

Yesterday I thought of you so much. Probably you must be on Honour Guard duties. Have you heard the Stalingrad speeches from Göring and Goebbels? One always wants to find hope but Mother and Father still see things very darkly.

On Friday the lessons began again and of course there is always so much post to deal with. Reports are due, the savings-bank duties and on top of that SS books to take back for the People's Book Library. From the Bundes Deutsche Madchen came the news that I should take responsibility for the Laukischken group, because there is no one else to do the task. So if I went there in summer and was also able to cope with working from Gertlauken, that would be acceptable, since because of the war it is compulsory that one takes on additional duties. But I really don't know what to do. Firstly it is still a long summer and secondly I can't travel for two days to Laukischken!

On Saturday after lessons Frau Stachel, Frau Kippar, Olga and I cleaned my room, and they gave me a couple of tablecloths and cushions that make the room more comfortable. I loathe the mice so much and despite the large cleaning-up operation, once again I found mouse droppings in a cup. I must acquire a mousetrap.

This afternoon I received from Frau Stachel half a pound of butter and a chicken as a token of her appreciation. With the half-pound of butter I baked a cake for Wolfgang and now I am invited to join Frau Stachel for roast chicken.

Gertlauken 3 February 1943

My dear Parents

The people here are so very kind to me, for I have been invited to go on a horse-drawn sleigh ride through the woods on Sunday.

Recently I spoke with a local farmer, a member of a pious sect and who sometimes seems to me to be a bit weird. He is, however, well read and clever, but also the meanest man in the village. He knows many interesting things about the earliest times in the village. When I told him that my home town was Köln, that it was founded by the Romans in 38 BC, also that fifty years after Christ was born it was raised to the status of a city by Agrippina, the mother of Emperor Nero, he clasped his hands together on his head and said, "What, before Christ was born?' He continued, 'I know quite a lot about things, but that I did not know.'

This morning a charming six-year-old girl gave apologies for her eight-year-old sister for not being present at school, in the following way: 'I want you to excuse my elder sister. She must stay at home to take care of the small ones.'

My dear Parents

Our sleigh ride came to nothing, as the weather was too bad. Anyway on Saturday Paula came with her cycle through storm, rain and snow-covered streets and Frau Kippar invited us to coffee. When Paula and I are together we philosophise never-endingly about life and its meaning, about our work and the frightful war. Paula is a very earnest person and I am more easy-going.

On Monday afternoon I went to Krakau with the Frenchman who works for Farmer Buttkus, in the old cart. I was invited to ride with him and he even gave me the reins. It had been a long-held wish of mine to steer a horse and cart, and with the peaceful surroundings and the straight road, it was fairly simple. The Frenchman was on his way to the station to collect Frau Buttkus. The French prisoners of war here are treated as if they were locals and they assist fully in the work and in the house, and belong to the family.

Frau Schulz and her husband are exceptionally friendly to me. He is a real East Prussian – above all things dependable. Full of pride, he showed me his rabbit-lined new waistcoat which he lay on his knee, stroked it lovingly and let it be admired. Then he put it on, even though the room was swelteringly hot, and wore it the entire day without taking it off.

Shortly before 7 o'clock I set out on the return journey when it was dark and no moon or stars to be seen. The wind blew strongly in the trees and nearly blew me over into the fields. When I'm outside and striding out strongly and am quite alone, I feel utterly free and forget all my cares and have the strength to face the future. In any case, after a visit to Herr Schulz I always feel refreshed, not only physically but mentally. I received another order to undertake the BDM work. It may be that Father is right that this work in my judgement is more important than my schoolwork, but despite this possibility, I cannot accept it as such. I am fully occupied with schoolwork, the distances are too great.

Besides, if it were good for me to organise the home evenings so that they could sing well, I know full well that I cannot do it successfully. In school I help with the accordion but how should I manage with a cycle in the wind and inclement weather! Besides, it is I who give the orders. There is a distinct obligation on my part to get to know the parents of my pupils and to be well informed of the individual family circumstances. So tomorrow I shall have a few of the village women for coffee. Now I shall bake once again fruit tart and potato croissants.

Gertlauken 15 February 1943

My dear Parents

In haste – how are you faring? Frau Stachel has just informed me that eight bombers were shot down over Köln. Hopefully you were lucky and nothing has happened to you. All goes well with me. On Saturday the large coffee gossip gathering took place. Frau Neumann, Frau Strupat, the two Fräulein Beckmanns and Frau Buttkus. On Friday afternoon with Frau Stachel I baked a cake. Firstly a pot cake (a pound of semolina, a pound of cooked mashed potatoes, half a pound of sugar, two eggs and a little fat). Secondly, a gooseberry tart (I sacrificed a bottle which I received from you). Thirdly, potato croissants and fourthly, a pudding tart (in which I used up the last of the cocoa, also received from you). My guests obviously believed I must be hungry and they brought cakes: two Madeira cakes, a yeast cake and a cheese tart. From that you can see how well we indulged ourselves! Soon there was a lively discussion in flow – no wonder, with six women! For the evening meal I didn't take anything. Instead, about 7 o'clock I had coffee for a second time and passed the cakes round yet again. About 8.30 p.m. I said goodbye to my guests – it was really pleasant having them. As they were leaving – Frau Stachel, Frau Kippar, Olga – a young non-commissioned officer who was visiting the Stachels appeared and was told by them that they had, alas, eaten up all the coupon-free cakes. It was all so nice.

On Saturday afternoon, Frau Kippar had invited us all, and once again Frau Kerwath the innkeeper and Herr von Cohs. He is the senior forester and a colleague of her husband. Apparently, Frau von Cohs is spending a short time visiting her parents on the Mosel, the NCO, a cousin of Frau Stachel, initiated us into the secrets of a card game *Doppelkopf*. Here there is a passion for playing cards – I too! I can visualise how Father would wrinkle his brow at that confession.

My dear, dear Parents

Today I received your loving letter of 17 February and I am overjoyed to hear from you and to know that everything is in order with you. But what Father writes about Hohe Pforte and Thieboldsgasse is terrible, the most heavily populated quarter. And those young girls with torn-off heads, upright and buried under rubble. The Hangebrucke also has been hit. I can well understand that the foundations of your house shook and especially understand your fear. It is much better if you go into the bunker. I wish so much I could share with you my peaceful evenings, where deep silence prevails in the house when I'm squatting by the tiled stove and writing.

I received, with a thousand thanks, your lovely parcel. Thank you yet again a thousand times for the hand towels and nightclothes. Such items I can most certainly use, and I have already drunk a little of the delicious juice. Also a package came from the Lowen pharmacy.

Gertlauken 26 February 1943

My dear Parents

I am writing in school during the lesson time. Does that amaze you? But this morning and also on Monday I had rotten days. We had to make fifty letter envelopes per child in the upper school, for our soldiers at the front. Yesterday I rushed about to acquire paper, most of all bundles of paper, but also one-sided paper to be able to print on. We had 2,500 envelopes to make. I divided the children into three groups, one group to sign, one to cut and fold and one to stick. Yesterday I had six hours of lessons, then from 2.30–4 p.m. lending out books [library duties], then I sat for an hour in vain at the post office waiting to have a conversation with Labiau, but it did not materialise. Then at 6.15 I cycled to Laukischken to a conference. It was very dark and my lamp did not work. The path was overgrown and full of potholes in the middle. I didn't dare go on the edge because of my previous fall over the heap of stones at the road edge. The conference should have begun at 7 p.m. but it had to be changed to 8 p.m. Once again, an hour of hanging around. On the return journey there were three of us and one had a cycle light. It makes for a completely different journey when one has a light.

The day before yesterday I had leave and travelled to Labiau to acquire, finally, my identity card. I went on the milk cart in the morning and it was lovely to roll along through the start of the day. Everywhere one sees smoke coming from the chimneys. The people, still half asleep, greet one. You see our life here is so peaceful and quiet. In comparison, when I think of you, not a night without air-raid alarms – awful.

I thank you so very much for Mother's loving letter. That Bruno Kahl has received the Knight's Cross must have made his mother so proud of him.

Gertlauken 2 March 1943

My dear Parents

The radio doesn't work properly. For the past few days I've had but a little reception – all shrieks, crackles, or silence – quite odd. What has happened I do not know. Perhaps it is the storm to blame, for the entire house shook, as if a huge overloaded cart went by.

Your telegram reached me early on Saturday. Then I was much more at peace for I had had such fear for you. Now I wait for Father's new report. One would think that there is nothing left in Köln to destroy. The storm broke off the beam on our well with loud crack.

Father, you warned about the passion for card playing – well, it is really nothing, but I would have you accept that these hours with the conversation, cheerfulness and laughter, make for much fun and it does make me feel happy. Next month I shall be twenty-two years old and somewhat more sociable and a little pleasanter I must be, despite the difficult times. All the young women here have their individual worries – their husbands being at the front, often brothers and cousins have been killed, so that they help each other, and in this reciprocating way they support each other. Their strength so impresses me. Besides, mutual laughter can be like medicine.

I have set myself a task – I would like to write a kind of Village Book or Village Chronicle – stories, customs and manners. The superstitions featured therein would be most interesting, the people here and their fate, and also the fate of the villagers who have died, I would like to record.

I have again left the BDM work in abeyance. How can I travel all the way there when the storm howls all day long, besides which there is always something happening all the time.

On Saturday there is a battle meeting to be held at a certain place and attendance there is compulsory. In the following week there is the Heroes Memorial Celebration in Laukischken, and on 28 March there is the solemn reception of the boys and girls in the Hitler Youth and in the BDM respectively. And before that there are still the confirmations.

Gertlauken 10 March 1943

My dear Parents

A peaceful week is over – hopefully for you also. Frau Kippar thought she had flu and I visited her yesterday and today for an hour each visit. After that I browsed through some books I had sent for previously for the people's library. My pupils are extraordinarily enthusiastic readers and I am so proud of this fact. The goings-on at the school make me very happy at the moment. Whether the school officer would say the same, I certainly don't know.

Today it was especially lovely. After a long winter we have an extra hour outside and the children use it to run wildly all over the place. At the end of the school day we have the folk dance *'Hab' den Wagen Vollgeladen'*.

The previous Sunday in artwork (gosh, how we had to learn this in high school!), I entered in the Village Book the list of honours for those of the village who fell in several wars. Up to the present there are twenty-three names relating to this war, thirty-six names from the First World War, 1 from the 1870/71 War, and none from the 1813 War. Above the names I have written these words of Walter Flex:

Wir sanken hin für Deutschlands Glanz,
Bluh, Deutschland, uns als Totenkranz.
Der Bruder, der den Acker pflugt,
Ist mir ein Denkmal, wohlgefugt.
Die Mutter, die ihr Kindlein hegt,
Ein Blumlein uberm Grab mir pflegt.
Die Bublien schlank, die Dirnlein rank
Bluhn mir also Totengartlein Dank.
Bluh, Deutschland, uberm Grabe mein
Jung, stark und schon als Heldenhain!

My dear, dear Parents

This afternoon I received two letters, one from you and one from Wolfgang. The fact that I now know he is in action gave me a powerful shock, the same as it must have given you. Poor mother, you must have cried all night. On the last few occasions, Wolfgang had after written that he desperately disliked the barracks goings-on, and had those constant thoughts about the front. It weighed him down this not being out of doors in the open air.

I am so pleased that when the alarm goes, Mother goes to the bunker. If you too would go, Father, I'd be a lot happier.

On Friday we had a conference in Labiau. It began at 10 a.m. but by Barn I was there, parked my cycle at the station and after a long absence visited a hairdresser. So, clean and up to scratch, I appeared ready for the great meeting of the local group leader of the Nationalist Socialist Party, Leuten, local group leader of the Peasants and Teachers, an administrative officer of the district, in broadest East Prussian dialect, about the 'Economic Balance Sheet of East Prussia'. For me, the best time is at the end of the conference when I meet with young colleagues in the Café Riemann.

Meanwhile, Hannelore Ribback took my cycle to Mauern on her railway ticket and I at 4 o'clock went to Königsberg. I had telephoned previously and booked a room with Frau Kinder in the Rossgarten Market, sited very favourably in the centre of the town. It is the district where cheap hotel accommodation is found by out; villagers and those from surrounding areas. All the forestry workers and teachers stay here overnight and in the evening, naturally, I was in the cinema.

On Saturday morning I looked for the Strength Through Joy house in order to speak with the district people's education officer about the formation of our Gertlauken Village Book. I was referred to a barracks where he was on duty as the chief superintendent and arranged to meet him in the Strength Through Joy house in two hours' time.

During the midday meal in the Berliner Hof two senior medical officers came to my table and conversed with me. They wanted us to link up in the cinema but as I was to be at the Strength Through Joy house at 2 o'clock and they had not at that moment got cinema tickets, I told them at once that I had to fetch my friend from the station at 4 p.m. and I could not disappear before going to meet the chief superintendent in the house. Once there, he showed me his recording of the East Prussian National History and promised to help me both in word and deed. He comes from a village near Angerburg and knows so much about his country. I parted from him full of thanks and bursting with the zeal to work at my project.

At 4 o'clock I was at the station but Paula was not there. The two doctors were already waiting there. We pushed off to the town and spent a stimulating coffee hour. Both were sons of teachers and could discuss much about Finland, Sweden and Norway. One was called Goring and had an enigmatic sense of humour. They were on their way to the Eastern Front and were due to depart the next morning. By evening I was in the cinema and as the cinema closed at 10 o'clock, what do you think? Until the police hour we sat in the Berliner Hof with a bottle of wine. I felt very comfortable in their company and also secure. Dear Father most certainly need not shake his head about his daughter spending the entire evening with two unknown gentlemen.

On Sunday I was at the station at 7 o'clock because I hoped Paula would come on the first train. No Paula. Then shortly after 9 o'clock I bade my two friends farewell. Behind the calmness and humour was their melancholy, which I felt also. The sun shone so brightly, so I strolled to the castle in order to take part in the 10 o'clock conducted tour, and who should I meet there but Paula who had arrived on Saturday evening. After the visit to the castle with its famous Bernstein room that impressed me greatly, we went into the zoo. It is considerably smaller than our zoo in Köln.

At 1917 hours my train took me sadly homewards. Throughout the journey from Mauern to Gertlauken the moon shone brightly. By 10 o'clock I was once again in my dwelling that Frau Stachel had cosily warmed.

Gertlauken 17 March 1943

My dear Parents

Only a short greeting. I believe we both think of the same subject – about Wolfgang. How is it going with him? How may he be when once again we see him? I have nothing especially to write about and I would like only to be with you again. The time flies and before I know it another day has arrived. Soon I shall be twenty-two. How may the picture turn out?

On Sunday in the village the confirmation takes place – there is good food. Couldn't you take part?

How is it going with you, Father? Your leave? Hopefully you do not have an alarm every night and again, hopefully, luck is close by for you. In Essen it is said to be very bad. Later I am going to Frau Kaise who has had two sons killed in the war and is to give me photos, letters and her life story, all for our Village Book.

Gertlauken 25 March 1943

My dear, dear Parents

Eight years ago today I was confirmed. How good it is that one cannot see into the future. Until we hear from Wolfgang time will appear to stand still. I suspect he is in action in the Charkow area.

Now you can hear how I spent the past week. Before 21 March we were all taken up with the confirmation, everywhere baking, roasting and cooking. All the kindred spirits contributing ingredients for the party that has been anticipated for months.

I got up at 7 a.m. on Sunday morning, for one just cannot lie abed with the early morning birds singing with all their might and the sun shining brightly in a dear sky. I quickly ironed my clothes, swept my room and rushed off to Laukischken. At 10 a.m. the Heroes Memorial Celebration was to begin, but it finally began at 11 a.m. – and what a bustle. Twenty, thirty horse and carts stood before the church and the Deutschen house and others round about in front of farms. At the Heroes Memorial Celebration, Herr Schulz spoke from the heart and moved those listening. With the wreath laying the celebration ended.

Coming back from the cemetery the visitors came pouring out of the place of worship. In the Laukischken church 128 children were seated (seventy-two boys and fifty-six girls including eleven from Gertlauken). And then you should have seen the train of wagons, about eighty to a hundred and everywhere festively costumed, happy people, greetings and talking, crying and laughing and congratulations abounding.

In Krakau I went at once to the family Schulz and naturally had to remain for the midday meal, despite the fact that I had previously

228

been invited by the Lemkes. (Still, in the hurly-burly it didn't matter one way or another.)

About 2 o'clock I was back home and an hour later we were ready to take Frau Stachel to a confirmation celebration with the Kaisers; Frau Kippar with Forester Appel and myself were invited by the Strupats. But when we met in Frau Stachel's kitchen we burst into laughter just as if the order had been given for such merriment. I had just put on my hat with the others likewise – it was very odd, as if we were strangers – so we immediately removed our hats.

With the Strupats were twenty-three guests and the tables had been placed in the form of a horseshoe, and sixteen tarts were on the table. Buttercream and sour-cream tart, cheese, poppy seed and mixed cakes. Seldom have I been so sorry that I was so quickly full. In addition there was really good strong bean coffee. I had to think constantly of my mother. About 6 o'clock I rushed to Lemkes and didn't return as quickly to the Strupats as I had done previously. Naturally I had to stay for the evening meal.

With the Lemkes were many youngsters. Six daughters are in the house, two of my age, thus the reason for friendliness. Herr Lemke is now a company sergeant major and he brought along a couple of his comrades. There was much joking and laughter and eventually a game of forfeits was played. So with cherry drinks and giving kisses, the voices were high. And of course the home-brewed schnapps and liquor in abundance. So I thought, warning – look out Marianne! At 10 o'clock despite protests I broke away and rushed to the Strupats and there found a happy, singing company. One song followed another, each one had their turn and always it went round in a circle. I found it most pleasant and it was well after midnight when I left.

But there is also great sorrow in the village and I learnt of this when compiling the Village History Book. Recently I was with the family Mauritz. He has a farming business and is a quiet, peaceful person. Two months ago their only son was killed. He was only nineteen years old and an industrious, friendly young man. He was a leader in the Hitler Youth and in April 1942 was called up. He had passed the examination to become a journeyman and worked in his father's business. Now there are only two daughters, aged seventeen and six years respectively. 'The Fatherland may claim from each of us a sacrifice,' said his mother quietly, but she and her husband wept just the same. I believe she finds some comfort in religion as she seems very pious and prays at table.

Yesterday no lessons as I had to go to Labiau and with all the teachers of the district underwent an X-ray examination. It commenced at 7.15 and there would be four hours of standing around before the first train from Mauern at 5.30 p.m. Frau Kippar and I planned to travel further to Königsberg to find some amusement. When Fräulein Eggerth heard that she cried, 'Children, there is a railway carriage travelling at eight so if you get yourselves called early, you could be in Königsberg by 10.' She suggested we were called at once and by 7.30 we were ready and a whole long day lay ahead of us.

We still had time for refreshments in the Café Riemann and we really were in Königsberg by 10 and at 11 we went to the cinema, at that time a film with Zara Lenader was showing. The next film called *Meine Freundin Josephine* [My Friend Josephine] was due to be shown at 2 o'clock, so between times we had time enough for a midday meal. Over coffee there was much laughter as to whether we should be hungry enough to permit ourselves watching a third film. We cinema rats decided that we would see it and afterwards we had a good evening meal. At 1927 hours the train left for Mauern. We were determined to make that a lovely day, even better still by taking a moonlight walk.

When we arrived at Mauern we waited to collect our cycles from the shed on the station, but were taken aback by the shed and station being closed. Despite rattling and shouting and calling out, the door didn't open. It was 2110 hours and so began our moonlit walk. Anyway, In Laukischken we found a military concert taking place in the Deutschen house. As pleasure seekers we naturally took our places. The hall was packed full and all the top representatives of the party and their members were there, and most certainly our cycle-shed owner. We stayed until the end. First melodies from operettas were played and then dance music. At the close we were hailed with loud greetings by Herr and Frau von Cohns who were there with their cycles. And on the way home, the journey went like this: Herr and Frau von Cohns rode on their cycles for a while, then placed their cycles against a tree and went ahead on foot. When we, on foot, reached the tree with the cycles, we cycled on and overtook both the Cohns and left the cycles beside another tree. And so it went on until we reached Gertlauken at 1130 hours. There we drummed Frau Stachel out of bed to tell her about everything. Yes and such it was that was pursued by your pleasure-seeking daughter!

Now I must write some school-leaving certificates, besides I must somehow close because this is my last sheet of writing paper. I would prefer to leave a wide margin, but the paper is too narrow.

Gertlauken 29 March 1943

Dear Parents

Yes, and I too think of Wolfgang often and hope soon for news. If he should send to you an army post office voucher for a parcel so that he can get two parcels each month, do please send me one of the vouchers. I know that you love to send him a parcel, but I can send him more nourishing things. I have already kept back a little German salami, pork and other things. Also I can bake him a Madeira cake that keeps fresh for a long time, also rolled out macaroons that he loves to eat.

Aunt Lies has written that Hermann is in hospital and should soon be home on sick leave, also that Willi visited her and is now a lance corporal. And that Rolf Hellman has been killed.

On Sunday, after the transfer of the young girls to the BD Madchen, I went to Schulz. I spent the entire day there working on things, especially the Village History Book and the schoolwork. But we had much else to talk about. Herr Schulz spoke about the campaigns in Poland then France and then about ancestry research. After the evening meal he wanted to play cards, 66 and *Herzblattchen*, but when one has learnt to play *Doppelkopf* one doesn't want to play anything else.

When I arrived home I found a familiar cycle outside. It was Paula's and she had sat in my cold room during the entire afternoon in my absence. It did so annoy me. However, we had an hour together before she had to leave. Besides, tomorrow after school I shall go to see her at Weidlacken.

31 March

I have opened the letter because the meat coupons I intended to send fell out before I posted it to you. I hope you can purchase some German salami and send it to me.

Yesterday after lessons I went straight away to Paula. I had twenty-one kilometres to travel despite a nasty wind against me, and did the journey in two hours. We then had a peaceful walk in the countryside and it was wonderful. The woods are full of anemones, liverwort, lungwort, wild lilac, golden stars and *Milzkraut*. It is an indescribable, luxuriant floral picture.

At evening time we read from Waiter Flex's *Klaus von Bismarck* and at 5 a.m. this morning it was time to get up. I was here punctually in time for the lessons.

Gertlauken 5 April 1943

My dear Parents

I have just received your letter No. 38 from 31 March. My grateful thanks for it. I wait, like you, for post from Wolfgang. But I should not be too impatient. He went off on 16 March precisely and we must reckon on it being five to six weeks before we receive post from him. This is the time factor in respect of Herr Kippar and Alga's brother.

Here I spend such a pleasant life that it weighs heavily on my conscience. So often do I hear the Armed Forces Report, and how objectively and militarily concise it sounds. 'The awaited attack of the Soviet Army on the Kuban Bridge had commenced yesterday – the battle continues.' And what lies behind this? Distress and death, grief and hardship and courage? One cannot express that in words.

Gertlauken 8 April 1943

My dear Parents

Today I received a card from Wolfgang. It reads, 'I send you very best wishes. With me all goes well.' Field Post No. 041124. I take it that you likewise received news from him and now finally you will be able to send him the letters and he will be so pleased to receive many postal items at one time. Frau Neumann gave me a Field Post voucher so that tomorrow I shall be able to send him a parcel. Where may Wolfgang be? I'm on tenterhooks awaiting his next news.

I was not too well this morning but everything is again in order. But I have fallen behind in the lessons. What would be best for me?

I thought. And decided that the best time would be when I am, undisturbed, to open your parcel that has lain here for several days unopened. So yes, I did that and I am unbelievably happy about it.

Above all, I am pleased with the clothing items. I know already exactly how the clothing will look. I thank you from the bottom of my heart. Also for the pen which now flies on the paper. Also for the sweets and oranges. You have no idea how I have hungered for such fruit. The food here is excellent but always potatoes, cream, gravy and meat. Jam I can eat by the spoonful! I am somewhat disappointed that Father didn't visit me during his holiday.

You claim that we children did not inherit your longing for the countryside. To that I can only say that I would be willing to live my life in the countryside, because I feel so closely bound to nature. Admittedly I can also fit into the life of a big city. We have always been very self-contained in Köln. What a big city offered, we enjoyed. The cinema for one thing and, unforgettable, are my visits with Mother to the theatre. She with a season ticket on the ground floor and I in No. 3 circle, middle row for 25 pfennigs, and my; school identity pass. And then in the interval, with Mother on the ground floor.

No, I still haven't received anything more; only through the school education and museum visits. Today I shall use another preference for another large city and in my education details enter sport and much, much more.

You ask if I am always brave in school? Oh you dear, unsuspecting Father. We have in our school a huge barn-door entrance. This opens into a vast floor space with the classrooms off each side and a normal door to the side with a staircase leading to it. Then ascends a wooden staircase of twenty-one steps leading to the first floor where, leading off to the right and to the left respectively, are the quarters of the chief and the first teacher. A further seventeen steps higher one finds Frau Stachel's room door and opposite this door, the living quarters of the second teacher, also my own quarters.

I hope you can follow this description. So, for the main door and the door leading to the staircase area, there are not any keys. That made it all quite insecure, especially if on an evening I arrive at the house in the dark and might find the light not working because of the lack of blackout paper for the higher windows. Then sometimes I think, 'Someone is standing in the corner and is lying in wait for me.' Well, such a thought sends cold shivers running down one's spine. But with time that feeling of apprehension went. In addition to this, Frau Berkan and Frau Stachel with their two children each live here. So there is enough life in the house.

In the complaints about the school I gave many an instance, such as an open window in the class of Frau Kippar (everywhere else we have double windows), with three panes of glass broken, and a pane of glass broken to my own room. Clothes hooks I've asked for since December have not arrived, and we do not have enough. So coats and hats are left on the floor and this gives rise to quarrels with the parents. My children do not have enough exercise books. At the same time school stamps are missing and we cannot fetch water from the well if, in a violent storm, the wooden arm above the well breaks. To that situation it is said, 'It is quite all right if the wooden arm is not working, so for health reasons the children will not be tempted to drink water from the well.' For we teachers the well water is good enough!

In summer I can use the pumps of Stachels and Berkans to fetch the water but in winter they are frozen up. This is when we fetch our water by the bucketful from the farmer opposite. One gets tired over these things and the town mayor is always 'frightfully' friendly and would most 'frightfully' like to help, 'But it is the war now and unfortunately there is nothing to be done.'

Gertlauken 11 April 1943

My dear Parents

The writing paper you sent me is simply delightful. It affords the writing double the space, such as if I hear Strauss waltzes played on the radio I am scarcely still and want most of all to dance.

I received a card from Wolfgang on 3 April. It was dated 27 March and then three days later a letter. He writes that he is at the front and that his wish to be here is finally fulfilled. But he is happy that he is together with Heinz Goldammer. I at once sent him a parcel but it is a pity he is not allowed to write where he is.

I advised him that he should be prepared in case of the slightest trouble – in his next letter to form the name of the town where he is in such a way that the letter at the beginning of the last sentence gives the approximate location details.

All goes excellently with me, only that I am waiting for the school chief before the Easter holidays and daily I am conscious of an uncomfortable feeling. This week I must have leave of absence to work with the planting in the fields.

My birthday I shall celebrate in a different way. I shall bake a small cake and a curd cheese and yeast cake for my schoolchildren. I have them until 4 p.m. in the afternoon and then we shall romp about in an orderly manner. And in the evening there is the 'Double-headed Club', Frau Stachel, Frau Kippar, Frau Kerwath and Herr & Frau von Cohs. On Saturday afternoon I am going to Frau Berkan and Frau Schustereit, the shopkeeper's wife, and on Sunday Paula comes.

Friday evening found us with Frau Kerwath and a 'little party'. Herr von Cohs spent so long hinting about cognac that the Kerwaths finally caught on and produced a bottle. The women, however, preferred egg liquor and so Herr von Cohs was sent to the Stachens to acquire ten eggs. Frau Kerwath supplied more, so fourteen eggs were beaten up, sugar and schnapps added and we had two bottles of egg liquor as a result – and the most lovely voices. As a result I had the beginning of a headache.

In the morning of that day when drawing with the children outside the school I was bitten near my eye by a bee. So in the course of the evening I became tired. For the first time since being here I smoked a cigarette, then a second one and they helped dear my headache.

Herr von Cohs introduced us to a card game he had learnt when he was under training as a forester in the Rhein area. His lovely, full-blooded wife comes from the Mosel. When we broke up at nearly 2 a.m. I had won 80 pfennigs from each of the men. Herr von Cohs who cannot take much drink, was nearly asleep. His forestry house lies ideally on the edge of the forest and he has a smallholding nearby and has two cows in his stables. On getting up from playing I felt my limbs somewhat heavy and my bones really unwilling to help matters, but at least my head was quite clear.

On Saturday it was the village social evening and it began at 8 o'clock. Herr Schulz made a speech, then there was singing and it closed with the Hitler Youth and BD Madchen dancing fun dances together. Naturally the adults took part and Herr Neumann took Frau von Cohs and myself in the polonaise dance. It was all terribly limited but I had most fun with the *Hopsen* (hops dancing around). Out of politeness I took myself off back to the missing members of our 'club' where, in the homely stillness and quietness of Frau Kerwath's kitchen, meringues from over fourteen eggs were consumed.

Now comes the best of all about my birthday – peacefulness and on the radio a cheering Wiener waltz and I am writing a letter to you.

On Tuesday with the Beckmanns and Neumanns we organised some good things to bake. In addition I was with the tailoress, Fräulein Dannat, where I heard all the latest news about the village, but it was not particularly worthy of note.

On Wednesday after the lessons I was with Frau Stachel doing a large bake. A semolina tart without fat but with eight eggs. A Frankfurt sausage ring and biscuits from 3 lb of flour. In the middle of baking, Paula came and helped considerably in the kneading and cutting-out. She presented me with a glass of jam, a delightful wooden plate and a picture of the Minnesangern. Before she left for her homeward journey, we had blancmange and tidied up the kitchen.

After that I went to Frau Kippar where I acted as her hairdresser, inasmuch as I did her freshly washed hair in a very artistic manner and with much squeezing and rolling did the waving and curling requirements. Then off to Frau Kerwath in good time for a cup of bean coffee and a piece of cake. Actually I would prefer not to play cards this evening but since Herr von Cohs will be absent I remain as the fourth person.

And then the great day broke. I was awake at 6 a.m. and got up and put my room in order. I then heard pleasant noises in the classroom below. At 8 a.m. when I went down all the stairs leading to my door were strewn with fir branches. It made me think instinctively of a wedding. When I opened the door of the classroom, once again the overwhelming impression as in the previous year. The entire room decorated with flowers – wherever one looked – snow flowers had already bloomed this year – anemones, liverwort, *Zillerchen*, golden stars and carnations. There was a twined garland on the desk and present upon present, all packed and tied up by loving hands. Also there were two thick, red, burning candles. And the children serious, good and as quiet as lambs. They looked at me so expectantly and I did not know then what I should say or what I should do. On such a day naturally nothing much is done in the way of learning.

Then in came Frau Kippar with a bouquet of flowers in her hand and leading in the first- and second-year pupils. They sang a song and each child greeted me with a flower. We all squeezed together and sang a few songs. Then I told a long fairy tale and we played the game 'All Birds Fly High' with forfeits. Every child paid a forfeit and provided us all with lots of laughter with their antics such as stargazing, teeth extracting and telephone building, and so on. We played outside from 11 to 12 and then we sent all the children home. Frau Kippar and I were quite dead beat by that time.

Then I wanted to phone Köln and go to the post office. I wanted so much to speak with you straight away on the day, but the official said that the connection would be engaged for several hours, so I left it at that.

In between times, at her own expense, Frau Stachel gave me as birthday presents, half a pound of butter, *Flinsen* and also baked potato waffles. Frau Kippar and I consumed at least twenty of them. Afterwards I rested for an hour. No, before that, there was another present all packed up – 166 eggs, two and a half pounds of butter and numerous things such as ham, pork and sausage. Naturally I was as happy as a Snow King.

About 4 o'clock I was again in the classroom having put on new clothing. It looks very nice as Fräulein Dannat sews very well and has such good taste. And now commenced the children's play with my children wearing their Sunday clothes. We danced a few simple folk dances, played races and finally a game of forfeits. And at the close at 7 o'clock we sang '*Gute Nacht Kameraden*' [Goodnight Comrades]. I believe it was a beautiful day for us all. There is one thing I do know for a certainty and that is that my boys and girls are very likeable and have much kindness towards others. I think I shall be celebrating again the next few days.

At midday Frau Kippar and Frau Stachel cleaned my room and polished the floor. I brought out my tarts, laid the table and decorated it with flowers. Then Frau Stachel said, "You must beat fifteen eggs to make egg cognac.' The Kerwaths had actually once again brought a bottle and each of us brought bean coffee. (Heaven knows where on earth the people here get hold of bean coffee!) However, at first we drank bean coffee and later ate tarts. Then I brought out the egg cognac and naturally we played cards. Finally we finished with bread and butter. Now, at the close of day, I am twenty-two years old and what a glorious, wonderful, full day of activity it was.

By the way, today a pair of storks with great flapping and noise returned to nest in the village. But during the entire day I have had but one thought, wishing that you and Wolfgang were here. You would most certainly be interested in the air battles going on over Königsberg. For hours on end we hear the planes flying over us in countless waves. In all directions round our village we saw thirty parachute flares and additionally we hear the anti-aircraft fire in Königsberg and other nearby towns.

By the way, yet again we sat playing the unavoidable game of cards when, at about 2215 hours, the whole house shuddered. Then excited cries, 'Lights Out!' The children – 'I must go home!' 'Where is my coat?' and so on, and all left at once. Frau Stachel got the children out of bed and we found out that a bomb had fallen off target near Krakau. In the nights following, the planes were there again. Naturally the women no longer have peace at night and from now on we listen out attentively with an extra ear. At present all is quiet.

Gertlauken 25 April 1943

My dear Parents

Hopefully the Easter period passed quietly and peacefully for you as it did for me, and hopefully you have received the two parcels I sent to you. I was so greatly pleased by your loving Easter greetings – a thousand thanks.

This morning I overslept and at 9 there was a knock on the door. It was the petite Helma who had brought me breakfast in bed, and a small nest with a coloured Easter egg and a few sweets, and then poppy seed cake, coffee and an egg, with a vase of spring flowers. I got up at 11 o'clock and soon Frau Buttkus came with the food. Plenty of meat, potatoes and blancmange. Then I sat by the window and read a story about Norway. Between whiles I admired the view of the lush meadows and the light-green woods – quietness and contemplative peace.

This afternoon I have been invited to Frau von Cohs and there is to be lots of company. The Stachels, Frau Kippar, the Stachelowskis, with Forester Krause and his wife. Early tomorrow Paula and I are to meet in Königsberg for a four-day Samland tour.

Yesterday was my great cleaning day and I took the bed and mattress outside and gave both a good beating. On Friday morning Frau Kippar and I went to Springlack to visit her sister-in-law there. She was my predecessor here and then had married Frau Kippar's brother. He is now a soldier. She still travels to see her first school. Unfortunately we didn't meet her and so we spent a nice day with Frau Kippar making *Flinsen* [small biscuits] and *Bisquitrolle* [sponge rolls]. And at evening time! Now what? Frau von Cohs sent over one of her apprentices to take part in a card game, *Doppelkopf*.

Gertlauken 1 May 1943

My dear Parents

Paula and I had planned to travel, partly on foot and partly by rail, from Cranz, always along the coast to Pillau. A wandering programme it would have been. But on Easter Monday I failed to meet Paula at the prearranged time in Königsberg. I waited until the next train arrived but then left alone and went from the north railway station on the Samland train to Neukuhren.

Neukuhren is a pretty place with many villas almost all fully occupied, so it took me a little while before I found a private room. Then I took a walk along the *Ufer* promenade and saw the view from the *Steilküste* of the Baltic Sea. Thereafter, because it was cold and windy, I didn't visit the small harbour but took myself very quickly back to my room and bed.

On Tuesday morning I took a long wander to the Wanger and to the Loppohnerspitze. Before me, always the sea and the coastal strip and the parapet. There were many soldiers there recovering from their wounds. A young corporal asked if he could accompany me. His forename was Wolfgang and, as he was a friendly and polite man, I had nothing against his request. It made for more fun being a couple. After the midday meal we went to Warnicken and strolled on from there along the steep coast over rushes, and back to Neukuhren. The *Ufer* is a small strip with fine sand and thick rock-like cliffs with incisions in them. Into these gaps come the white waves and the water constantly changes colour. These colours are of the clouds or of the sun as it glistens on the sea.

On Wednesday morning, again on my own, I went to Rauschen where there is a large millpond, more like a large lake in fact, with wonderful grounds and naturally many woods. And always there is the view of the coastal strip and the sea – indescribable!

At midday I returned to Königsberg and obtained, wonder of wonders, a ticket for the Waffenschmied from Lortzing and that was a beautiful ending to the day. On the next morning I travelled to Pillau by way of the Frischen Nehrung. Pillau is, so to speak, the harbour of Königsberg and leads to it through a sea canal via the Frische Haff, but now it is full of military personnel. In the harbour lay the ship *Robert Ley* and even the larger ship *Pretoria*. The latter ship I greeted like an old acquaintance for I had heard so much about it. In peacetime it travelled to Africa. After this I went on the Norderrnole as far as the lighthouse and looked for a while at the fishing going on. Then I strolled along the beach to Neuhausen, a pretty place with villas, a nice sandy beach, weeds and many, many soldiers. On the whole, however, there is still an air of much peacefulness. By evening I was again in Königsberg with Frau Kinder and lived through a four-hour air-raid alarm. It wasn't too bad and I had to think of you in Köln.

Then on Friday I used up my time with a little shopping and a lengthy stroll through the town to Preger and its harbour with its old, tall, gabled and timber-framed stone houses. Especially charming is the fish market and nearby I came across the house where Kant was born. His gravestone is an impressive monument, as you can see from the enclosed postcard depicting it. It lies on the Kneiphof, a Pregel island, near the cathedral. The Kneiphof gymnasium is said to be the oldest school in Prussia. First of all I saw the cathedral, a very solid, Gothic, brick stoned building with broad facades and many apertures and arches. In its interior are many gravestone memorials of important Prussian personalities. Especially noteworthy to me were those of Herzog Albrech I and his two wives. I found the town to be especially rich in memorials. In front of the castle is a high pedestal of Bismarck and on the castle terrace on the side a monument of Kaiser Wilhelm I swinging his sword, and on the other side of the castle one meets Herzog Albrech the last Hochmeister [high official] of the German Order and First Duke of Prussia, as well as King Friedrich I. His memorial is by Andreas Schluter and stands with all its vigour, apart from the others.

Out on the parade square and to its rear stands the mounted statue of King Friedrich Wilhelm III with a laurel-leaf wreath on his head, and the significantly modest statue of Immanuel Kant. This parade square makes an unforgettable impression on one – a broad walled enclosure on one side restricted by the university where in 1544 the Albertina was founded by Duke Albrecht. Through the long arcades the building appears, bright and imposing. Its roof has a decorated balustrade with quite a lot of figures on the corners and central parts. The figures of Luther and Melanchthon stand. A daughter of Melanchthon should have been the wife of the first rector of the university, and a son of Luther died in Königsberg. On the other side of the university there is a huge bookshop, the largest I have ever seen – its name Grafe and Unzer. In its four floors one can browse and bury themselves for days on end. A real find and a pleasure beyond words. Our bookshop Gonski in the Neumarkt in Köln bears no comparison.

About ten that evening I arrived in Gertlauken safe and dog-tired. There was a letter from Paula awaiting me. She had been ill and therefore was unable to accompany me. If possible I shall visit her tomorrow. I think that when one travels alone one is receptive to the entire world. But perhaps the pair of us will travel to Palmnicken if our original plan stands. The obtaining of amber by open mining and the whole story of amber now definitely belongs to a teacher (myself) in East Prussia. Is that not so?

P.S. Heinz Licht is also now a soldier. He is stationed in Holland and enclosed is his Field Post number.

Gertlauken 10 May 1943

My dear Parents

Once again I am sitting, sunning myself, on the bank behind the toilet in Stachel's garden. I have examined 100 exercise books and the essays of the older children make me very happy. They are better at expressing themselves, and above all their accounts of their experiences are very good.

Have you received any post from Wolfgang? I received a short letter and he writes always of unimportant stuff, nothing about what one would like to know. But of that, probably, he may not write.

In the long holidays we shall again be needed for employment. We shall each receive fourteen days' leave and I am now trying to seek such employment, perhaps manufacturing work in Köln. Have you heard of any about? Or shall I write to Uncle August and ask him?

In the Armed Forces Reports one hears frequently nowadays of the attacks on the large cities in the west of Germany. The last was

Dortmund, just one in a series of raids. God willing, you will be spared!

In Wolfgang's letter there were four vouchers for Field Post parcels. I at once baked him a cake as I had ¾ lb flour and ¼ lb potato flour. About 3 o'clock Frau Stachel asked if I would like to go with her and Frau Kippar through the woods to a market garden. I really wanted to look through several exercise books but I let myself be talked into it. The woods are never more beautiful than in May. On the way we called in to Forester Krause where we were invited for coffee and cake. The forestry cottage, like all the others, lies beautifully in the woods. In the stall were eight cows and two horses. On this same afternoon the three Krause children came home from school in Labiau. They are a fourteen-year-old boy, a thirteen-year-old girl and an eleven-year-old girl, all healthy and blooming, fair with rosy cheeks. I thought at the time that there stood before me was a future forester, yet to be a man. I would keep my eyes open as to his future.

After much conversation we took our leave and went on to the market garden. The gardener himself was an original and gave us fresh heads of lettuces, whereupon Frau Kippar spontaneously invited us to an evening meal and Frau Stachel offered to make the salad cream. That evening we indulged terribly in the first fresh vegetables of the year.

On Sunday morning I travelled to Paula. We enjoy ourselves so much when we are together. Paula suffers very much from homesickness and there is no one in her village with whom she associates. The journey to her was an experience as it had rained and the air was warm and full-scented. Although apple and pear blossom is lovely, the loveliest above all is the cherry blossom – such wonderful, wonderful blossom. Paula and I wandered through the woods for a few hours. We know a wonderful place in a high position above where the wild animals feed. At evening time I was so tired that I slept at Paula's.

It seems to be very bad in North Africa.

Gertlauken 21 May 1943

My dear Parents

I am well as always. Herr Berkan is here on leave and he is extraordinarily kind to me. Above all he takes his calling as a teacher very seriously. To find in him a fellow-teacher is good for me and already I have been affected and have more zeal for schoolwork. Last week there were vaccinations for everybody in Krakau and last Wednesday Herr Schulz became a soldier again and his wife took the news very badly. Also our town mayor is to be called up for military service.

Paula went home last Saturday as her sister marries on Wednesday and Paula will return on Sunday.

Have you, in between your experiences, found which Talsperren was destroyed? That must have been an inconceivable catastrophe.

As I have told you previously, I work even more intensively for the lessons, since Herr Berkan is here. With him I can talk about all my preparation and the results achieved. He is not only a good teacher but he also encourages inexperienced colleagues in such a manner that the work becomes fun.

Soon I have to go to Laukischken on duty grounds regarding the BDM. The weather has again turned warmer after all the tomato plants and many other vegetable flowers were attacked by frost. Also rain is needed. How is it looking in our garden?

Yesterday I was with the Neumanns and fetched some geese and duck eggs for Frau Stachel. The chicks are so cute and follow one everywhere and always are under one's feet. In the evenings they are kept in a box near the stove.

On the train to Marienburg 30 May 1943

My dear Parents

'Anne has written very little recently' – that's what you mean, Father, when you write 'Anne seems to have a terrible amount of work.'

I have actually achieved more than normal recently and it is such a pity that Herr Berkan has once again left. He had made me into a good teacher.

In your previous letter you informed me that both the large Eder and the Mohnetalsperre dams had been hit and shattered. One simply cannot imagine the catastrophe in its entirety with its terror let loose and the merciless flood of the water. From the force of the water there was no escape. The poor, poor people. For the East Prussians here it was hard to understand and I had to give an explanation and a drawing to enable them to realise how dreadful it was.

Yesterday was the day for the State's Youngsters Contest for those aged between ten to fourteen years. Later on Saturday I travelled to Königsberg, I had telephoned already and ordered a cinema ticket. Then I travelled with the first train to Marienburg in order to see the old Ordensburg. Later I was to meet up with Frau Neumann as we wanted to visit her son who was in the vicinity training in a National Socialist model estate.

Have you heard from Wolfgang?

Gertlauken 5 June 1943

In school today there was much fun and confusion. I wanted us to complete our handicraft work on the Punch and Judy show puppets to enable us to stage a puppet show at the beginning of the school holidays. The youngsters had cut out the puppets' heads and were now ready to affix hair and body. The girls sewed the clothing, especially Death, the Devil and the Witch. These are exceptionally good and successful.

By the way I did not meet Frau Neumann on Saturday in Marienburg as she did not come, because of bad weather. Therefore I saw the Ordensburg on my own. After the last war the Poles wanted to claim it, but in the 1920 plebiscite they obtained only 191 votes. Marienburg lies on the Nogat at the junction of the border that from 1918 had become the boundary of the Free State of Danzig. From the riverbank one sees the castle at its most impressive with its two massive, solid round towers either side of the bridge door. There is the High Castle, the chief official's palace, and the gabled glazed roofs are wonderful to see. The room of the *Sommerremter* – the chief official – was the best. He possessed a Star Vault that rested on a solitary slim column. In 1410 when the city was besieged by the Poles they wanted to destroy this column. A stone ball is still embedded in the wall over the chimney to this day. The Castle Church displays a picture of Marien and from whichever side one looks at the picture, her eyes always follow you. The town has a heavily tree-lined road, the houses being shaded by the foliage. Such houses surround the market square. Although there was much more I wanted to see, there was insufficient time as I had to catch a train.

The next part of the journey is well-known to me from old

times; over Elbing, along to Frischenhaff, on the way passing Frauenburg with its exceptionally visible cathedral, of which Nikolaus Kopernikus [the great German astronomer] was the Cathedral Master. I must one day avail myself of an opportunity to go to Frauenburg.

On Monday we had a conference in HaffWinkel, an especially lovely piece of earth. I should give a lecture on 'The Helpful Aids of the Knowledge of the Earth, and Their Use'!

After the conference Frau Kippar and I indulged in roast beef in a restaurant we found quite by chance. Some quite choice things were to be had there, such as eels. We ate together with the local teachers and after the eel we had a bowl of blancmange.

On Tuesday evening I was invited to the Berkans where we sang and played, and on Wednesday evening Frau Stachel celebrated her 10th wedding anniversary. Naturally she misses her husband very much and the whole card club endeavoured to cheer her up. Frau Kippar brought her ten lovely dark red Whitsun roses. Herr Stachel is at present in Karlsruhe and Frau Stachel and Frau Kippar want to visit him during the holidays, and perhaps thereby come to Köln!

Gertlauken 7 June 1943

My dear Parents

Just a short few lines. Kinni arrived here safely today. I could scarcely concentrate on schoolwork and the subjects to be studied. I went on my cycle for a while to meet her. I had begged Herr Beckmann to fetch her from the station and there she sat, laughing, near him on the seat of the carriage. It was her first carriage ride.

We then ate fried potatoes with fried eggs and at supper curd cheese and sugar. Then Kinni lay down and went to sleep. Then, after I had washed, I opened my parcel. One was just like a small child and wanted most of all to ask "What have you brought me?' In order not to disturb Kinni I took a quick, fleeting look then firmly closed up the parcel on the sheer lovely things inside. So first of all, thank you so sincerely for all the things enclosed.

Kinni had at once told me of all the latest news. That Elli had got engaged, that Karl Schuller had been wounded and that you had visited him (I would love to see him once again), and that Erni had been taken prisoner in Africa.

My dear Parents

We spent our time beautifully. Kinni loves the peace and quietness. She sleeps so soundly and when I come from school, she has the place cleared and has cooked a small meal. Frau Buttkus can no longer cook my midday meal because she has commenced work in the fields and spends the entire day outside. But she has spoken around the village that I have a visitor and all the people are extremely kind. We take small walks in the woods but best of all, Kinni likes to sit in the garden in the sunshine. She sits quietly and enjoys the quietness and the peacefulness in Gertlauken.

Once again this year the Whitsun holidays have been restricted to but two days. Father should be against this, but I have on my own account given the school Whitsun Saturday free, while Kinni and I travel along the Nehrung to Nidden, and in respect of which she has been always spending the mornings cycling. Today real 'holiday voices' prevail as I sat at the window in the evening sunshine and played just simple folk songs on the accordion. And Kinni lacquered her fingernails. Now she sleeps soundly and I shall say, 'Goodnight.'

My dear Parents

We have spent fabulous Whitsun days and I am annoyed with myself only because I didn't give myself Tuesday as a school-free day. For only half of the children appeared anyway for the lessons. The East Prussians like to celebrate their holidays in a long and merry fashion.

On Whit Saturday we set off cycling very early. It was a lovely sunny morning and the saddle on my bike had been lowered for Kinni, while I cycled on Frau Kippar's bike. The small person felt herself quite brave on the wide straight road from Laukischken to Labiau. It might become dangerous if vehicles came from each direction, particularly towards us, perhaps containing a school official. So each time this occurred we jumped off our cycles and went into hiding. Luckily this only occurred three times.

The boat was packed with soldiers and soon we were entertained by two nice, pleasant, somewhat seasoned warriors of about thirty-five years of age. One came from Köln and the other from

Wuppertal. The one from Köln was in the State Civil Prosecutor's office and let off much steam immediately about his changed circumstances. He was really angry about this. He had then to go to the writing room to sharpen the under-officer's pencils – earlier, such persons had had this chore done for themselves. The one from Wuppertal was a quiet and humorous man who, when he learnt we had no accommodation booked in Nidden, thought it looked a dark prospect for us. We then agreed to stay together and they would contact the *Kommandantur* [commander] and request a room for us, for members of the armed forces were afforded special treatment. So we went at once to the beach.

I was daring enough to bathe but only for a short swim as the water was freezing. Although it was hot in the sunshine the soldier from Wuppertal and I began to build a windbreak, so if it became cooler we could sunbathe in it. He told me about his family and later we spoke about *Barrines of William von Simpson*, an East Prussian Estate novel, a book we had both read. Then suddenly I heard Kinni crying out. She sprang out of the windbreak that the soldier from Köln had slavishly built and ran towards the water, and I ran after her. Apparently the chap had been rather pushy. On the beach we discussed what to do and came to the conclusion to overlook the occurrence.

Then about 5 p.m. the two soldiers had obtained two rooms from the *Kommandantur* and wanted to give us one of them. When we had come from the beach, the soldier from Köln apologised and the soldier from Wuppertal found the whole incident embarrassing.

Thereafter everything was in order and at 5 o'clock we obtained a private room in a tiny, reed-covered, coloured and so picturesque fisherman's house. We met in the Hotel Zur Nordische Linnaa for the evening meal. There we met another friend of the two soldiers. He was from Wien and during the meal, which he quite ignored, he turned his full charm on Kinni.

On Whit Sunday I was early out of bed. The sun shone and I got out through the window of our doll's house into the open air, otherwise I would have had to go through the bedroom of our landlord, had I used the door. I strolled alone through the place in the still morning air and returned for breakfast. After that we met up with our friends and looked at the pretty houses and the harbour of Nidden.

The Niddeners go in for cattle breeding and they have part of the meadowland on the other side of the lagoon. They bring the hay to the cattle in barges. But of course their main occupation is fishing. And the harbour is full of fishing boats. We arranged to go for a long walk in the afternoon to the Tal des Schweigens [Valley of Silence] and to the Toten Dune [Death Dunes], the latter being two vast, changing dunes in which there were small waves of fine sand.

The soldier from Köln missed this outing and shut himself out in the hotel, mumbling away and mocking the pleasure we took in our ramblings. He was a queer fellow at times, arrogant on occasion, then at other times extremely kind. When we met in the hotel for the evening meal he surprised us with a truly festive spread in which, because we had good wine, the voices rose. The landlady told us about the curious name of the hotel – the Nordisch Linnaa is the name of a very rare local plant. Later, the soldier from Köln and I argued about who had built the first bridge over the Rhein and then we all tried to see if we could walk a straight line – and we could! At the end, the soldier from Köln suggested we took a night stroll along the Nehrung to the Baltic Sea. That was very romantic but no one was inclined for a midnight dip in the sea. Finally, Kinni and I landed back in our cottage room, which we entered via the window. My last words to Kinni were, 'Kinni, we have landed ourselves in a cosy little sugar house.'

Gertlauken 21 June 1943

My dear Parents

When Kinni and I returned from Königsberg yesterday evening we found your telegram. It was such a huge relief to receive it. The attack on Köln must have been appalling. Kinni always says she is lucky she is to be away from it. Now we await Father's report.

Now, briefly, we have spent a wonderful weekend in Königsberg. On Saturday afternoon we sat in the Café Alhambra and on Sunday morning we did a conducted tour of the castle and rowed a boat on the castle pond. After the midday meal we meet Herr and Frau Kippar in the Hotel Kreutz. Herr Kippar is on leave and Frau Kippar is free from school duties until 3 July. Soon Kinni will be with you again and can tell you all about the happenings.

My dear Parents

Today I received Father's letter No. 56 (about Aunt Lies) and No. 57 for 17 and 19 June. The misery so terrible and here it is impossible to conceive it. No, I cannot conceive of such a life of fear and terror with sleepless nights and I ask myself how you can bear it. Of Köln nothing more is standing and how can one count the dead?

Kinni set out today with a heavy heart and when I got back from the station the dwelling was quite empty. She was so content here and we have had many lovely hours together. In Berlin she will stay overnight with her relatives and the next day will travel on to you and tell you all of our time together.

On Monday we took our last cycle ride and went to Tapiau, to the birthplace of Lovis Corinth. It was to the gloomy Ordensburg, those who were to be reformed were brought. In the Café den Wiener we met the soldier from Wuppertal an acquaintance from our Whitsun outing. The soldier from Köln had gone home on leave because his family had become air-raid victims for the second time. On the return journey we cycled for a long time through the Gertlauken forests and in the middle of a wood we saw a Russian prisoner-of-war camp. From there came the pretty wooden playing toy in the village, the toy the children love so much. It is a quite fantastic toy, so colourfully painted. It is a round board on top of which there is a cock, hens and small chicks. These can be moved by hand from underneath. I had no idea such a camp existed. The poor souls, but by making such toys perhaps their food is improved.

But it was quite dark, so we quickly tramped on in silence in order to get out of the gloom of the forest.

My dear Parents

I'm sick of the Latin script which we should use in our lessons. It should be the German Sutterlin script to be used. The writing is very slow in consequence. At the end of the week I was once again working on the hay, and day after day the people are working in the meadows. But yesterday it rained heavily and Frau Stachel came and said, 'The correct weather for a little party.' So I went along as the fourth person in their company, to Frau Kerwath. I forgot for a while all my troubles. And at 3 o'clock today the Kippars came to the village and it was once again card-playing time. Frau Stachel had quickly baked waffles – there's nothing more delicious than waffles with honey. I like Herr Kippar a lot, he is tall and slim and has a long, narrow face, light-coloured hair and dark blue eyes. He and his wife are a lovely pair. I had placed him before in a mocking context, but he is good-natured, merry and there is always a liveliness about him. On Friday he returns once again to the front. That will be hard for both of them, especially Frau Kippar.

Gertlauken 5 July 1943

My dear Parents

Today I received Father's report of 30 June. Between times you have become homeless for the second time. What will the English actually do to Köln? When only you are left to destroy! I am quite upset because I did not receive a telegram. Couldn't you come here where the people live in peace?

When yesterday I was in the Nehrung and in Pillkoppen standing on a high dune of shifting sand, I looked about me and saw the small village with, at most, its twenty houses. Then at the potato fields ringing it and the sparse meadows, I thought, 'What a picture of peacefulness.' Of all the things here, one sees especially clearly above all, the shifting sand dunes. One house has already half its garden covered in sand. The poem *Die Frauen von Nidden* [The Women from Nidden] by Agnes Miegel, came to mind.

> *Die Frauen von Nidden standen am Strand*
> *Uber spahenden Augen die braune Hand*
> *Und de Bote nahten in wilder Hast*
> *Schwarze Wimpel flogen zungelnd am Mast.*
> *Die Manner banden de Kahna fest*
> *Und schrieen: Druben wutet die Pest!*
> *In der Niedrung von Heydekrug bis Schaaken*
> *Gehn die Leute in Trauerlaken . . .*
> *Sieh, wir liegen and warten in Ruh,*
> *Und die Dune kam*
> *Und deckte sie zu.*

In Nidden there is still a plague cemetery and I saw a whole hamlet there, and looked out over the lagoon. I was startled by a man standing suddenly behind me. He was a native of the area and was on leave from the front. He told me of the present situation at the front and of his experiences there. His account almost made my heart turn over in anxiety. And then, in the evening, I heard in the Armed Forces Report about the attack on Köln. If only you are safe, for the house to be destroyed would not be so important in the scheme of things. That you are alive is the most important thing!

Gertlauken 12 July 1943

My dear Parents

Thank you for your short report. It must have been devastating for you and I am so happy that you are still alive. Soon we shall see each other again.

I find it extraordinarily important for my pupils to learn about their surroundings, so I have therefore organised a boat trip to my beloved Nehrung. For almost all the children it was their first trip on the railway and with such a lively crowd one had to take extreme care in their supervision.

The railway journey, the ship journey, the water and later the high dunes in Rossitten made for huge excitement. They were up and down, and round and round the sandhills, and I could readily understand their excitement and energy from my own experience of the dunes. Then we camped on the Baltic Sea beach. We had brought our swimming things with us and I went out into the water for a short distance to show the limit the gang should observe, once they entered the water.

Suddenly, as I stood there, a wave came from behind me and submerged me. When I surfaced, my hand towel that I had wrapped around my head as a turban had disappeared. Still worse, my spectacles had vanished. No amount of groping or looking for them helped. They had vanished. Then later, all safe and sound, we returned to our village. The children's main theme of conversation was not about the Nehrung or the sea, but instead 'Our fräulein lost her spectacles in the water.'

Without spectacles I am a little insecure but one gets quickly used to it. Nevertheless I do see leaves and trees rather clearer and in any case, I use my spectacles during the lessons.

Now the holidays are fast approaching and in Labiau and

Königsberg, where I telephoned and made enquiries about the new pair, I was informed that in spite of my Office Certificate of Urgency, it could take a week or a month to provide a new pair of spectacles. I shall try for myself in Osnabrück to obtain a pair, as I don't know whether there is any place in Köln still standing where a pair could be made. But perhaps Ebmeyers in Euskirchen can help? If, despite all your cares, you could enquire on my behalf, I would be so grateful to you.

I'm a little anxious about the journey on account of the crush of people boarding the train. Perhaps, like last time, I shall be lucky and find myself heaved into the compartment through the window by a group of friendly soldiers!

Bad Reinerz 9 August 1943

Dear Parents

I still hold in fond memory the weeks spent with you, even if at the end the sad report came from Wolfgang. But the most important thing is that he is, once again, quite lively.

The journey went well and I travelled second class and had an excellent place. The travellers in the third class are certainly much more friendly than those in the second class and change places more often. Probably the second-class travellers believe that the higher price they paid and also the glue for their behinds keep them in one place. At least these are my views, based on my experiences. In Berlin that was an instruction almost impossible to envisage or describe. Dr Goebbels had called upon the population of Berlin to leave the city. Now the Berliners are fleeing, panic-stricken. Their plight is pitiful.

About 2130 hours I was in Charlottenberg with Frau Ribback. I got up at 4.30 a.m. the next morning and at 6.20 a.m. I was on the Gorlitzer railway. It was a long, tedious route for I had to travel on both underground railway and a street car. It is far from being the most pleasing quarter of Berlin and many bombs had fallen there. The train was packed to capacity but I hoped nothing more would trouble me or cause me anxiety. The day before I had had actually a spot of bad luck on getting out of the underground. In the crush I caught my right hand in the door and it was very painful. The middle finger is swollen and I believe I have a small haemorrhage for I cannot lift my arm very high. I must use my left arm to wash and comb my hair and I am unable to carry my luggage with my right arm. Altogether it makes getting in and out of a heavily crowded train almost impossible.

I had to stand in the corridor of the train for a few hours before I obtained a seat. The train halted only at Cottbus, Hirschburg and Glatz where we arrived at 1400 hours. Three-quarters of an hour later the connecting train to Reinerz left. It was about an hour's journey and there I was lucky. I accompanied a porter who took the luggage on a hand wagon to the town. He took me to the Haus Cornelia. The station lay a little higher up than the town, which lies in a valley below. From the town one goes through a nice alley, about twenty minutes' journey, to the Kurark in which is the large villa, now used as a hospital. The Haus Cornelia is but a short distance away.

I was feeling so happy at the thought of seeing Wolfgang again. I asked after him and they fetched him to me. It is almost impossible to say how happy I was at that moment. Only his arm he had in a sling and we sat on a bank in the garden and talked. He wore his fatigue dress, the same clothing he wore when he was wounded and transported here. The splinter had hit him as he was opening a cake parcel from Aunt Lies. But I need not write further on that score as he, himself, will tell you. In between time he had obtained another uniform and was pleased as a child about it.

I am ending this letter in Gertlauken. It is 2100 hours on 16 August and I am sitting once again in my favourite place by the fireside. I have my table lamp on so that the greater part of the room is in darkness. I am listening to quiet music on the radio as I write. How wonderful is the space and freedom here, for after the weeks in Köln I find the difference so stark. The constant alarms, the nights in the air-raid shelter and the unrest – and here the quietness and peacefulness.

In Reinerz we walked about a great deal. One evening after our meal we went to the Gondelteich and climbed up the hill almost to Ziegenbockbaude [Goat House]. It was such a lovely, peaceful summer evening. Another occasion we went over to the Waldmuhle along a path through the meadow and climbed the hill and from there had a wonderful view of the valley. To our front were meadows hemmed in by the woods and in the valley were small farmyards, and beyond other forested hills. I tried to sleep for a little while, during which time Wolfgang with his one good hand worked zealously at sewing a button on his army jacket. I told him that the end result was not good enough. By the way your vain daughter hardly wears her glasses, although they suit her very well. In fact, Wolfgang thought that if I didn't need them, then why wear them!

At evening time we spent a little time in a very homely restaurant and once we went to the cinema where a very nice friend of Wolfgang met us. I must say that all of those members of the Leibstandarte Adolf Hitler Division I have seen and spoken to were splendid fellows. Wolfgang is still as serious as ever and he hates this lack of comradeship here behind the front. He was particularly indignant about those behind the front who, if not smartly saluted, say to the offender that they would be sent back to the front a lot quicker.

Once I undertook an outing on my own and on one lovely early morning went to the Hindenburg Building. The way went first through Schmelzetal and then a fairly steep climb to the building itself. Everywhere bordering the path were small buttercups and from above one has a vast view over the hills, valleys, fields and meadows. And always there are woods to view, woods that overlook woods, in fact. The building was made of wood, all the furniture painted in colours and on long bookcases there were plates, often with sayings on them, one such being 'Oh, how pleasant it is to do nothing and then take a rest afterwards.' In the Hindenburg Building were youngsters who were enjoying a stay in the countryside.

I strolled further to a higher-placed building to the south which had been built by the Czechs. Its site was about 1,000 metres high. I went further along the ridge and on top the wind blew and blustered. The conifer trees were crippled and all bent in one direction. This building was occupied by soldiers, so I went on further through a wood. Suddenly it lightened and I stood before the Schierlichmule. There I had an excellent midday meal. Later I went past the Hindenburg Building on the Kaiserweg and so back to Reinerz. By this time I had travelled part of the former borderline between Germany and Czechoslovakia, and after a good hour's walk, reached the Hohe Mense. From this building one has a panoramic view just as if one is in an aeroplane, so tiny lie the woods and meadows, villages and fields.

Towering above all is the Bergkuppen. I could not stay too long to admire this outstanding, distant view. But in clear weather one should be able to see Prague, and blueberries grew there in abundance.

In the early evening about 6 o'clock I was again with Wolfgang and a nursing sister from his hospital had obtained for me a tiny room in Reinerz.

On the return journey I stayed in Glatz for two hours but was not inclined to look around the town, as I felt so despondent at parting from Wolfgang. Instead I spent the waiting time with a pleasant elderly couple from East Prussia. They came from Kudowa (sixteen kilometres from Reinerz) in which there is a guest house, they told me, where one can eat and drink the choicest things without food coupons. The old man was enthusiastic about liquor, cognac and wine, whereas his wife's tastes ran to genuine coffee. Both enthused about roast goose and delightful fish, one portion only fifteen marks. One calculates that a meal with drinks would cost thirty marks, so for every meal for five persons the bill would amount to 150 marks – almost as much as my monthly salary!

The train came about 11 o'clock at night and once under way stopped for about an hour on an open stretch and was so packed full of passengers that for the entire twelve hours we stood in the gangway until Allenstein. About three and a half hours later we got to Königsberg, where it rained in streams.

Gertlauken 25 August 1943

My dear Parents

Today I received the first letter from you. I would have loved to have seen your faces when Wolfgang so unexpectedly stood before you. Hopefully it will be the same when Wolfgang visits me, so that we can have the same experience. Already I am saving some foodstuffs to make a well-fed warrior.

The school term has begun again. One has, at the beginning of the school year, an exceptional amount of work – but still I have been well prepared: yearly material, quarterly material, another year's plans for the itemised classes, and so on. The newcomers vary in their abilities and that makes the lessons difficult. For them we have a solitary guest teacher from Berlin and one from

Hamburg. I give six hours' extra teaching at that level personally.

Today Frau Kippar has got a lady from Berlin with four children in her house. Please send me as soon as possible a feather quilt as I must give up mine, for the family wants it for their evacuated relatives from Berlin. And should you, by chance, find an old pencil case, please give it to Wolfgang for Peter Stachel.

As I came back from Reinerz I had a spot of luck on the station at Mauern. There were two cart drivers from Gertlauken and with one of them I got a lift to the village. Frau Stachel and Frau Kippar welcomed me. They had made themselves up very nicely and were so sad that Wolfgang had not come with me. And how tastefully they had done up my room! Everywhere flowers and they had also lit a fire. That was just as well because the weather was wet and cold. The table had been decorated for Wolfgang and me, and a terrific amount of apple cakes awaited the hungry soldier. Then I begged them to stay after thanking them so much, and we had so much to talk about. Herr Stachel wanted his wife to travel to the West – too dangerous! Then at evening time we played cards with the von Cohs family. Frau Kerwath did not play with us – her brother has been killed near Bjelgorod.

Gertlauken 2 September 1943

My dear Parents

Now that Wolfgang has left, both you and the house feel great emptiness. Don't let your heads droop. I'm hoping that Wolfgang can come from Berlin to Gertlauken when he gets his annual leave. Couldn't you manage the journey here?

On Saturday we had a working committee in Haffwerder and in the afternoon Paula visited me. There was much to talk about when we went for a walk in the woods for hours. On Sunday we went by cycle to Rathswalde and swam in a local pond. Before that, however, on Sunday I went to Rossitten, despite all my work. I believe I did not tell you this in my letter, but the weather was good, real summer weather called to me and at 5 a.m. I cycled there. The day was heavenly and I obtained a place on the ship and in good company. In Rossitten, however, I preferred to be on my own. Once on the beach there one is all alone with the sky, sand, water and sun, and one can bathe without a swimming costume. I swam out a fair distance and there is nothing better than with strong strokes to glide through the water, with overhead the vast sky, and before one the unending, forever glistening surface of the water.

When I was once again on the ship on the return journey I was once again ready to speak with people and the world at large. Among the passengers was a nice, regular soldier from Darmstadt, who through his firm AEG, in peacetime went often to foreign parts hereabouts, but I didn't want to be in correspondence with him. I had no pleasure in being such a pen pal. It is understandable that one can find pleasure in the company of a passing acquaintance, especially on a ship such as this, and the person concerned is kindly disposed towards one!

Gertlauken 10 September 1943

My dear Parents

After a long time I received two of the familiar detailed letters from Köln – two at one time! I was quite troubled in the interim period when I hadn't heard from you and as the days passed, I feared that something bad had befallen you, or each of you had been ill. Always at 1 o'clock I sent a girl to the post to ask if there was a letter for me.

Now I am really happy and first of all I know you wish to have news of Wolfgang. Today I received post from him in Berlin and it does not seem at all promising regarding his leave, since the Americans have landed in Italy and I know that the Leibstandarte division is stationed there. I believe it is unlikely for me to bank on his coming here. But in spite of that, I am more pleased that he has been sent to Italy rather than to Russia. So after lessons today, I baked a lot of small biscuits, also some of those rolled-oat biscuits he especially likes. They were made of: 12 cups flour, 2 cups rolled oats sifted through a mincer, 2 cups sugar, 1 teaspoon staghorn; all mixed up and left standing.

From Father's letter I gather that Wolfgang has received the decoration for being wounded and will be promoted to a storm trooper. He seems to know nothing about it and it will make him happy. I don't think soldiers deliberately seek danger in battle but rather that they endeavour to complete a task or mission. What does this expression 'self-will' mean? I feel that this war for me and for so many other like-minded is a case of being driven to endure it. Just now on the radio somebody announced that the Führer is to speak.

It is a pity you cannot hear it, being without a radio. I will no longer deny and no further believe that the war is going to end favourably for us.

Dear Father, now briefly to your points. 1) Travel. What you say I also think. I have spent the most beautiful hours of my life living with nature. I think especially fondly of our lovely days in Attendorn. 2) Furniture/dowry in the case of my marriage. There is still time for that. So many will have been killed that many women must perforce remain unmarried. Up to the present I have not met a man with whom I would wish to spend my whole life. I shall be older, and particular, also I love my freedom and independence. 3) Card playing. You warned me before about too much playing and parrying, and reminded me about the second examination. I shall tackle this as and when necessary. But as far as the card playing, it makes me happy, especially as it takes place in such a nice circle of friends. But the reading aspect I love just as much.

After my cold and sore throat things are going again well for me. As my swollen right middle finger didn't go down and it gave me severe pain, I went to a doctor in Laukischken. He said a small piece of bone had splintered, and put a bandage on the finger. On the return journey I looked in on Frau Schulz whose husband is in France. I have since seen a specialist in Königsberg who took an X-ray and it revealed not just the one splinter but many more tiny bone fragments. He wrote out for me a prescription for an oily liquid that I have to rub into the affected finger. In the holidays (on 20 September I am to get twenty-four days!) I shall once again come to you.

Gertlauken 16 September 1943

My dear Mother

You will now be fifty-five years old. A year full of work and cares is behind you. What the future will bring, we do not know. I wish for you all in the future good health and the strength to cope with all the things you encounter. I wish you both a pleasant and alarm-free peaceful birthday.

Last Sunday I travelled to Königsberg with seven of the eldest pupils. At 4.30 a.m. they drummed me up early out of bed. Fifteen minutes later our journey started and a little before 8 a.m. we were in Königsberg.

First of all we strengthened ourselves with a cup of coffee in the waiting room. Then for one and a half hours we strolled through the old town and the harbour quarter. We saw the storehouses, the cathedral and the courthouse. I looked for a property of Gothic origin to explain its history – remembrance of same is always satisfying to one. At 10 o'clock we had a conducted tour of the castle. The children had enormous fun with the felt slippers but they obeyed all the instructions most attentively. There was so much now for them to see, all the large rooms with smooth parquet floors, artistic stucco ceilings, mirrors, chandeliers, beautiful heavy woodcut and gilded furniture. In the Coronation Room there was a powerfully deep silence as all listened intently to the guide as he intoned, 'And here sat Frederick, the first king of Prussia, one-handed he held the crown over his head and then subsequently over his wife, Charlotte.' I heard some splashing sounds near me and a girl, seeing me, turned scarlet red and needed help. The crowd of people then went off to the next hall and all went through the puddle in their felt slippers. Then the guide suddenly cried, "What is that? Who was that?' Then I had to whisper to him quietly that one of my girls had had an accident, a most human one, in that she had accidentally wet herself. Now our visit was over. The caretaker brought us a bucket, a scrubbing brush and cloth to clean the Coronation Hall.

Next we went to the Prussian Museum. In the castle the children had had the opportunity to see how well those resident in the castle lived with their beautiful rooms and expensive furniture, but here in the museum they saw for themselves old farming and fishing living quarters, such as they personally knew and lived in. At midday, in order to take a rest from all our viewing activities, we all went in a boat on the castle pond. For the children this was most certainly the high point of the day, as each of them took turns to row. The afternoon we spent in the zoo, where the monkeys had most of our attention. Also of course the bears. Finally at 10.30 p.m., dead tired, we were once again safely back in our village.

It is just as well we have a holiday on Monday. At the moment the schoolwork is not so good, because always more of the children are absent. They must be at home to help with the potato harvest.

My dear Father

I wish so much heartfelt happiness to you on this, your 57th birthday. Hopefully all our wishes will be fulfilled and we shall all see one another safe and well again after this war. How will you spend your birthday? And how did Mother spend hers? Here I think often about you.

The day of 23 September was spent here in the following manner. At 8 o'clock, got up, room brought to order and something mended. Actually I wanted to do laundry but the weather was too bad, autumnally cool, stormy and raining. At 11 o'clock I went to the post but there was nothing there. Then I worked on my Village History Book. For a few moments I read the school chronicle in order to get together an overall view about the development of the Gertlauken school. The chronicle was begun over 100 years ago and it is really a fine actual account of the village story. Many teachers before me have worked on it, with diligence and love.

For the midday meal Frau Stachel gave us *Schiroggen*, that is a kind of cooked egg which in the end is rolled in sugared curd cheese (they are those Wolfgang also likes). In the main I eat with Frau Stachel at midday, afternoons or evenings. If she has something delicious she calls to me. Now it is harvest time, Frau Buttkus cooks quite irregularly. But if a midday meal has to be cancelled, I can always fetch a litre of fresh milk in the evening. It will all get better once the potatoes are harvested and in the cellar.

At midday Frau Stachel called me again. She had soft baked rolls in milk, baked them in butter and then sprinkled them with sugar. We always have a brief chat when eating. In her kitchen it is cosy and warm since in it stands a gigantic cooker, three times as large as a normal one. Whereas with me upstairs I freeze, despite many woollen clothes and covers. Still, for the first time today I'm really warm and I can stand that.

During our coffee (it was real coffee and so good of her to give me some of it) Frau Kerwath came and invited us for the evening to her parents. Her father, the guest landlord is at present on leave. Herr and Frau von Cohs likewise came. Only Frau Kippar was absent as she is at present visiting her parents in Christburg. At the welcoming party there were chocolate cakes and real coffee. Then we played two games of cards and at intervals, strengthened ourselves with liquor and pumpernickel bread and butter with cheese. So I spent my holiday.

On Tuesday at 11 a.m. there was a conference with the leader of the People's Library in the district of Labiau presiding. Fifteen persons were in attendance, nearly all of them teachers, most of whom I know well. The conference was held in the large meeting hall of the Labiau courthouse. I felt quite strange sitting in a massive armchair at the long table, also that I was part of a conference of great importance.

Later we ate in the Hotel Zum Kronprinz, There was a huge amount of fish with tasty sauce and potatoes. I couldn't eat it all and that, for me, was quite something, for Frau Berkan has called my stomach 'a barrel without a bottom'. The cost was borne by the town as we were its guests. After the conference I went on my cycle to a nearby aerodrome, but at present there are only a few machines there.

Although it is naturally impossible, your daughter harbours the dream that one day a flier would come to her and say, 'I have waited for you and the plane is ready for taking-off. Would you like to step aboard and take a long-distance flight, or just a short trip round the drome?'

At 8 o'clock I was once again in Gertlauken. Oh yes, before I went to Labiau, I visited Dr Ohlsen as, in the last couple of weeks, my foot swelled to such an extent that one saw little of the ankle. It gave me no pain but still it did look nasty. He gave me something to rub in and it is now better. Also, my finger is healing slowly.

The previous Saturday evening we were invited by Herr and Frau von Cohs to a meal of liver. He had recently killed a stag and an elk in quick succession, from which he received the innards. Before that, at midday, Frau Stachel, Helma, Peter and I took a wonderful walk in the woods. Like a flash, three hours went by.

On Wednesday, the day after the conference in Labiau, I slept for a long time during the entire afternoon, and then baked two cheese cakes, both of which turned out well. One was for Frau Stachel and the other for myself, but by evening time we had eaten them, as Herr and Frau von Cohs came to our small party. Next week, either in the mornings or the evenings, I am to accompany Herr and Frau von Cohs to the forest to observe the wildlife there. The hunting season is at its busiest now and almost daily there are special guests with the chief forestry official. Also the season extends to neighbouring Sternberg.

I do so hope you can make sense of this mixed-up letter. By the way, I have got fifty new books from the People's Library. Hans Bucket has sent me a novel by a Bulgarian authoress, the book's title *The Last of the Assenows*. Now to end the letter and I shall go to post it in the box.

Gertlauken 2 October 1943

My dear Parents

I have been reading and looking out for a long time at the close of this autumn day, as the soft darkness descends.

Hour after hour I have thought about my vocation. On the whole I do not feel wholly satisfied. The wealth of subjects to be studied and mastered, rather than the many passing years, sometimes overwhelms me. One lives in rare highs and frequent lows about the end result of one's labours.

After my leaving school and the official decision-making as to a vocation, I made the decision to become a teacher in a primary school, as such work seemed so worthwhile to me. Also, I was free from the *Arbeitsdienst* [labour service] if so employed. The studies in the university were of not long duration and the career with its valuable tasks (as they still are) seemed to be acceptable and important.

You know that the outside life here is such that I could scarcely have anything better. Sometimes I'm almost lulled to sleep by it. But then, especially on peaceful and contemplative days such as today, I am assailed by doubt as to whether the school and the lessons provide me with a complete life. I feel, in myself, to be somewhat immature to lead people. But I have within me the burning desire to learn about myself, to widen my points of view and my range of experiences.

I know you are pleased about my secure future, but I would like to know how you both stand about it, if one day eventually I take up with a new university and whether, if so, I can reckon on your support. Now don't let this letter startle you, as it is for once me just speaking out. It is a question of how broad the future is to be seen.

My dear Wolfgang

You will now be in Italy. How often must your ears have rung, for so often I have thought about you. I cannot think of anything more peaceful, sitting and reading here, and then hearing your step and voice outside. When I am out in the afternoon I step expectantly into my room and, in my absence, you have arrived and are here in the room. Such self-optimism and anticipation are lovely things when one is full of hope and can imagine all kinds of self-pleasing things really happening.

I am once again in Königsberg and have this strong desire to chat to you. Sometimes the pleasant Gertlauken is too limited and so I must then go out and have this burning wish to learn, to obtain stimulation and to be with learned people. So yesterday I went to Königsberg and my local landlady, Frau Kinder, was quite surprised that I had not brought you. At evening time Frau Stachel and Frau Kippar came and Frau Kinder had obtained cinema tickets for the film *The Spouse* with Jenny Jugo and Willi Fritsch. Afterwards we sat in the Café Bauer, not a pleasant place for the room is too high, too bright and too bare. The air was full of thick, black smoke and noise, and the so-called vegetable dish, cold and stale.

On the next morning, both the others made purchases, during which time I was in Grafe and Unzer, the booksellers. Before that I went by tram to the final stopping place and indeed only because I overhead pure Kolsch [Cologne dialect] being spoken. Midday the three of us went into the Blutgericat, the historical wine cellar, in the castle. After the meal, cinema, then into Café Gehlhar which serves good cakes and finally we had a small local wine.

The next morning Frau Kippar and Frau Stachel went home. I meanwhile sought the man in charge of the State Education Office, in order to get further suggestions for my Village History Book. He was an elderly man, tall, gaunt and bespectacled, a good narrator. In fact, a model citizen, does not smoke and lives only to extend his knowledge. A non-drinker too, and constantly learning. He invited me to visit him in Rauschen where he lives and no doubt should possess a worthwhile library.

At every time the place is full to capacity with locals and service personnel.

Two under-officers in the Luftwaffe [German Air Force] sat

themselves at my table. Initially I had no pleasure in their company nor wish to be entertained, but despite that very soon a lively conversation ensued. The first one was twenty-three years old and came from Thuringen, the other was nineteen years old and an East Prussian. They were engaged in the building of wireless communications in the vicinity of Königsberg. They wanted to meet me without fail today, but you know for me, it has a meaningful effect only when the partner in every way knows more than I do, is superior to me and if I like him as a person out of the ordinary run of man.

Today I strolled for a long time through the town and had a good browse in Grafe and Unzer and in the evening ate in the Berliner Hof. I like best of all to sit there as it is so homely and warm. A lady from Osnabrück district sat at my table – one hears the region of origin immediately from the speech. Also a middle-aged lieutenant, an artist/painter, from Düsseldorf by the name of Cleff. At present, he is a war correspondent and has painted the celebrated and famous airmen, such as Molders and Marsaille. Tomorrow, Christel Lange is coming and I have obtained two tickets for *Madame Butterfly*.

Gertlauken 18 October 1943

My dear Parents

The school term began here on Friday. A mistake in our teaching books complicated the lessons and always I have to give six hours extra work in the week. Frau Kippar had an especially difficult time with the first-year pupils. Firstly there were no panels or slate pencils because their manufacture is not important to the war effort, and secondly our new first-year books for the first-year pupils will not be here until shortly before Christmas. How shall the children learn to read without them? Now I shall get the bigger pupils each to bring a first-year reading book for the first-year pupils.

After the lessons today I cycled to Laukischken about the Village History Book. I had the wind at my back and went like greased lightning. The sky was quite clear and blue, the woods wore their autumn colours and the wind blew strongly through the trees, and it caused leaves to fall like rain.

The registrar who wishes to speak to me in Laukischken was not there. Instead I saw his wife who is fresh, friendly, outwardly homely and talkative. I soon knew the entire family history. She offered me a piece of cheesecake, instead of what I always got, a cup of hot milk and an apple or something similar.

I obtained the following details. Two-thirds of those who have died since 1874 with the particulars of their gender. From the books I have examined I've tried to establish if possible the causes of death of the elderly. Total number of marriages and births. Such of these earlier details are shattering about the deaths of infants and small children, so many of whom died from the *Braune*, that is diphtheria.

When I become deeply engrossed in this work I am oblivious to all that is happening outside. Unfortunately it was very dark when I made the return journey. I had the storm against me and once I reached home, the first thing I had was a milk soup I cooked immediately. Now I am sitting with Frau Stachel. She knits, I write and the radio plays its quiet music.

On Sunday afternoon we ladies had a card-playing party with Frau Stachel. In the evening there was a battle meeting and a similar one on the evening before that in Laukischken, and the Deputy District Leader Grossherr spoke. From our village the women and girls were taken there on a tractor and trailer. Two successive evenings of battle meetings – that is definitely too much.

Gertlauken 22 October 1943

My dear Parents

Before I commence answering your two letters I will first of all describe briefly my daily routine as of today. At 7 o'clock I get up. From 8 until 2 lessons.

Yesterday a few children during the break placed an apple on my desk and again today. I find it very touching but I have made it clear to the children that the mother had not given them apples for me, and that young children need the necessary nourishment to enable them to grow up and become adults.

After school I had my meal and then went on my cycle to a Frau Kanscheit. For some time now I have experienced a resistance against my compiling the Village History Book. Naturally I have explained the reason for such a compilation of village occurrences for later generations to read and write about. If on occasion I visit a possible source of information and obtain nothing, I always politely request that on my next visit if possible they produce letters from those who had died in the war and a picture, if possible, that

I could insert in the book. I've stressed always my gratitude for any help given or promised. But when I visit a few days later, they have in the meantime discussed the matter with others and come to a different viewpoint altogether, as if there were a catch somewhere in my request for historically important items.

Apparently the town mayor seems to support their views – 'The dead are dead, let them rest in peace' is the favoured reaction. An understandable viewpoint indeed. But others who do not share these views are most ready to help, so I will not allow myself to be discouraged. I shall therefore only compile my village chronicle as completely as possible, from facts I hear, to record the fate of the people in the village, especially those who have died in the war. The two books I've compiled to date do not contain very much but when one travels around one observes so much. It always requires a personal effort of will on my part to approach these strange people, but invariably a friendly approach is always acceptable.

Indeed, yesterday a farmer spoke to me about his dead brother who in early 1933 was in the party and in the SA. Once apparently this brother had been approached by a local group leader of the National Socialist Party [Nazi] who got stuck with his car near the farm. The Nazi official requested that the brother use his two horses to pull and extricate the vehicle. The brother had only two mares and they were frightened of the car, so the brother said that his suggestion to use the horses was useless. Whereupon the official said, 'Now, you wish one day to become a settler?' And much later when the brother applied for his certificate stating that he was a newly settled farmer after two years of training, his application was turned down.

Also I heard that a woman in the village was arrested for consorting with French prisoners of war.

Father's letter of 17 October came today, also from Wolfgang an actual airmail field letter. Even the newspaper from Köln with the appallingly long casualty list. From Osnabrück there is nothing new but from Spenge the news of the engagement of Heinz Kleymann. From Wolfgang today came brief greetings, 'Thank you for the address of Erni, now a prisoner of war of the Canadians, and good luck and good fortune to Hans Fischer on his engagement.'

Dear Parents

It is early on Sunday morning, so I will write a letter quickly, as at 10 o'clock they are holding the Heroes Memorial Service in Laukischken, so I must cycle there and can take this letter with me at the same time to post it.

I know only too well that you are awaiting news from me. Saturday is the best day of the week as it involves our card playing, and yesterday evening we spent with Frau Kerwath and it was very homely.

Now I must first of all thank you for your letters of 24, 25 and 31 October. I do find the schoolwork hard, in fact sometimes I feel quite desperate about it. I feel so absolutely alone and lost. Just for once to be able to confess one's thoughts and worries to another person. Just for once, for a short time not to have responsibilities and to be able not to bother with anything. Whenever this feeling comes over me I feel I must carry on alone, despite everything.

Previously I have always collected the old schoolbooks for use in the classes yet to come into the school. Unfortunately new instructions have been issued recently, that the old books are no longer to be used. At the same time, we are told no longer to use the old Sutterlin script, but instead to use the new normal script.

I've set out in detail in a letter I've written to Wolfgang who Christel Wange is. He will send the letter on to you.

Paula was at home during the autumn holidays and yesterday she was with me, although it was unfortunately a brief visit and she does not feel happy here in East Prussia. In between times I was with Frau Schulz once again. She has become very thin and worries herself about her husband and the whole war, just like all of us. Where she is, she is very much alone, whereas here we have more young women who get on well together and help each other. This of course helps keep at bay the duller hours. I would like to travel to Frau Schulz more often but since I have lessons until 2 o'clock and the twice weekly afternoons, I am only too happy to be sitting in my warm room and no longer have to go out on my cycle. It gets dark so early and already it is very cold.

By the way Peter Stachel is delighted with the pencil case. Helma does not have such a lovely one. Helga was enthusiastic about the many glossy coloured pictures. She sat squatting on the floor playing with them for the whole day long. Mother asks about panels and slate pencils. One cannot get them here at all. In the first-year school class we need enough for twenty children but I let them write with them until the fourth year because so few exercise books are available. In such circumstances I take all I can get, but how will Mother obtain them? The Hoffmans and the valerian drops are for Frau Neumann, who complains of 'restlessness'.

I have so far put my winter things in order. Now it is only the trousers I shall send to Aunt Lies to sew up. I am so happy over the splendid set of woollen underwear, vests and trousers that Aunt Lies has knitted and presented to me in the holidays as a birthday gift. Already it is freezing here and now it is bitterly cold. Please send the wool I brought with me the Christmas before last to Aunt Lies. She will then very kindly knit me a pair of mittens.

Gertlauken 11 November 1943

My dear Parents

It is a pleasure to write on Mother's lovely notepaper and Father himself would be satisfied with the margin. I feel myself to be a king with all my treasures – apples, nuts and pudding. What a treat Mother has put together and I am so very grateful and send many, many thanks. For Wolfgang's Field Post parcels I have two marks. I shall bake a Madeira cake and on top of that I shall enclose a small German salami, two duck eggs, and naturally apples and nuts, so that he will not want for anything. Such activity makes it easy to remember that Christmas feeling, the house full of cooking and baking on Holy Night [Christmas Eve] and Mother's small iced cakes and the beautiful coloured plates.

I have received Father's letter of 7 November together with the two newspapers. In the list of those killed recently there are many acquaintances listed. The cathedral is badly damaged and your life can scarcely be called safe. Come at once here!

On the late afternoon there was a meeting about air-raid protection and such things are taken very seriously here. I am the amateur lady assistant responsible for bandaging and such. Stachelowski took over the air-raid protection questions. They ran to two pages long about the siren warning, etc. Because of his monotonous voice it was not at all interesting. After the meeting, Frau Kaiser, who has lost two sons in the field, came with me upstairs and looked at the Village

History Chronicle and I believe she will help me in my work. She seems on the outside to be coarse and self-controlled, so that one doesn't notice how hard for her is her immense sorrow. As I stood once again in the presence of such deep sorrow, one seeks hard for good, comforting, consoling words to say, but it is ever too small to convey one's truly compassionate feelings.

My dear Father, from each of your letters I read of the spoken and unspoken worries you have about Wolfgang's future. I think that to him the war itself must be considered a closed thing. Certain people do that, compress their feelings and limit their horizons. And if after the war he has the will to open up, he will do just that. After the war there will be work enough available. If Wolfgang comes out of the war in sound health and is determined to take his school-leaving examination [A levels] once more I cannot see anything standing in his way. Above all things I believe that one should not reproach him, neither now at his present age, nor after the war.

In this manner I would speak and advise you and I don't find it easy or simple to write as such. I have thought so long and so much about this matter and should 'our Wolfgang' need any help whatsoever I will do all I can that is possible in my position to help him.

Gertlauken 16 November 1943

My dear Parents

A mammoth storm rages and howls outside. I have written about being with Frau Stachel and the Neumanns the previous Friday. Then on Sunday we were invited to the family von Cohs as Frau von Cohs had a birthday. The table groaned under the good things and it made me feel very sorry that I had to leave so quickly.

Yesterday evening I travelled to Herrn Schulz as I had heard that he was expected on leave. I was really pleased to see him again. And what do you think his first words were to me as I stood by the tiled stove and after such a long parting between us? 'But you have become fat,' he said.

Tomorrow I shall send off my Christmas present to you. It is a goose and I shall send it by express to Köln-Deutz. Ask there the time to telephone. I have written on the parcel, 'At once inform by telephone no. 12016'.

With much love yesterday I baked several biscuits for Wolfgang. Today I must acquire and hoard a few eggs. The people I get them from always ask me in for coffee and conversation with them for hours on end. Tomorrow I shall send everything on its way. On 13 October Wolfgang wrote to me at last, perhaps his letter was delayed in the post. At 5 a.m. tomorrow I shall go to the Neumanns and pack the goose. He will then take it with him on his milk wagon to the post.

Gertlauken 27 November 1943

My dear Parents

The week's letter is unfortunately not punctual when it comes on Friday. Today it is already Saturday. Important happenings do not have to be reported to Köln; only how an unimportant girl experiences the wartime in Germany. In my last letter I mentioned that I was waiting around at Neumanns for the goose. Hopefully the splendid specimen will reach you safely. There was quite a sight when I came to the Neumanns, ten geese were hanging there, one much better than the others, many over 23 lb in weight, a truly splendid sight for sore eyes.

When I came out of school on Saturday I first of all cleaned out the week's dust in my room and then went to Christel Lange because I had a few things to talk about and naturally did not leave them without real coffee and cakes being given to me. Once back home I got out a couple of buckets of hot water and washed myself from head to foot with the greatest of pleasure, then combed my hair high. Afterwards we all set off to the Kerwaths for our Saturday evening card-playing session. Also Frau Kerwath had, a few days before, slaughtered her goose and so gave us the first part of the goose liver with roast potatoes, followed later by rolls and cocoa.

On Monday I had to go to Frau Stachelowski for coffee as it was her birthday. Her sister-in-law from Köln was there with the small girl who had once visited us. They each warmly welcomed me and I was so pleased to hear again the old familiar sounds of Köln speech. She said that her most terrible experience was when she had been in a train in Hannover during a huge air raid.

After the lessons on Tuesday I sought out Fräulein Dannat our tailoress but she put me off and I must make another visit next week. Subsequently I had to rush off to Frau Kippar as I had a headache and a sore throat and didn't want to stay there very long, but I didn't get away quickly. For the evening meal she had made roast potatoes with fried eggs and a delicious blueberry stoup. It was so cosy being with her. Of course, at our place the huge tiled stove is not known, but here by it are two deep armchairs, a small smoking table and a standard lamp. And if outside a storm raves and howls, it cannot dispel the feeling of well-being one has inside by the stove.

In the night I felt quite unwell and could not sleep, so the next morning I did not go to school but remained in bed. In the afternoon Frau Kippar came to see me and brought a quite mysterious pot. She got out the small lace tablecloth, laid the table and placed a plate with milk cakes on it. I like Frau Kippar very much, she is so quiet and fine and ladylike, and we get along together excellently. Later we deliberated as to whether on the following day we should go to the teachers' conference in Labiau, through storm and rain, on our cycles, and I so full of a cold.

Frau Kippar then telephoned and told me that the children were to be given Thursday off from school and that I was to remain in bed until midday. Subsequently I went shopping. Paula had invited herself here for the evening and I decided that milk soup, roast potatoes and bread and butter should be instantly the nourishment she needed after she had endured the terrible weather to get here. It is already dark at 3 p.m. in the afternoon and she had a nasty journey behind her, always a headwind to combat and frozen through and hungry as a result of cycling through the rain-drenched streets.

The following evening I again felt unwell. I then bathed quickly in hot water in my bowl, so unlike being at home in a bath, as I have to bring up buckets of water and heat them on the stove. At 9 o'clock I lay in bed and thought, 'Tomorrow you'll get up fresh and lively.' But this morning I awoke at just after 8 o'clock as the alarm on my clock does not work. Instead, Olga bangs on the outside of the door at 7.30 a.m. with a broomstick until I answer. Today she forgot to do so. Like lightning I was up, dressed and downstairs.

After the lessons the older children came to me and said they wanted to put on a Christmas play. As a textbook about *Snow White*, the play chosen, we are writing the words ourselves. Each one has something to do and all are enthusiastic about the idea.

Tomorrow there is to be a large meeting of the Nationalist Socialist Party conducted by the district leader in Laukischken. All party members who have not got an appointment or specific department shall have the chance to speak. I would like to know most of all how I shall get to Laukischken. The storm howls, the rain pelts against the windowpanes, all the roads are muddy like the tracks in Russia, and cycling in such conditions is dangerous to life!

Gertlauken 5 December 1943

My dear Parents

You must be angry that I write so little but my time is still more than limited. Every day after the lessons we practise for the Christmas holiday play, so once again this week has flown. By the way, before this letter reaches you, Fräulein Stachelowski will visit you and report on my welfare and how things are going with me.

Wednesday afternoon was a great dress rehearsal and with indefatigable zeal and much imagination the children fully entered into the spirit of the thing. In addition to *Snow White* we are staging a second play, *In the Spinning Room*. That too we have written ourselves. The seven dwarves have each themselves cut out the same pointed caps and made their own genuinely effective beards from flax and wool. They look enchanting. And the others taking part have burrowed through mothers' and grandmothers' wardrobes and really wonderful old-fashioned clothes, skirts, blouses and suchlike retrieved as useful adjuncts in the play. Also an old spinning wheel and a genuine cradle have been acquired.

On Friday I have to get out of bed early to do the cattle count and this time I have been allotted a part of the village I am conversant with. This particular area lies two to three kilometres from our village and sometimes particularly muddy paths lead to the isolated farmsteads. So my high brown boots are exactly the things to wear. Sometimes these farmsteads lie like islands in the middle of meadows, which in springtime and autumn are flooded, so that one needs a boat to reach them. There are three such boats with different names. In winter there is neither a path nor a small bridge giving access thereto. It is astonishing that the children from these farmsteads only seldom, and that in very bad weather, fail to get to school.

Also the family of the former Chief Gamekeeper Appel lives in this district on the edge of the woods. Herr Appel died the previous month aged sixty-eight and his wife now lives alone and runs the farm, covering ninety acres with ten cows, four horses and a vast number of poultry belonging to her. Her help includes a Pole and two Ukrainians. Frau Appel suffers acutely from loneliness and is more than twenty-five years younger than her dead husband, and lavishes all her love on her son, a delicate boy in his third year at school.

From many households I have been warned, 'Don't go backwards at any time with the pigs!' Meaning, I suppose, not even a pig would go in there! But of course there are exceptions. Many a time a pig would be slaughtered as it was just before Christmas time and gifts such as meatballs or fresh sausage were given to me. Sometimes I'd give them to Frau Stachel, otherwise preserve them for myself. In each family I have stayed for a short while and chatted, and such easy-going conversations such as I had never previously experienced, they were. But it is always good to open one's heart to such people and equally good to listen, for one learns so much about life and oneself.

Yesterday Frau von Cohs informed me that the living quarters of the third teacher are to be occupied by a family from Berlin. Also that I must vacate my room and go back to living in Frau Stachel's small attic room. Both Frau Stachel and Alga helped me with the move but the stove has got to be repaired, a wall socket is missing and the windows are leaking.

Herr von Cohs shot a deer and took it to Frau Kippar's place where it was cut up. On Tuesday evening we shall arrange to have a community feast and all invited shall contribute something to it.

Gertlauken 11 December 1943

My dear Parents

Today your loving letter of 5 December came. Also Wolfgang has written and he has received the Iron Cross, 2nd Class. I know nothing about it and suspect only where he is. Since 13 October I have not received any more lines from him and I have had serious and worried thoughts about him. Sometimes it all overcomes me and I want to have a good cry. The cousin of Frau Stachel, the one who two years ago taught us the card game *Doppelkoptspiel*, is missing. I see him still before me, a fresh youngster of twenty-four or twenty-five years of age. After his leave he went off to Russia and by coincidence was in Herr Kippar's battalion. He was wounded and in the retreat was left behind lying down.

Our Community Feast on Tuesday last was festively decorated. We all wore our best clothes and one could almost believe it was peacetime. But in reality all the young women were thinking about their husbands at the front. And I? I thought about Wolfgang.

This morning in school we helped Father Christmas with his baking! We had about a half-hundredweight of wheat flour, 8 lb of butter and 50 eggs. We baked as if in peacetime and now have two large washbowls full of cakes of all kinds. For one youngster from Hamburg it was quite a special experience. He spent the entire morning cutting out from the dough. I was nearby when I heard him tell his cousin, 'And as for butter, like a mountain! And eggs! You've got to see it!'

You know already that I am once again in Frau Stachel's attic room. Power and power points were put in for me by Herr Stachelowski in the meantime. In the meantime surely his sister has visited you? Tomorrow at 10 a.m. the children are coming to practise. In the afternoon a Christmas celebration for the NS women's group is to take place. To that, unfortunately, I must go.

I am incredibly happy that at Christmas time I shall be with you in Köln.

Labiau 13 January 1944

My dear Parents

I am writing in a public house while I am waiting for the train and my thoughts are constantly with you. Also, during the journey my thoughts range, 'Now Father is at the office', 'Now Mother is having an afternoon nap', 'Now Father is going home from work', 'First post from Wolfgang there?' 'It will soon be 10 o'clock at night and Mother stands nearby with her suitcase packed prepared for any air raid', and so on. Hopefully though you can remain in the house.

My journey from Köln passed off well. I had a very pleasant

second-class corner seat. The plump, blond, freshly dressed haired lady from Köln near me related without pause, dot or comma, her entire family history. But I was always thinking of you. In Bielefeld she got out and her place was taken by a flight lieutenant who previously had stood in the gangway. He was as tall as myself much stronger and slimmer in figure. Most of all I fell for his large, bright eyes of unbelievable blueness. He looked so honest and I estimated his age as being between twenty-eight and thirty. For a few hours we conversed together. In the compartment one sat as if in a hatching box and it was frightfully overheated. I had a splitting headache and regretted I was so warmly clad. A young girl in the gangway gave me two tablets and a woman gave me a drop of coffee to take them with. The *Oberleutnant* saw this and as we sat down again he offered me tablets likewise. He was so genuinely concerned about me and as a result, I felt much better. During our conversation I must admit that he made an impression on me. We talked almost the whole night through.

He was in the Luftwaffe and was shot down near Dunkirk in 1940 and had spent three and a half years in an English prisoner-of-war camp before, as a wounded serviceman, he was exchanged with similarly wounded British prisoners in Germany. In England he had been in a number of hospitals and the English doctors had saved his shot-up arm.

The average English person is indifferent to the war, of which they are tired and very much want it to end. The relationship between the English servicemen and the masses of American servicemen there in the UK is extremely strained. The Americans get five times as much money as the English soldier (Tommy) does. They sit in expensive public houses and bars, and attract all the girls. The food in England is very scarce, only tinned foods. As prisoners, the German POWs had the same subsistence as the English soldier received and therefore had sometimes been hungry.

By way of an occupation he is a secondary school teacher in Godesberg school. Now he has to report himself in Bromberg. Perhaps he will be discharged! He was shot in the left arm. I had to get out in Schneidemuhl and because there was a delay, the connecting train had gone. It was about 4 a.m. in the morning and despite this fact, there were enormous comings and goings. Although at this hour, normally station waiting rooms are ghostly and empty, the waiting hall where I was, was packed to the limit with soldiers. At about 7 a.m. a passenger train came from Berlin and so, finally at 4.30 p.m. I arrived in Königsberg. I purchased at once a ticket to Mauern and there went to Frau Kinder who had not received the postcard I had sent to her but was able to accommodate me after all. That was a priceless gift to me, for you cannot imagine how difficult it is to find a room in Königsberg.

First of all I had a good wash and had a warm meal of kale, and was lucky enough to get a ticket for the cinema. It looks as if it is going to snow, although at present it is raining.

Gertlauken 19 January 1944

My dear Parents

Now I want you to know how my non-approved Christmas holiday went down with the school council official, 'Come what may,' I thought, 'count to three and go in to see him.'

He was very reserved and did not shake hands when we met. In his mode of expression he was certainly moderate and also showed understanding of my position. I'm sure Father and he would have understood each other, since both hold similar views about duty and the same opinion about women. He used the same way of expression as Father and referred to the 'women's clique'. He is concerned that I should give him news as to why I could not have taken part in the sports course in Königsberg. Everything would then have been in order he said, but I doubted that. Finally he told me that he could have informed me earlier about the course that took place exactly over the Christmas period. The letter of information he referred to had been handed over to me when I was ready with packed cases on the waiting wagon about to leave. It was an instant, spontaneous decision on my part to ignore the letter as 'not received by me'.

Anyway, thereafter I rang the Kerwathens in Gertlauken and requested that they obtain a wagon for me but they said it would be better if I caught the train tomorrow and they would meet me at the station. So I tramped on foot to Gertlauken in the afternoon, but after Krakau I met a gentleman driving a sledge who gave me a lift. Here in Gertlauken first of all I fetched my letters and parcels from the post and chatted a long time with Frau Stachel and Frau Kippar. So it was later or rather early morning but I was happy about sleeping late on Sunday in order to catch my breath before schoolwork. Then about 9 a.m. a banging on my door and Frau Stachelowski passed on to me in a breathless manner that an *Oberleutnant* so and so, who I knew already from Bromberg, had telephoned. He was in Königsberg and that I should meet him there. The train left at 10.21 hours but how should I manage the ten kilometres to the station? There was no longer any time to order a sledge!

Within ten minutes I was clothed and took my chance with the cycle. I found it impossible to cycle as deep snow was everywhere. At the end of the village I was overtaken by a sledge. I left my cycle at the Neumanns and went on the sledge to the station and was in good time to get a ticket and catch the train. At the station in Königsberg, the *Oberleutnant* was waiting for me. He had to return to the West on Tuesday and therefore had taken the complicated journey from Bromberg to Königsberg at short notice. His journey had taken him ten hours.

He pleases me very much, being very serious and quiet, a Westerner and not a chattering one from Köln. He is thirty-four years old and comes from a farm near Hagen. Unfortunately the weather was bad and we had to move to a public house for the rest of our meeting.

I later travelled with the last train to Mauern. I had been prepared for a long night's travelling, but how glad I was when, at a waiting halt, I saw a horse-drawn sledge and one of my pupils from the upper classes called to me, 'Fräulein Günther – is that you?' He was fetching his mother and I was carefully packed in covers and enjoyed the sledge journey through the night.

Gertlauken 31 January 1944

My dear Parents

After a thorough examination of the facts I have come to the convincing conclusion that between Olga and myself, apart from the fact that we are both women, a significant change no longer exists. Olga is eighteen years old and has six friends and nothing else in her head. I shall be twenty-three and until now have never been seriously involved with men. How was it with you, dear Father, when you were twenty-three years old?

My dear Parents

How shall I begin after so long a time? First then my heartfelt thanks for your loving letters No. 79 to 81. They all came on Monday 7 February and today No. 82 came. All were so lovely and nice and I am so pleased with them, more than I can possibly say.

My schoolwork I take very conscientiously and one can do no more than that. There was first the preparation for the next day's lessons for five hours and six different class years. For instance, I make a division from the student plans with two sections, one for the five to six school years and another for the seven to eight years. Both have different things that I must somehow, if possible, combine but I have to judge it to a nicety when to stop, myself. I allow each section a half-hour for its completion. That is very little time for them to pick out the points of significance. Before the beginning of each subject, five minutes are taken up by revision of the subject matter. This is particularly necessary, as at the end of the hour there is a summarising. This relates to all subjects, German, arithmetic, nature study and geography.

Also I must myself use more than five hours in doing the groundwork for lesson preparation. During the lessons children come to me regarding this or that matter. For instance, my signature being required regarding the receipt of an exercise book. One day after the classes left the room I observed three mice quietly playing on the tiled stove. In any case it is usually 2 o'clock before I fetch my midday meal. Quite often also, I have one 'kept-in culprit' after school hours and that makes me a 'kept-in' supervisor too! I have noticed, by the way, that some of the children find pleasure in being kept in. Is there something wrong?

Additionally I have reports to write and facts to collect relative to such reports. In respect of children from a bombed-out area, I must submit a long report – names, place of residence, occupation of father, etc. There are already forty to fifty such children here. Often I have to write to the previous schools of the children and demand reports and documents.

On Wednesday afternoon I have Hitler Youth Duty which entails beforehand collecting and bringing scrap materials required for the war effort. Each quarter of a kilo of iron, paper, rags and bones will be needed, and the children earn good marks on a points system regarding what is brought.

To the vast number of rules there are always amendments, additions, etc. My head sometimes reels from it all. I suppose it all gives some people to thinking, 'So, the teachers have it made – the whole afternoon free.' My post I quite often neglect, concentrating on writing to you, Wolfgang and Aunt Lies. I am sorry that I can no longer write to friends and hear from Osnabrück.

Perhaps you each can understand how I long for Saturdays to arrive when the afternoons bring the necessary rest and relaxation, and on Sunday I can sleep in. Even now I am tired, with writing I tire even more. Perhaps Father now understands also, the reason I like playing cards at small parties. During such times I'm not assailed by the thoughts such as, 'You must do that and not that,' and 'You may not, God willing, forget such and such.' Besides, Saturday is my main bath day.

By the way it is the time once again to tackle the extra duties. First of all I have, until 31 January, all the school reports to write (and that, as even you, Father, know, is to be done in a conscientious manner). And now I must also stand in for Frau Kippar, whose husband Herr Kippar I found standing in the school hall on 28 or 29 January. The children had streamed in from their morning break and I saw this tall, slim soldier, Herr Kippar. He was looking for his wife in the school, who had been free after the third hour of class. Sadly, he looks in a very bad way, so bad in fact that I did not at first recognise him.

Later, feeling fresh and strong, I found the week between 31 January and 5 February went very swiftly. Since I know that Wolfgang is lying in hospital in Leslau, I thought to myself, I shall visit him. The railway connections are as follows: Mauern – Königsberg – Thorn – Leslau. Father is correct, Leslau is the former Polish town Wlozlawsk on the Weichsel. I can manage the journey between midday Saturday after school closes and Monday morning before the school opens. But it would be better if I had an additional day's leave. On Wednesday afternoon I baked cakes and biscuits for Wolfgang and on Thursday I said to myself, be a bit cheeky and send a request in writing to the school official (the same one I had to see about the Christmas holiday situation), informing him that a short leave period was requested to enable me to visit my brother. I'd add that I had not seen my brother for a long time, and he was always away on active service and was now lying in a hospital in Leslau, and in the next few weeks would be returning to the front.

The letter did not get a reply and as I did not hear from him, I telephoned him, but he was still not available. In the afternoon we were all with Frau Kerwath at her birthday celebrations. The two Kippars were present, with Herr and Frau von Cohs, Frau Stachel and myself. Herr Kippar suggested I ring the school official again and I did so and was terribly excited. Although he had depressed me about the Christmas situation, he gave me the whole of Saturday off school. I was quite dazed and sent Wolfgang a telegram with reply paid, asking if he would be definitely in Leslau. The reply came very quickly and quite laconic, 'Can come. Wolfgang.'

The entire celebration evening pleased me so much. It was so unendingly pleasant and all there so kind and nice to me. But further details I can't clearly remember. I know I was in fine voice with the drinks we had and became suddenly tired and wished only to be in bed. When I woke up I was fully clothed, lying on Frau Stachel's couch, and wondered what the bucket was doing near me. But since I had slept strongly and soundly, my head was clear.

On Friday at close of school I set off. I obtained a second-class ticket and was lucky enough to get a corner seat. It was an easy journey with my small case containing only washing things, night clothes and the cakes for Wolfgang. I wore my costume and over it my overcoat. I had to get out in the middle of the night at Thorn and a strange railway station at night is a melancholy sight. But in the waiting hall I met up with a pleasant man from a business firm in Bielefeld. He was called Freitag and was an architect and built the savings bank in Spenge (he knows you), and is now employed in Litzmanstadt. He showed me photos of his wife and his sweet, small daughters, a genuine pair of twins. He didn't speak well of teachers. He thought the war will only end when all the teachers become captains!

About 8 a.m. I was in Leslau, such an easterly town. You will know it, Father, from the First World War. It lies on the Weichsel and looks quite imposing. The houses are mostly grey and flat, but there is a beautiful church and a cathedral. The town must have about 60,000 inhabitants – 50,000 Poles and 10,000 Germans.

The streets were, naturally, all renamed. Adolf-Hitler-Strasse, Herman-Göring-Platz and then on to the Goethestrasse. Here I was reminded of the horrors of the ghetto in Plohnen. Grey, dirty houses, broken windows, doors torn off and everywhere dirt, where the Polish women, wrapped in their dark-coloured clothes and head scarves, simply scurry along.

I was frozen when I reached the hospital, an enormous, magnificent building, such as I never expected to see in this town. At the enquiry desk I asked about Wolfgang but since there was a little time to go before official visiting hours, I was not allowed entry. Eventually, however, he came. A short while ago he was only 108 lb in weight but now I saw he looked much better. He had not wanted to leave his company but his jaundice had weakened him to such an extent that he could no longer carry his firearm. All the inmates of the hospital go about in huge slippers and in blue and white striped suits, looking like criminals.

At 3 p.m. Wolfgang received permission to go out. Until then I had looked for a room myself. There were only two hotels but they were fully occupied, even the strangers' homes were full. For two whole hours I searched and I was utterly desperate. Eventually I returned to the hospital where I thought I might procure a private bed. In the room I found slept two other women who were visiting relatives in hospital. As 2 o'clock was visiting time I went to Wolfgang's room and was introduced to his comrades. They would not believe I was his sister. Some of his comrades were there because of the terror of the bombing in which they had lost all their worldly goods and possessions.

Wolfgang had been allowed to wear a uniform and at 3 o'clock off we went. First of all we had a nice coffee and we were so pleased to be together again and had so much to talk about, until a couple of his room comrades came and sat at our table. But we soon broke away and went walking to the Weichsel and he told me how he had knocked out a tank. He had been in a small wood, and he and his comrades were sent on an observation patrol to establish whether the Russians were in the vicinity. But as soon as they left the wood, five enemy tanks approached them. He and his comrade sought cover and protection in a hole in the ground and let the tanks bypass them. But the tanks halted between them and the wood, and after a time the turret hatch opened on one of the tanks and a Russian soldier looked out. The comrade next to Wolfgang was terrified out of his skin and prayed and spoke about his wife and children. Wolfgang succeeded in creeping closer to the tank and threw a hand grenade through the open hatch. It exploded and the other tanks withdrew.

For knocking out the tank he was given fourteen days' special leave. I was happy to have Wolfgang safe and sound and with me to talk to and touch, but I thought also about the poor young men in the tank who must have died, and felt very sad.

We next went into the German House where it was most pleasant and the food was excellent. However, once again his comrades came and sat at our table, despite the fact that there were other tables free. We quickly finished our meal and went out walking for half an hour on the Weichselufer. The air was quite still and only the river murmured quietly as the town was outlined against the night sky. Wolfgang gave me the highest praise that I could possibly ever receive when he said, 'My wife-to-be must, above all, be like you in temperament and nature, but she can also be like you in beautiful looks.'

At 9 o'clock Wolfgang's leave ended and I accompanied him to the hospital. There all the soldiers strolled about together like streams of bees in a hive. Many rolled up in carriages, so I took one of them and in it went to my quarters. I was more than a little cold in the night, despite the fact I wore my underclothes and a pullover.

The next morning Wolfgang told me that he could not obtain leave in the morning but could have leave at 3 o'clock. But my train left at 1445 hours and I had to take my hand luggage. A girl often achieves more than a soldier in such circumstances, especially as the duty officer was a sergeant, also by chance a glider pilot. We at once got into conversation about our mutual interest – seaplanes. It resulted in instant permission for Wolfgang to have leave. At the end, the sergeant said, 'Pass on to your brother my greetings, but next time he should not send his sister with such a request but come himself.' As his room comrades heard that, they said to Wolfgang, 'The Waffen SS has no fighting spirit – they must send a woman first.'

We waited together until the arrival of my train and had a meal promptly at 2 o'clock. Wolfgang told me he would be leaving the hospital on 10 February and then go to a troop training unit in Dresden. There he hoped he would be granted his sick leave and could then visit me in Gertlauken.

The train connections on the return journey were good. In Thorn I used the stopping halt to make a short visit to the town and saw the Kopernikus memorial. I stayed for a long time in the

Gothic stone church of St Johannes where someone played the organ beautifully. Such playing in the empty church reflected, as it were, my own voice.

We got to Allenstein three-quarters of an hour later and I caught the Königsberg train at the last minute. I had scarcely time to sit down and off it went. At 0045 hours we arrived in Mauern. The night, being clear and not cold, lent itself to a pleasant walk. Once when I was in a wood I heard voices afar off, so I took a large stone from a pile at the roadside as a potential weapon. They, the voices, were of the rural guards who mistrusted me as I did them. Finally we all had to laugh. The encounter made me think of a similar walk from the Dülmen station to Dernckamp, when a caring father gave me his stick as a weapon. Do you still remember?

By 2 o'clock I was home and I wondered if I would find anything open. I then heard a sound coming from my room, gripped my stone firmly and pressed down the door handle, and . . . Paula lay in my bed! I had not seen her for over two months, so you can understand what a lengthy chat we had. Paula could not put up with Weidlacken any more and wanted once again to speak with national people. She left shortly before eight and we had not had a wink of sleep. She had left me her typed work for the teacher's examination No. 2. At 8.30 a.m. I reported by telephone to the school official who was very pleased about my return and enquired as to the course of my journey.

Now, as a result of the latter, there is much to hoard. I noticed how Wolfgang ate readily his fill because he had a respectable appetite and had to go out to eat. So yesterday I made some dripping and baked some biscuits and a Madeira cake afterwards. I then ironed all my clothes and cleaned the room. So if small brother comes, all will be well and in order. I will also have more time for him, and all here in the village take an interest in him.

Do please always send me the newspaper as Wolfgang is always happy when one is available, as it is a piece and breath of home. In one of them I read of the death of Frau Walden.

During the break in the school playground we all had a huge snowball fight, boys versus girls, and I was the main target.

If Wolfgang came now I could collect him with the sledge. My Königsberg address is: Frau Elly Kinder, Königsberg (PR) Fremdenheim, Rossgarten 6.

My dear Parents

On Monday there were no lessons. Instead there was an unscheduled meeting of the teachers' school helpers and temporary teachers' helpers, held in Gross Scharlack. I set off at 4 a.m. on my cycle and it was pitch-black and an icy-smooth surface on the roads. On top of the ice lay at least five centimetres of water in depth.

The train to Labiau left at 5.35 a.m. From Labiau a small railway line runs in the direction of Tapiau until Klein Scharlack and then there is a kilometre walk on foot over the muddy roads to the Gross Scharlack school. The school official either had no more petrol or no car, since he tramped along with us. He is a man of slight and delicate build and a person one can read like a book.

Firstly was an hour of German with the introduction of a new reading piece relating to the five to six year class, then a history hour in respect of the seven to eight school year and for us, the teachers, etc., an excellent hour about good organisation possibilities. But the teachers in front of him dozed and the children slept on. The discussion about the reading matter should have taken about ten minutes but instead went on for half an hour. And the history hour! Themes related to the transfer of territory as a result of the Versailles Treaty. From there to the signatories to the armistice signed in the Forest of Compiègne, France. The school official released us all to wake the children up.

After the hours mentioned, two lectures followed. One was good and the other involved the new BDM group leader, quite a BDM type, talking with her hands and feet, who believed all the small girls were hers to possess. I visualised very few from my village contacting her as the village is some distance away.

At the conclusion of the meeting subsistence money matters were addressed and the school official said that because of the early hour of my reveille I could receive overnight payment. We had to make haste in order to catch the train which was dead on time, to convey us to Tilsker. It was ready to depart and was unbelievably full of Königsberg folk and no space at all to be had. Terrible!

I stayed with Fräulein Weiss during the entire journey and she had acted as the representative of Herr Schulz and Krakau. She had many of his similarities in her ways and comes from a farm holding, like he does. The farm covers 300 acres and has twenty-six cows. In her manner she is particularly self-assured, loyal, reliable, dependable and so correct an East Prussian! And I like her very much.

I was too tired to travel to see Frau Schulz as I normally do. Besides, on the journey the weather turned so nasty that I thought only of getting home. That I was able to manage, but nothing more. Instead I had to take a rest with Frau Neumann. Since I was feeling sick, I was given a schnapps and had to lie down until I felt better. Recently, I've had many stomach upsets.

I have spent this week waiting for Wolfgang. I've had hand towels and coloureds washed and ironed and baked many biscuits as well as 3 lb flour pepper cakes. Today also aniseed biscuits made from a recipe of Aunt Lies. Frau Stachel went off today to spend two days with her parents in Deutsch-Eylau. If Wolfgang comes he can sleep in my bed and I can sleep on the wide couch at Frau Stachel's.

Today I received mail from Wolfgang that he will leave Dresden on Wednesday or Thursday and then come here, perhaps getting here by tomorrow. I expect him at any moment and the entire village too, as the people here are already curious. So this afternoon I have this feeling that tomorrow evening I shall be with my brother, and after meeting him we can go for a walk together . . .

Sunday 20 February

I couldn't write any more the day before yesterday. It was shortly before midnight when there was a sudden knock. I had the radio on and heard but a light sound, but didn't take much notice. Then I called, 'Who is there?' No answer but again a knock. Once again I called, 'Who is there?' A deep voice answered, 'For goodness' sake, open the door.' Wolfgang it was and you cannot understand how I felt at that moment.

Now, I don't know where to start in this report. First though, about Wolfgang. During the entire journey from Dresden he and two other soldiers had to stand in the train's toilet compartment. He arrived in Königsberg four hours late, so that he was unable to catch the 13.26 train to Tilsit. First of all he thought of staying in Königsberg overnight, but he had had enough of sitting around in waiting rooms, so he caught the 19.17 train which reached Mauern at 2115 hours. He found that despite the darkness he was able somewhat to find his way about and with luck obtained a lift in a cart that took him to Krakau. Now came the route march but luckily he found the walk not too difficult. He found Gertlauken and the schoolhouse, both not too hard to find. It is, after all, the largest building in the village and can't be overlooked.

At first his search revealed many entrances to the house as he went round the building. He then put on three lights, banged loudly on the door, rapped on the garden door and whistled. Nobody stirred. Unfortunately he had no matches and it was very dark. Eventually after making further noises he felt his way to the main floor and would have stayed there overnight on one of the benches in a classroom. Finally, he saw the staircase, felt his way to the first floor, rattling every door. No reply, as all were abed. He felt his way upstairs where he banged on another door for a long time before realising it was the door to the closet. Next he tried the adjoining room, the door of which was open, and switched on the light above a basin and found a washing line.

The next day after my lessons we went to the Neumanns and there learnt at once about a typical, open-hearted East Prussian family. They liked him very much and today Sunday, I slept in a while and wondered what to cook for the midday meal. Then Christel Beckmann came and brought an invitation to their midday meal. Naturally we accepted it and afterwards had coffee and pancakes. Wolfgang was quite taken with the cordiality of the people and the lavishness of the meals given to him. Then I wanted to introduce him to Frau Kippar who came round at once and was happy that Wolfgang had at last really arrived. She'd quickly brewed a cup of real coffee. A little later Herr and Frau von Cohs came and eventually all went to Frau Kerwath for a small party. But best of all, I have Frau Kippar and Frau Stachel as friends. But at this time when I am so happy and lucky having Wolfgang here, Frau Kippar has her own sorrows to bear at saying farewell to her husband.

Gertlauken 24 February 1944

My dear Parents
Yesterday I received an additional visit. The *Oberleutnant* Peyinghaus had leave and telegraphed his arrival. I was quite excited and happy that Wolfgang is here also. First of all I had

to organise a sledge and a horse, both of which I obtained from the Beckmanns. Herr Beckmann had, however, no time to travel to Laukischken. Wolfgang also was not willing to do it, so yours truly alone had to drive. The horse was quite tame, even through Laukischken where I was spared much traffic. Herr Peyinghaus, who understands horses, took over the reins for the return journey.

As we got to the road crossing in Gertlauken and in front of the Krug, I saw behind the window the three women and Wolfgang laughing and winking. As I jolted round the corner they rushed to another window and made faces at me again. They and Wolfgang certainly had fun watching us.

In my room Olga had laid the table very prettily and, bursting with curiosity, brought hot waffles from upstairs. Gradually my shyness left me as Fritz Peyinghaus is, in his quiet, caring way, very likeable. After the coffee, he made a proposal of marriage to me. I was completely surprised and asked for time to consider, and that he understood. I scarcely know what to think about it all. My two guests are the talking point in the entire village. Besides, Frau Kippar was so kind as to accommodate the *Oberleutnant* as a guest in her house.

Now I must close because I still have Paula's work to type. She brought it to me eight days ago and I've only done a quarter of it.

Gertlauken 2 March 1944

My dear Parents

Eight small and large alarms you have endured and nights spent in the bomb shelter. Colleagues from Father's department are to become frontier guards and sent to the Dutch border, but Father is over fifty years old and, thank heavens, is discharged from the armed forces. Poor Mother, 63 cwt of briquettes through the cellar hole, no wonder that the back aches. And instead of 3 lb potatoes, you get turnips! What luck that we have the garden. I shall give to Wolfgang whatever he can carry.

Yesterday Fritz left as he had to be in Münster on 1 March, and will visit you as soon as possible. I had the opportunity this week to learn a little about his character and naturally I asked Wolfgang, "What do you make of him?' He thought he was different from all the other men he knew and also different from his officers. That is correct. He is warm-hearted, ready to help and more intelligent than all the men I know. I can but wonder why he has fallen for me!

All in the village wish us well and await only the invitation! In the school I have done only that which is necessary and in between times have typed Paula's work. The invitation to Neumanns last Saturday I did not want to accept and wanted Wolfgang and Fritz to go there alone. Both would not entertain the idea and finally Fritz remained in my other room and typed Paula's work, while Wolfgang and I plodded through the deep snow to Neumanns for coffee. But they were disappointed not to see him and they sent Wolfgang back on a cycle to fetch Fritz. It was a picture how they came back. The saddle was too low for Wolfgang's long legs, while Fritz sat on the crossbar and both balanced uneasily over the snow-covered and ice-covered street.

About midnight Wolfgang and I took the opportunity to go outdoors from the Neumanns to get some fresh air. It was cold, with a clear velvet sky full of glistening stars that curved itself over the quiet, white landscape. And I congratulated Wolfgang on his 21st birthday. Now the neighbours all heard about Wolfgang's birthday and wished him good luck and there were happy greetings without end. It was 2 o'clock before we broke away. Both Wolfgang and Fritz in unison said they would buy me a riding horse in the Wehlau horse market and then they both marched off as if on parade, singing loudly in the night air. I walked alongside them, urging them to be quiet, otherwise they would awaken the village. My grumbling was ignored and they just laughed at me.

The next day Frau Stachel held a banquet and for birthday coffee the whole lot of them came to me. I had baked quite a lot of things and after that we played cards, and after the evening meal once again played cards. I thought always to myself, 'Hopefully they won't stay long as I must finish typing the last quarter of Paula's work and she is coming tomorrow to fetch it.' But she came instead on Sunday evening about 2200 hours and her arrival accelerated the break-up of the party. Wolfgang, for once, slept in Frau Stachel's living room, and Paula and I spent the entire night typing. She read to me and I typed. By the break of dawn we had finished and she went off to Wehlau and I went to school.

On Wednesday Fritz received news that on 1 March he had to be in Münster, so we organised a horse and sleigh for him and I took him to the station at Mauern. We arrived there punctually and he carefully fastened the reins to a long wooden pole behind the waiting room. He was so anxious about me and advised me most strongly to return safely to Gertlauken on the horse-drawn sleigh. I know most certainly that I shall soon get to know more about him.

Gertlauken 7 March 1944

My dear Parents

I have such worries about you and Wolfgang. Please write to me at once. I am always thinking of Wolfgang and his train journey. He must have arrived in Berlin in the middle of a huge air raid. Please write at once. He has forgotten his cigarette case and I have sent it on to him with a few photographs.

Gertlauken 17 March 1944

My dear Parents

I am furious. I have always subscribed to the view that I do as little as possible to pester the school official, especially never over a trivial mater. When I have school problems, does he help me? During the last two and a half years I have asked him for advice on, at most, six occasions.

In the upper class I have two rogues who are cheeky to me. Actually it is only one, the tall Mahnke, who is the leader. Today, the Forestry Leader came and requested the aid of a couple of youngsters to help him carry the bedding required by the NSV [National Socialist League for Public Welfare] for the Berlin evacuees. I allowed him three pupils and what did they do? They simply placed the bedding behind the bend of the road and left it there. And when I took them to task about it, they were cheeky and ran off under the leadership of Mahnke.

Then I rang the school official at midday and he ordered me to beat the offender. I thought, 'Am I hearing this correctly?' I said, 'He is bigger than I am and I don't think I dare do it.' The school official will now send Herr Drabe, but that did not pacify me. For over a year, Herr Drabe the teacher at Laukischken has not been here. Then one day he arrived on his cycle quite unexpectedly, asked whether I had anything to ask, or any complaints, and then said he would come over once a week to see if everything was all right. And that is how it has remained, since he never came again. Before he left on that occasion, he wished me well and that if I had any questions to ask I should, first of all, refer them to him. Then after the Christmas holiday when I had again questions to ask, I jumped on my bike and cycled to Herr Drabe. The result was unsatisfactory – almost indifference on his part and useless to ask him for anything. I don't wish to think about him again, for I am so damned angry.

Since Christmas the school official was supposed to have made a visit but up to the present nobody has appeared. When one is stuck in an out-of-the-way place like this, one simply has to see how one can cope with any problem. Those stupid chaps, they can take a running jump somewhere. . . .

Gertlauken 22 March 1944

My dear Parents
In my letter I feel I have only disturbed you by writing as I did. When one has a problem and sleeps on it, one sees things more clearly. Up until today no one has been here, neither the school official nor Herr Drabe, but I have again spoken to the offending pupils about their behaviour and the atmosphere is certainly better.

The weather is atrocious – Christmas in clover, Easter in snow. Outside it looks like Christmas and the snow crocuses are already in bloom. In the forest one finds liverwort and the first *Stare* are already there. Many of the children are away from school because of influenza, scarlet fever or diphtheria. Also Frau Kippar, Frau Stachel and Helma are off with high fever.

Has Wolfgang written recently? And for Mother it's time for work to be done in the garden. It is good to know that the radio now announces whether the enemy bombers are approaching. I can see now Mother taking the radio set on a child's cart to be repaired at Merheim – the picture is ever before me. I received Father's loving letter of 11 March on 18 March. That was the time things were not going well for me. Then I was particularly pleased to read and reread his letter.

Gertlauken 29 March 1944

My dear Parents
I can so easily imagine your last few days. How quickly the time flies by. The main thing is that Wolfgang came home in good health. Poor, dear Mother, not being able to give Wolfgang the butter cake

because his train set off so quickly. Wolfgang described his abrupt leave-taking of you in his letter to me. It was his first letter from Dresden.

He sounds quite sorrowful about seeing you standing by the train with the cake in your hands. What the father of Wolfgang said of his son, I've said likewise. Wolfgang has become mature. But Wolfgang was actually always very serious and had always an open countenance. One can despair a little at his not saying much about things, but once one discusses serious matters and themes with him, it is a different matter. He opens up fully and one realises how pleasant a person he is.

I am sorry to disappoint you about the coffee as I was able to obtain only half a pound and it cost fifty marks. But I shall shortly try again to get some. The half-pound I purchased I gave to Fritz, whose letter I received today informing me of a visit he hopes to make to me this week.

Over Easter, Paula was here visiting me on Sunday. Frau Stachel and Frau Kippar travelled to their parents, even Frau Kerwath was away. So without Paula's visit it would have been lonely here.

I don't know how long Fritz will be able to stay. Two days ago I went to Königsberg to acquire some books and exercise books. On the previous Friday I went to Krakau to Frau Schulz and Fräulein Weiss. The last-named is sick with scarlet fever and so the school official ordered that the children should be dismissed from school. This I did and no further lessons will take place until the Easter holidays fall due.

With us here, deep winter rules, with two days of unbroken snowfalls. All the ways, roads and paths are blocked.

Gertlauken 3 April 1944

My dear Parents

I would like to write a long letter to you but I cannot concentrate. Tomorrow is the final day of the holidays and since Friday, Fritz has visited me. He stays with Frau Kerwath and over the Easter holidays we were both with Paula. On the Tuesday after Easter Fritz had to leave again and Paula and I accompanied him to Königsberg and we (Paula and I) spent a few days there. I must once again be in Gertlauken for my birthday. I know the children are sorry that my birthday falls in the holiday period but I shall invite them all, as I did last year.

Yesterday was a blessing day in the village, in which the Berkans' Elka was baptised. We should have been in three places at one time. At midday we were at the Beckmanns who gave us the most delicious things that I'd better not tell you about, in case it makes your mouths water. The Beckmanns simply would not let us go and we had to stay for coffee. One by one, all the families I knew best appeared and it was a huge, merry, social party with lots of young folk. Together we were about thirty persons and about twenty-three of us were invited for coffee and the delicious tarts that were brought in. That was only half of it, the table couldn't bear it all.

Gertlauken 21 April 1944

My dear Parents

Fritz received a telegram that he should start his course in Bad Nauheim without delay, so we then had to make other holiday arrangements. As a result Paula and I spent the Easter holiday together on our own – how wonderful! Frau Stachel and her children were away, also Olga for a short time had gone home, so we had the entire kitchen with cooker and electric plate just for ourselves – a delightful household! On the first Friday we had *Flinsen* on two hot waffles. Immediately after leaving the table we went for a long walk in the woods.

The snow is slowly melting and it was sunny and warm, and in the woods bloomed liverwort, golden stars, *Milzkraut* and I know not what else. The lavish shoots of the *Bachen* and the small *Teichen* spring up everywhere. In the distance we heard the frogs croaking, and in a sunny clearing we found a pile of timber on which we lay and sunned ourselves. We also went to the woods on the following day.

Just now I have heard the Armed Forces Report and Köln was mentioned once again. Even if nothing occurred, dear Mother, I hope you were in the air-raid shelter. Perhaps Father has heard whether anything has happened in Dresden where Wolfgang is?

But I will continue with my description of my Easter activities. On Easter Tuesday I thought to myself, you still have holiday time left, why don't you travel to Dresden to visit Wolfgang and Father? The deed followed the words and Paula and I quickly baked a cake, packed it in the small case, and on Wednesday at 10 a.m. I was able to travel in a cart to the station. We actually wanted to travel together to Königsberg but Paula had such a severe attack of stomach ache that she could not, unfortunately, come with me.

During the afternoon I went twice to the cinema and then left on the 2200 hours train to Berlin. The train was terribly crowded and I had to stand in the gangway. Near me stood a young girl from Halle who had been a hospital sister and later married a baker. She told me of her entire life history. At the end she gave me her address so that I could at some time write to her. She was so frank and open, honest and friendly. Such acquaintances I always seem to encounter.

The train reached Berlin on time to meet up with the other connection but the latter was full up. But, in another half-hour I was in Dresden. There I had first to find out where the barracks were and found, very fortunately, they lay in a place surrounded by woods. Then I washed thoroughly in the station washroom and, thus refreshed, went out to the barracks. There, a soldier on guard took me to the canteen and when I met Wolfgang he was quite astonished! 'How did you get here? I thought Father was coming?' he said. He then went to the company commander and obtained leave until 2200 hours.

We went into the town first of all to seek accommodation for me. From hotel to hotel in the hot sunshine we went, but the result? A dead loss! Eventually from a hotel waitress I got a private address and rang there immediately, and was told I could be accommodated. The room was in a house that lay in the centre of the town and after the arrangements there, we went off to eat somewhere. Seemingly I had fetched Wolfgang from his midday meal. He was in the process of peeling his first potato when interrupted by my presence in the barracks. In the afternoon we strolled through the town and then went for our evening meal. We parted at about 8 o'clock because Wolfgang had an exercise the following night.

On Friday morning we strolled again in the town, which impressed me very much. The traffic density was nothing like that we have in Köln in peacetime. A real, proper picture of what a large town should be – countless people, broad streets, beautiful shops and shop windows, imposing buildings and not a solitary ruin.

We have our venerable, romantic church in Köln but never did I think that I would be so enraptured to such an extent by the Baroque.

The Zwinger, as all call the Frauenkirche with their tremendous domes on which an angel soars, then the beautiful Adolf-Hitler-Platz with the State Opera House, a part of the Zwinger, and the castle. The *Platz* lies on the River Elbe, there a few steps to climb and then come onto the Bruhlsche Terrace. From there one has a splendid view over the Elbe with its three bridges. On either side of the riverbanks there are beautiful, artistic buildings laid out. There is too the so-called *Neustadt* [new town].

I regret very much that I could not buy any of the town's souvenirs but it is such a beautiful place in which to make delightful strolls, and aimlessly wander through it and let its effect – overwhelm you. I took my time rambling and then about 3 p.m. Wolfgang wanted to go to my room to have a sleep before we went out again until 2200 hours, his leave finishing time, and after, the start of his night exercise, and the following day he had duty. Such a programme would defeat the strongest soldier.

I'd bought some cakes before I met Wolfgang, who had decided against sleeping. So we drank some tasty coffee and eventually wandered around the town. He knew of a local pub in which good Wiener schnitzel was served. Father in the meantime will have got to know about this. Still, a very tired, slow waiter could manage to bring something to fill the two growling, hungry stomachs.

On the next day, my birthday, Wolfgang was free of duty and I waited for him to come to breakfast with me. He had wished to bring Heinz Goldammer with him and I had bought rolls and laid the table with the delicacies I had available. But unfortunately Heinz Goldammer was required to stay in barracks despite the fact he had leave granted to him. So Wolfgang came alone. After breakfast Wolfgang and I looked for a photographer in the town. We found one but had to wait an hour in the waiting room. Wolfgang was so tired he fell asleep sitting in his chair. The photographer was an old, pious man from Königsberg and expressed his Christian feelings to the lovely brother and sister. The photograph he will send to you in Köln.

After the midday meal, without potatoes as they are very scarce in Dresden, but with bread instead, we went by train line No. 18 to Pillnitz. Despite its neglected state, the castle and its surroundings are quite delightful to look at. To the River Elbe below, a broad staircase leads to a parapet on which are two watchful sphinx figures. We were on our own as we walked and I thought how thankful we should be to the princes of days long ago who left so much beauty behind them, especially if one considers that in that age, the majority of people lived in abject poverty.

In the evening we fetched tired Father from the station, but that said he was still quite fresh. We greeted each other and with him between us went to my dwelling place to see if Father could be accommodated there. Then Father produced a package, and, Mother, I must grumble about you, what have you not packed? The lovely blouse and the lovely light jacket and the coat! They are all your things and you simply should not have sent them to me. Nevertheless I had to put on the brown blouse immediately.

Wolfgang and I are so pleased with the vast amount of foodstuffs and he had to indulge his love of sweet things at once. No wonder when you have two children who eat a lot!

Father at once ate two portions from the foodstuffs. But I can most certainly use the comb and hairslides, buttons, needles and towels. Thank you so much for giving me so much pleasure. Also there is the toothbrush, one I have sought for ages. So, my dearest Mother, I thank you from the bottom of my heart for all your loving presents on my birthday.

22 April

On Sunday Father and I wandered through Dresden and had a huge portion of meat in a local pub – actually with potatoes too! Then we returned on foot. The walks in the town in the warm weather with one still wearing a warm coat, make one tired.

In the evening Father, Wolfgang and I visited the Circus Sarrasani. The programme consisted of a quarter of an operetta, a quarter of variety and a quarter of *Café Haus* and circus, but it is terrific that in wartime they can manage to put together such a show. The best part of the evening was that the three of us were able to be together. Only you, Mother, were missing and we would have loved you to have been present.

On Monday, the last day, Father and I went to the Elbsand-Steingebirge. It is always pleasant to have walks with Father, a fact I had already noted in Attendorn we frequented so often. We went to Bad Rathen on the Elbe, a little way behind Pirna. The steep, similarly shaped rocks of the Elbsandgebirge rise up on the other side of the river and give quite a romantic view. We were allowed to sit with the driver and it caused me to think of a previous instance of Moritz von Schwind. In the mountains one sees an indescribable mass of different rocks, all of a tangle. We saw the Lilienstein and the Königstein Fortress and hoped to have been able to get something to eat at the Gasthaus den Bastei [guest house], but on Mondays it is closed. We wanted to climb up a different path at the top and at first the route was a quiet, broad, tree-lined way, and being in the shade, pleased Father. But once we reached the so-called Schwedenlocher [Swedish Holes] we began a wildly romantic climb up through rocky paths, access being only possible if one stooped. Often we splashed through a lively stream. It was heavenly, summery and peaceful, and one had time to enjoy it all to the full.

Gertlauken 2 May 1944

My dear Parents
Your first letter after the air raid I received today. I was so full of worries. From Saturday to Monday I was in Königsberg and there met Elesa Heller and her husband, as well as Helga Ibing and Paula. The day after tomorrow we have a conference and there I will see the school official and request leave regarding my engagement party.

Gertlauken 7 May 1944

My dear Parents
I shall leave it to you how you wish to celebrate the engagement party, who you wish to invite and so on. But please, not too big a party. I have written to Aunt Lies, and Uncle Hermann could also come. I have written off quickly for special leave and as soon as I get an answer I shall write to you. Probably I should be able to meet you with Kinni in Köln on 26 May. She will be here on Thursday. Here it is raining steadily.

Gertlauken 11 May 1944

Dear Parents
Again, but a short greeting. It was again reported that today enemy planes were in the West. It was certainly a difficult day for you. If only everything goes well!

Yesterday Kinni came here safe and well and was dead-tired after almost thirty hours of travelling. The school official has not yet replied to my request and no doubt will wish to know where Fritz is located. We won't invite many people – the times are too terrible. In the school there is an outbreak of several cases of scabies and I too have been affected, and tomorrow I shall visit the doctor. Is Wolfgang still in Dresden? He has not written to me in a long time.

Gertlauken 15 May 1944

My dear Mother

Here a wonderful peace prevails, whereas you must stay in an air-raid shelter. How exhausted you must be. I can see from Kinni's appearance that she wants only to rest and sleep. Köln was mentioned again in today's Armed Forces Report and yesterday it was Osnabrück. Please obtain from the post office an emergency card – the one you get after a raid – one is allowed to write only ten words on them but they are despatched more quickly. I received such a card from Aunt Lies on 9 May.

Fritz has written from Mulheim that he will be able to come here for a week and then at Easter I shall travel with him. I expect him tomorrow or the day after. I still have not received an answer from the school official and if there is no post from him tomorrow I shall ring him.

Gertlauken 4 June 1944

My dear Parents

The previous Sunday we were all sitting together at coffee. What are you doing today? Hopefully you have a little peace after all the work that Mother had to do. Yesterday I wanted to write to you but I lay down on my bed to rest for a few minutes beforehand. This was at 6 o'clock in the evening, and it was 8 o'clock this morning before I woke up.

Has Fritz left already? Did Father take him to the station? Was his train as full as mine? In our compartment three people were standing and one didn't know where one's legs were, and in the gangway it was even worse, full to capacity. Until KLO was reached, one was constantly contorted and it was distressingly hot. But we arrived in Berlin fairly punctually and after Berlin I sat between two men. One was large and made up of mainly flesh and fat. He lay himself back comfortably in his corner cushion, expanded his broad chest and said, 'Now make yourself also comfortable, little lady.' I had to laugh. He lives in Hadersleben and his conversation about the march into Denmark was very interesting. But I thought so much about Fritz and hoped he had arrived safely in Mourmelon without any incidents.

The train went along at a spanking rate until suddenly at the rear of Stargard it halted – the reason why we never knew. So I arrived in Königsberg at 1000 hours instead of 1822 hours and my connecting train had vanished. So first of all I washed myself, placed my case in the luggage room and had a meal of spinach and salad in the waiting hall. And afterwards I went to Frau Kinder. She still had a room for me. The next morning I set off again and a strange man took me in his cart from Laukischken to Krakau. From there within an hour I was in Gertlauken. Frau Stachel and Frau Kippar had decorated my room with lilac, tulips and narcissi.

Because of smallpox vaccinations the lessons on Thursday and Friday were cancelled. Saturday was taken up with the German Youth Contests, so I had the opportunity of really spending a few days longer with you, had I known. I could have howled!

We really had to graft at midday on Saturday for Gertlauken became like a nursery-school area. On Friday the nursery-school teacher came and the furniture also. I am still amazed how well the NSV cooperate with those needing their help, suddenly all that is required is there.

Our third school room (the one used for further education) had to be made more spacious and so two cupboards had to go out. That enabled me to quickly contact the carpenter and to have one of them reconstructed as a clothes wardrobe for myself.

On Friday before the class vaccinations I entered the classroom and all the children sat at their places with floral bouquets. Each came individually to me and congratulated me on my engagement. My room at present is just like a full-scented lake of flowers. All in the village congratulated me also.

Gertlauken 9 June 1944

My dear Parents
In between times the invasion has begun and when on Tuesday I heard about it on the Armed Forces Report, my knees trembled. What will the decision be next time? What do you think? Specially

now Wolfgang is in the West! Yesterday I received the newspaper you sent me, for which many thanks, and it came very quickly in only eight days. Wolfgang's Field Post number is 58281C.

Here there was no need for me to adjust my way of living. Nevertheless there is a vast difference between the harassment you get in Köln and the quietness and peacefulness I enjoy here in Gertlauken. I feel this difference most strongly.

On Sunday morning the mayor came, and needs me and Frau Kippar to do the cattle count and listing, and in the afternoon Paula came. We went into the woods and discovered an especially beautiful place. At 5 o'clock on Monday morning she went off again.

It is particularly beautiful here in the mornings when the landscape, beasts and people awake and begin a new day. Because of this I began the cattle count quite early. I know my area inside out and everywhere I make a brief stay for a chat.

This time each of them asked about Köln, the air raids and your welfare, also congratulated me on my engagement. By late afternoon I had quickly finished the count and then it became acceptable to babble on.

Regarding the quantity of water that falls from the heavens here, you have no idea, for gardens and fields are swamped. Many people have been unable to plant their potatoes. There is another heavy thunderstorm today and it is time for the sun to shine once again without fail.

The nursery-school wing within the school has been operating since Monday and the children, aged between two and six years, are cute and are here from 0800 hours. A nursery-school teacher is no occupation for me, playing *Haschen in der Grube*, and *Zeigt her eure Fusschen*, with the children the whole day long – terrible! Horrible thought!

Most of the children had never been away from their mother before and made a dreadful row when they were left alone. Many also tried to leave.

I must close as it is already 7 o'clock and I have still shopping to do. Paula came yesterday and stayed for an hour merely to tell me that in the Minden district of Westfalen a teacher from East Prussia would like to exchange places with us. But I will remain here and after the summer holidays will take my examination, for which my occupation report is almost ready. Also, who knows what may happen in the autumn? Besides which, in four to six weeks' time, the major school holiday is here.

Gertlauken 15 June 1944

My dear Parents

Now I can thank you for all your mail. At the beginning of the week your thick letter of 8 June arrived and took only four days in the post. Today I received your letter of 5th with two newspapers, in one of which the engagement notice is shown. I am horrified about the bombing attack on Cimbernstrasse. Life in Köln is like being in hell and here one cannot possibly understand it.

Has Wolfgang in the meantime written? Please send me the letter from Erni Jennings, so that I can write to him in Canada.

Yesterday I visited Frau Strupat who has not been well but still makes real coffee and looks after her lady, who has been evacuated from Königsberg and whose husband is on leave here. We enjoyed ourselves very much and later we ladies had a little time on our own, during which time a lot was discussed about the wedding. Don't laugh, but between Christmas and now I have learnt so much about the relationship between husband and wife, about which I shall not write, as to what I think and what is eventful for me. It has been strongly impressed on me that many people in their life play a part, more necessary than I ever thought would be the case.

Today Helma had her birthday and there have been many visits warning adults to be ready this evening, and I must dress in my finery. Frau Stachel and her sister are always very chic!

Here it is always fairly cold since it has rained almost every day. In the fields the potatoes rot and the haymaking cannot begin because the meadows are underwater. I shall travel to Paula on Sunday.

This week in the school I have again looked at all the heads. One mother from the Rheinland came storming in late, and quite noisily in a flood of words complained about Frau Kippar and myself – her children simply did 'not' have lice and that was that! Frau Kippar only understood half of the outburst and that was the wrong way round. But in such situations I always stay calm.

My dear Parents

Many thanks for your letter No. 106 that came today. Father must have been in an appalling, growling voice – Brrr! I am always pleased that I am not there in the immediate vicinity. Only I must make one thing clear. Indeed, I have often been in Königsberg, but always only on holidays. If I go there on Saturdays it is always late afternoon and then all the well-known shops are already closed. And I would not be my father's daughter if everything was not in order and organised, and I have never made a secret of it.

Naturally I have often asked myself whether or not I should go out sightseeing, and perhaps my work suffers in consequence. But the East Prussians are very sociable and love visiting and that togetherness with relations, friends and neighbours. That is all we have here in the village, so different to the town, and it makes me happy and I feel myself somewhat safe where I belong.

So on Saturday at 5 o'clock Frau Kippar fetched me and we went to Frau Appel who had invited us both. She lives some distance away in a forestry house and is so pleased to have a visitor because of her loneliness after the death of her husband. We spent the entire afternoon cooking, baking, gardening and with the cattle. Besides us, there was also Frau Ander, also a forestry wife. The hospitality was like in peacetime, overwhelming, during the afternoon and evening. It is such a proper old house and if guests are there you get what you can from the cellar and the small room. It was midnight when I got back home.

On Tuesday at 9.30 p.m. I once again visited Frau Berkan below because I saw Drohlsen leaving on his motorbike. The small six-month-old Elke had had whooping cough for eight days but today she was getting a little better. She had eaten and in the afternoon lay in the sunshine and laughed whenever she saw anyone.

Just now she is struggling for breath, has spat blood and had a fever of over forty degrees. Pneumonia had set in. It was terrible, the poor little tot, so full of fight and so shocking to see. For hours on end her eyes were opening and closing themselves in the battle with the fever. The doctor had given her injections. Frau Berkan had not slept at all, all though the night, and herself is sick with rheumatism. The small one was a little more peaceful but naturally could not be left on her own. I offered to keep watch myself. Early, about 5 o'clock I heard a chorale – that was the death of little Elke.

It is the day of her burial here today and yesterday was the death wake. It is the custom here for the neighbours on the last evening before the burial to sit and keep watch until midnight and sing. That was the chorale I heard. The small corpse looked like a doll, so pretty in the long white dress with my flowers round her. With the watchers was an old social welfare worker who said a few well-meaning words and then we sang some holy songs. At 1800 hours the undertaker was there and at the end there was the usual meal with Frau Berkan, and I helped as much as I could. Of the five women watchers, each of them had lost a child, one of them had a son killed at the front.

Fritz wrote that he needs the following from me: copy of the family tree of descendants inclusive of grandparents; a police certificate of good conduct; a medical certificate regarding marriage suitability; names of two citizens and state nationals. For the registry office I need, besides the birth certificate of my parents, my own birth certificate and a certificate of baptism.

Gertlauken 2 July 1944

If it is cold we moan, when it is unceasingly hot one moans just the same. I have only one wish, to be in water and swimming. It is correct, I was at the Nehrung today but I did not get a ticket as the ship still travels only on a Sunday and for that, the available tickets are already purchased on Tuesday.

In the afternoon I was invited by Christel Beckmann for coffee as it was her birthday. The Beckmanns are a charming family and especially nice, the grandmother a proper picture-book grandmother. She was married three times and had fifteen children, of whom six are dead. One fell in the First World War, two are in America, the remainder live in the village or the surrounding area. She takes care of the house and the animals while the rest of the family work in the fields. She cooks, collects wild berries, and other berries and mushrooms, for hours on end. In winter she spins and knits, and when she starts talking about the old days . . . ! Early in the mornings she would go on foot to the market in Königsberg in order to sell the wild berries. She is a particularly rich source for me regarding recipes – for example, how one wins a man!

I have received only a brief note from Wolfgang. Together with his old company commander he is once again in No. 19 Company.

On Thursday afternoon we had a working committee in Mauern and the school official was there and said that we should be getting a third-course teacher in Gertlauken. I don't believe I'll be happy about it. After the summer holidays we are to get a twenty-six-year-old school teacher, a beginner. We have here 150 children, among them being several from Berlin and Königsberg, In these towns the schools are as good as empty, often just three or four children in each class.

Gertlauken 8 July 1944

For over three weeks now we have had a tropical heatwave and today I gave the school a free day off for the first time, as about 9 a.m. it was already thirty degrees in the shade. All our heads were drooping and for once there was simply nothing to do but send the children home.

The report from Frau Hunger is shattering. You wrote that the daughter from the top floor was unconscious and helpless. How was she rescued? And the father burnt?

I received a parcel from Fritz with two pairs of stockings, face cream and a pretty, blue leather money purse. He gave the parcel to a comrade who was travelling to East Prussia. I was also pleased to receive a letter in the week and in plenty of time to reply to it. On Sunday I made a proposal to him that the wedding should be postponed until next summer. To me this seems very correct and right, for perhaps in a year's time one can see the future more clearly.

Today at last after a long time I received a few lines from Wolfgang – whether he is in action?

Yesterday I received a pound of garden berries as a present and I am absolutely delighted with it. This week I have made three jars of jam from 5 lb gooseberries, so tiny that one could scarcely imagine how small they were. I had the sugar from Mother already. Also this week I did a large laundry, helped by Paula once again as she so often does. We chatted away in the house and sang in between and then we don't find the work so hard.

On Thursday we had a conference in Labiau. The district leader spoke to the mayor, local farmers' leader and teachers about the importance of the school. In a week's time it will be the holidays and issue of school certificates.

In Krakau the new teacher is already in place, an old eccentric who has had only the third year to teach. At first she set herself out to be the teacher-in-charge, but has since climbed down in her aspirations. Fräulein Weiss suggested to her that she should deal with the schoolmaster's basic tasks, such as report writing and similar things, and that she, the newcomer, will then have but her signature to append below the reports. Here also, Fräulein Weiss pointed out to her that since she had only twelve hours teaching per week and had only nineteen pupils, whereas she, Fräulein Weiss, had seventy-two pupils, the newcomer might take on teaching more of the school leavers. I was a bit curious as to how this arrangement will work in our school!

Gertlauken 16 July 1944

My dear Parents

It is 9 o'clock on Sunday morning and you are most certainly drinking your coffee or sitting in the cellar, should flights over south-west Germany have been reported. And what may Wolfgang be doing? I am expecting Paula to come for the midday meal but before that I shall write the marks in the exercise books. After which I shall have a lecture and a demonstration lesson to prepare for our conference.

In the week Herr Bachert, our head director, will be buried. When I came back from the Nehrung on Sunday I was overtaken by an ambulance from Labiau. I had encountered it previously near Laukischken and probably it had been in Krakau or Gertlauken. Herr Bachert was very helpful, and for a long time he had been sick with a head cold, from which an ear infection developed. He looked very thin and pale as if he should have been in hospital. Shortly after that occasion I met him on the street and spoke a little with him. I thought, 'My God, he is looking so sorry for himself.' Now I feel so sorry for having had such a thought. On Sunday his condition deteriorated and he was accepted into hospital in Königsberg, There was a spark of hope with his operation but it was in vain. Now his wife, with a horse and cart must fetch him from Königsberg. For an entire day and night, the village people were travelling with the corpse. Now the poor wife with her sixteen-year-old daughter are alone, since the son is at the front. When Herr Bachert died he was fifty-four years of age and the whole village took part in the burial service. When I came from the cemetery I thought how doubly fortunate I was with life, the sun and the sky. And when I too die it shall be in peace. That is a thought I think of occasionally, but I would like a short space of time before parting from this world, to thank God for all the beauty I have been allowed to enjoy.

At the burial space we heard in the distance the roar of the guns shooting at the front, but for two days now it has grown much quieter. You need not have any worries on my account. I stand here alone on my own two feet and those who stand thus can always help themselves and others if needs be. For the first time there is nervousness in the village about the war situation. This is because Grodno lies not really far from the East Prussian border. I wrote to you that suddenly twenty-five men from the village were told at 5 a.m. to report with side arms and spades at 8 a.m. Probably they were to work on the East Wall, and other men will be required for the same task. Herr Schustereit and Herr Neumann have also gone. Sometimes it was merely a request for their services, but as of now, they must go off in the middle of the harvest time.

Today also the young boys born in 1929 must go and even those born in 1930 can volunteer. One young boy from the school must go and said his goodbyes to me yesterday. I accept it is in order that full measures as possible be taken to safeguard East Prussia and to ensure it is not lost – but – schoolchildren?

This morning the General Journey Ban came into effect so that I cannot travel to you in Köln. Should the position improve there is always a little ground for hope. The Führer cares for those evacuated from Lithuania and the other Baltic people and that is why they are not allowed to rest here. Here everywhere quiet and peace prevail. I wonder to myself why the Russians have not made air attacks on the towns and railway lines.

The previous Sunday was the first time this year I had been on the Nehrung. In the sticky heat it was almost impossible to walk barefooted through the sand dunes. I went a long way along the beach until I was quite alone with only sand and water, sky and sun.

I swam a little way out without a bathing costume and lay in the nude on the sand, and let the air dry me. Unfortunately I could only stay an hour and had to get back to the boat in a rush, and reached it at the last moment. Wearily I sat down on a bench and after a while could only see the gloomy side of things. I could only think about Mother. But soon I felt better and then cycled the whole way back to Gertlauken.

Liebenfelde 20 July 1944

My dear Parents

You are astonished at the name of this place, is that not so? It came about like this. On Sunday Paula visited me, probably for the last time, for she has obtained a place in the main school in the district of Bartenstein. That amazes you also, correct? Paula has passed the second part of the teacher's examination with good marks, and I am so pleased for her. She is so fussy and didn't want to tell anyone about it. It was left to me to trumpet it all over the world. I had not to tell anyone about it. I would have liked to have told you about it before but have written about it now. If I had passed my examination with but adequate marks I would have been very satisfied. In addition to this, Paula has had three especially difficult weeks with school lessons. Three times in the week in Weidlacken and three times in Schirrau, three kilometres distant.

So Paula was with me on Sunday and is the best comrade and the most reliable friend that one can think of. Naturally we were both concerned about the nearness of the front line. Paula was very worried and had sent nearly all her things home, and asked my advice about it. From the local farmers' leader in her home village she has received information that she is requested at the harvest action. Perhaps she will get permission to travel, despite the travelling ban in operation. I have decided that likewise I too shall travel home in the holidays, if the school official allows it. In the evening we quickly packed two parcels, one to go to Köln and the other to Osnabrück, especially as on Sunday we heard artillery fire from the front line. There were also a few bombers over Schirrau.

During the break on Monday I phoned the school official and he was very pleasant but seemed undecided as to what he should do. He said he could not give me a travel pass because the new regulations are not exactly clear. We should speak to the authorities in Elchwerder about such travel arrangements when we attended the conference there.

On Tuesday the holidays and school-certificates time. I have a few children not transferred or placed in a department, only at the moment on approval. Their problems relate especially to the children in the upper classes, for whom recently I have not set any homework. Everything at present rests on the harvest work proceeding and the children's teacher being granted leave.

First thing on Tuesday afternoon I could devote myself to working on my homework in respect of the forthcoming conference. These relate to my subjects for my lecture and the demonstration:

Local History: With the Fishermen in the Moosbruch
Geology: Ground Shapes Used in Sandpits
Singing: A Singing Hour
Preparation and Analysis of an Outing (Lecture)
Preparation for a Village Social Evening (Lecture)

By evening I had finished two demonstrations (Singing, and With the Fishermen). Then I thought, 'To heck with it, I'm going to bed,' but I got up at 4 a.m., finished the rest of the homework, wrote the necessary reports, packed my clothing and set off. I wanted to meet two colleagues in the early morning in Elchwerder. So I set off on thirty kilometres against the wind. The route was very pretty until Laukischken. I know it by heart and I was once before with Paula in Elchwerder. Before Laukischken, one travels through the woods until the harbour is reached, and then on the right is the Grossen Friedrichsgraben. Using the ferry twice, one arrives in Elchwerder which lies behind the Grossenmoosbruch on the Nemonienstrom in the territory of Memel deltas. Russ and Gilge are the two main junctions on which Memel itself lies. The entire district is protected from the sea by a high dyke, behind which lies the fertile Elchniederung with fat cattle in the meadows. Just think of Tilsker cheese! But in front of the dyke, lying one behind another on the harbour beach, are the villages of Elchwerder, Gilge, Tawe and Inse. Here in the high water in spring and autumn, the villages are cut off and isolated. It is especially bad in spring when the high water and the ice in the harbour blocks the estuaries. The water then becomes dammed up and overflows the banks.

It is an unending view here, nothing but meadows and hay. In between the river and countless drainage canals there is, here and there, a tree or a bush. There are also vast flocks of waterbirds such as storks, who have their nests on the reed-thatched roofs of the houses of the fisherfolk. The birds mass and strut together in the meadows.

The youngsters in the hotel, ready to take part in the conference, have a pleasant situation, for on three sides the water joins from the Nemonienfluss and from the direction of the Seckenburger canal (the latter a continuation of the Grossen Friedrichgrabens).

As I entered the conference place I wondered about the utter silence. I knocked at the door. No reply. And I wondered if the conference had taken place. When I called on the school official he had little information to give me and I wanted then to return home to Gertlauken. However, I met up with a colleague from Dortmund who is a teacher in Elchwerder. She is called Hanna Stiefermann and we had not met for one year. A lovely afternoon and evening followed and we went for a long walk during which time the noise from the front line was heard like background music to the peacefulness of the evening and the countryside. Before that we had sought out the head teacher, whose wife led us through a garden like paradise – gooseberries, strawberries, redcurrants, raspberries and all kinds of fruit trees, including a peach tree. I was thrilled, as we were allowed to eat redcurrants from a bush and also fill a bag with them to eat on our way.

Elchwerder is a fishing village, its houses being constructed of wood with fieldstone base, and small huts serve as barns. Each dwelling backs onto the river and behind each one is a small stretch of land containing a number of boats. The broad Kekel boats are found everywhere here with their cut-out coloured flag on the mast. It all smells of fish. At the present moment eels, perch and *Plötze* are caught. On the mudflats thrive potatoes, carrots and onions, but most of all onions. The vegetable beds are exceptionally long and intersected throughout by drainage canals.

In Elchwerder I am always reminded of my cycle ride with Paula. We went through the Grosse Moosbruch to the Grossbaumerwald and I can never forget the spicy scents of the woods at night. Then on we went, straight as an arrow, to Timerberkanal and from Erle and its flooded ditches, full of dark water. Sometimes a boat came by and then further on we went to the village of Mauschern just lying in the sun. And everywhere quietness repeatedly. Of course the Moosbruch was encountered with its flesh-eating plants.

But back now to Elchwerder and Hanna. She gets on well with its people but still has not got the two promised trainee teachers. In the evening she produced a small fish meal and that greatly impressed us before, just after midnight, we went to sleep. It smelled of onions in her room and in the stillness of the night one heard quite clearly the noise from the front.

At 4 a.m. we got up as Hanna had to go to Labiau and the best method of transport is the steamer, which leaves at 5.30 a.m. and returns at 3 p.m. At first I wanted to travel with her but then thought of the lovely cycle tour over Hohenbruch (formerly Lauknen) to Liebenfelde (formerly Mehlauken), all in all about 28 kilometres. From there I would catch the train to Mauern. But from Liebenfelde cycles were no longer transported on the trains, so yet again a thirty-kilometre ride and I am already quite whacked and feel limp all over like an old woman, especially in the oppressive heat. But I rested for the first time in Hotel Beuder Rast and sorted myself out before I embarked on the last part of the cycle ride. Apparently the conference did not take place because the school official and the other teachers were, at short notice, ordered to do fieldwork on the East Wall. Daily one sees men going eastwards. It is now believed that every man and every boy of fourteen years of age must go.

So now I have been recovering from my recent journey and my writing paper is running out, so it's listening to the radio for now. Yesterday Köln was mentioned in the Armed Forces Report.

Gertlauken 23 July 1944

My dear Parents

Have you received my letter from Liebenfelde safely? At 8.30 a.m. on Thursday I was again in Gertlauken after calling in to see Frau Schulz, and there heard on the radio about the attempt on the life of the Führer. That was a shock, but he should recover. It was certainly a wonder that he escaped with his life. I cannot comprehend it and we were speechless.

On the same evening information was given out about the evacuation of women from Berlin and Hamburg to Thuringen, the Sudeten district. It is to take place on Saturday and most of them will feel the parting terribly. They had a good life and now it is once more with bag and baggage into uncertainty. Many have fifteen or twenty pieces of baggage, their entire property. Those resident in Königsberg are at liberty to leave on the journey to the West but countless rumours are going about. One such is that the first places are reserved for the military who have to prepare defences, etc. In Labiau, Tapiau, Wehlau and so on all the schools are temporarily closed until December, as they are to be utilised as hospitals.

Yesterday and on Friday I cleaned my room, checked on my supplies, washed my clothes and early this morning ironed them. It is wonderful to have time to do everything and one is not harassed. Today I shall reply to the post lying around requiring an answer. You will be the first to receive an answer!

On Friday I went into the woods with Herr Beckmann in order to fetch my four metres of party wood. On account of the gnats I wore my training suit and a blouse with long sleeves. Christel also accompanied me and looked after the horses, and used a brand to frighten away the horseflies which torment the beasts dreadfully. I have loaded on half my wood and Herr Beckmann will also bring the wood for the school. I shall help him with it as his fifteen-year-old son has been sent to work with a shovel on the fieldworks on the Eastern Wall. It is quite understandable that Frau Beckmann worries terribly about him and we spoke about the possibility of me taking a basket of food items to him on my cycle.

In the evening Frau Kerwath brought a bowl of strawberries which she had picked herself and after such a long time we once again had a party and played cards. We were all in good voice except Frau Kippar who has not received news or a report about her husband for more than five weeks. Seemingly, his division has been decimated. She soon returned to her house. We others spent an hour with Frau Reiche and Frau Frank. They had to help themselves to the remainder of the strawberries in the bowl and we helped with their packing.

I'm sleeping at present at Frau Stachel's because – yes, but don't laugh – so many rumours abound about partisans being around, and as I am anxious, I moved in with her.

Königsberg 28 July 1944

My dear Parents
This morning I went to Königsberg with Frau Berkan and tomorrow we shall return to Gertlauken. The little one, Sigrid, must visit the ear

specialist, and I had a few purchases to take care of, one of which was to fetch the enclosed photographs that were taken on the Sunday before Whitsun when we were with the Neumanns. Have you had any post from Wolfgang?

From our village we can observe the Russian planes flying over Tilsit and Insterburg. Three nights ago they were over Tilsit and there a trainload of munitions was blown up. Yesterday for about one hour we saw parachute flares over Insterburg. So far in our village we have not been so illuminated. In addition, the anti-aircraft fire could be seen clearly.

Frau Berkan, Sigrid and I will take a small boat trip round the castle pond, as it is frightfully hot.

Gertlauken 1 August 1944

My dear Parents

I have just received a letter from Aunt Lies with the shattering news that Heinz Licht is dead, apparently dying of his wounds in a hospital in Posen. Uncle Hermann has nothing left to live for. Poor Uncle Hermann, he must be quite heart-broken.

Even the 2 o'clock news is to end, and no news at all about the Eastern Front in the Armed Forces News Report. We ask ourselves again and again, what will happen? I keep active. Nevertheless the uncertainty, above all the approach of the Russians, weighs heavily on all we do and think. Here the measures taken are being intensified and all the men here expect their call-up at any hour. No one is to be seen on the streets after 9 o'clock and the railways seem to be at a standstill. Frau Kippar, who has still not received any news of her husband, went to Königsberg today to see the wife of a comrade of her husband. She has just returned. The train was cancelled ten minutes before the time of its departure.

If I am not required to help in the village harvest I shall do some of my examination work, about which I am now unenthusiastic. The main area of work as it stands is a historical work in a rough draft. I shall send a carbon copy to Father shortly.

Gertlauken 5 August 1944

My dear Parents

This is to be but a short letter, an expression that you both should not worry about me. Within a week's time the lessons are to begin again, or not, depending upon whether one believes the rumours. On Thursday I was in Labiau to establish the facts regarding the school, but no one there could give me any information.

Should it happened that there are to be three months without lessons I would like to establish whether I might be permitted to come to Köln. In Labiau I saw the movement of those persons from Memel and Tilsit, who came on a steamer across the lagoon. There are many soldiers with military vehicles from the East who are regrouping in a large area.

The Armed Forces Reports of the last two days have been favourable but soldiers from the Eastern Front come with dreadful reports and the fear here daily is about the Russians.

From our village today twenty-five older men have again gone away and their wives must get in the harvest alone with the aid of the Italian prisoners of war. Herr von Cohs has also gone and his wife who is expecting their child in two months' time went off yesterday to her parents in Germany. Frau Kerwath accompanied her as far as Berlin and the train journey must have been terrible. A woman from Essen spent four days travelling here. The railway traffic is now quite irregular, besides which it is almost impossible to obtain a travel permit. Without the permission of the school official I cannot travel and as there is no deputy school official either, I must perforce wait. A short time ago it was announced that it is to be regarded as desertion if one travels without security permission.

I received a brief letter from Wolfgang yesterday, and tomorrow Frau Kippar has her birthday. Frau Stachel and I will celebrate it with her.

Gertlauken 11 August 1944

My dear Parents

I shall write to Father about his request for me to put down the expenses of my last journey. That is because he wanted to give his poor daughter a helping hand out of his fatherly concern for her. The second-class ticket costs quite a lot, from Gertlauken to Köln return, 160 marks. A month's wages! No more needs to be said about it, besides which, Father, thank you for helping with regard to Fritz. The names of two in respect of the Marriage Approval Certificate Guarantees. These documents I received with many thanks.

In today's Prussian newspaper there was a report about the proceedings regarding the assassination attempt on 20 July. What will happen to their families? Does one punish the wives and children also?

I think constantly about Heinz Licht. I cannot believe his death actually happened. Always I see before me Heinz, Father and I on the Osnabrück Railway Station. He was full of hope and loved his young wife so very much. Poor Uncle Hermann, his only child!

For three days now we have had to accommodate those from Heidekrug and Memel. The population of the rural and town areas have had to vacate those places at once. In horse and carts they arrived here and in No. 3 Teacher's Room is quartered a woman with three children from one of the towns vacated. The first evacuees were so pleased to be in Gertlauken that they contributed 360 marks and gave the sum to the mayor to aid the efforts of the NSV. They were Lithuanians, mostly a good class of people, tall, slim, fair men in German uniform, border guards who had obtained leave to bring their families to safety.

Frau Stachel received the news yesterday that her brother-in-law has been killed on the Eastern Front, so she went off at once with her children to her sister in Wehlau.

There are scarcely any men left in our village. All aged between fifteen and sixty years of age have gone.

I have bought six pounds of honey. I could have purchased more if I had bottles. The school is still supposed to begin on 16 August.

Gertlauken 22 August 1944

My dear Parents

Please do not be angry because I have written so little, but have no worries, you can be sure that all is well with me. It would take more than this to finish me off.

Yesterday I had my suspicions confirmed, for parts of the SS Divisions, Hitler Youth and the Leibstandarte Adolf Hitler were in danger of being encircled in the Western Front.

For Bucker's sorrow I cannot find words. Now she has lost her third son and I had grown up with Theo, Frans and Hans, but the latter was almost like a brother to me. On his journey to the Eastern Front he wrote me a brief greetings card with his new Field Post number. He wrote that he had nearly called in the village to see me but the time did not allow it. I wrote to him in reply at once and received my letter back. He must have been killed in his first action or he was murdered by the partisans.

Kinni asked me for the negatives of the photos that I took at Christmas of herself and Hans in the doorway of our house and I have sent them. I've enclosed a copy for the Buckers also and I shall write to Frau Bucker. It will be a difficult letter for me to try, for what else is there to say?

Gertlauken 8 September 1944

My dear Parents
The first happy news you have given me is that you have received a letter from Wolfgang on 3 August. I had not heard anything from him since 24 July. At that time he was in position near Caen, Normandy. Where is he stationed now? My worries about you grow even worse. Hopefully the front won't come near you. But we still have the West Wall.

Here the excitement has abated. For weeks now the enemy has not advanced. After the large air attack on Königsberg, ashes rained on us here the next day as the wind direction blew ashes and burnt pieces of paper sixty kilometres further on from us!

We live again in peacefulness. Those from the Memelands and Heidekruger can tomorrow return again to their homelands. A rumour is going the rounds that we are getting 500 soldiers coming to Gertlauken, but according to the forestry official barely ten men of the forestry guard are coming. They are to be quartered in the No. 3 classroom. The nursery school will then be closed. In any case, three to four children come there daily. One recounts the most adventurous stories and tales now.

For a few weeks now at evening time or twilight or in the darkness, there appear mysterious men in the vicinity of this or that farm, or on the outskirts of the village. These persons are said to be looking out for something to eat and all of them speak good German. Some allow themselves to be given food but others take what they can, pigs, sheep or fowl. The forestry official has lost fourteen hens and ten geese, all taken by stealth, up until today. Only the dogs have barked a warning. Each forestry area has had such a visit by these persons. Most of the people live happily on their own in the forest area and to date no harm has come to them physically.

Frau von Cohs and Frau Kerwath came back from the West at the beginning of the week, even Herr von Cohs has returned from his shovelling duties in the East. The men were employed on the East Wall for a period of three to four weeks. We have had no alarms here in the area but with you it must be terrible. For in addition to the raids you must still work ten hours daily. How terrible are the terror bombers. It is simply murder, hitting peaceful people in the fields.

On 18 September we are having a harvest holiday. I would like to come home for the party, the birthdays and the silver wedding anniversary, but the latter is not an acceptable reason for travelling. I cannot even manage to visit Fritz in Neustettin. Despite that I shall see what I can manage to do.

Paula wrote from Bartenstein. It does not please her a bit being there, and in the main school there are one sixty-one-year-old teacher and a forty-year-old teacher. Paula's bed and board are bad and her accommodation not to her liking, for she so feels the cold in winter. I am happy that I am warm here in Gertlauken and wish only I could, just once, come and fetch you here.

Gertlauken 29 September 1944

Dear Father

Unfortunately my birthday greetings card reached you too late but despite that I think often of you also when you think of me angrily. From Mother I heard that you are to go to the West Wall and work on the fortifications, also that Wolfgang called from Euskirchen. He wrote that he was quite sorry that he had not seen you. For fourteen days he was stationed in Herrenstruden quite near his old Stinklochs of the young people's time with Karl Schuller. What sort of memories must he have had there? I always tend to think now of the lovely peacetime.

Where may you be stationed? And how goes it with your health? How are you looked after? The men working on the East Wall sleep on straw in barns and have daily air attacks and almost constant alarms. Always there are more towns mentioned in the Armed Forces Report, always more destroyed. Poor Germany.

In comparison to that way of life, my own here is almost sinful, but it doesn't help to reproach myself for I am happy, despite the loss of a holiday with you. I have never spent a summer in such a worthless way than I have this one. But what else is there for us to do but to wait?

At the end of the previous week we heard that all the Königsberg people must leave and be transported to Saxony. The women of Königsberg are becoming angry at being in our primitive villages and think it best not to leave at all. Here there are undisturbed nights and sufficient food. What more can one want, especially when one has children.

For two hours yesterday I helped our Königsberg folk to pack. Their furniture items such as they have and can't be stored in Königsberg must stay here, only bedding may be taken. Their entire property consisting of clothes, washing items and household goods required packing and binding up in cases, sacks and tubs. I wrote out sixty name tags to stick on or to hang on such items.

And this morning, with bag and baggage and children, they set off into the unknown. It was so sorrowful to see such a departure. Who knows whether we may also have to make such a departure, because one must take into account the strong attacks of the Russians.

Also helping with the packing were two forestry guards who are quartered in one of our school classrooms. One was small and fat, the other light of build, tall and gaunt. The tall one is more sympathetic in his tone and speech. He comes from Detmold district and also knows Bartrup. We had a nice long chat about Detmold and its surroundings, about the mountains and woods of the Hermann and the Exterstine, while we were packing.

Because Frau Berkan was helping with the transporting of the Königsberg people, she asked two soldiers if her children Sigrid and Henning could eat with them. They agreed immediately and after the meal Sigrid said to one of the soldiers, 'Henning must have a sleep now and you must look after him.' That he did and put both children to bed after the meal and also took them home again.

Naturally the wives wash, darn and mend for the soldiers and also bake the cakes. The soldiers, on other occasions, reciprocate with vegetables or, such as this morning, with fish, pike and perch that they caught in the River Nehne. We are sorry that they leave us tomorrow. They were assigned to the forestry district and farm holdings.

Now in the holidays I have so much time to myself and above all am aware every passing day that I am allowed to stay here in peace. Often of an evening we make music in the house and Frau Kippar likes to sing the ballads of Loewe, her best piece is '*Die Uhr*'. Frau Stachel accompanies her on the violin. I have learnt from them both all *Lonslieder*, such cheerful, cheeky songs and so full of longing. It makes for such a lovely picture when the two pretty young wives make music together. Also I read a lot during the sunny autumn days when I sit in the Stachel's garden at the rear of the toilet. And when the sun goes down over the woods, the meadows touched with twilight, I close my book and listen to the last sounds of the day. The birds go silent, here and there a cow moos and stillness lies over the land. Perhaps a deceptive peace?

> *Ein Traum, ein Traum ist unser Leben*
> *Auf Erden hier*
> *Wie Schatten auf den Wogen schweben*
> *Und schwinden wir . . .*

(Words from our East Prussian shepherd.)

Gertlauken 7 October 1944

My dear Parents

When I returned from Paula in Bartenstein I found your long letter awaiting me about the attacks you had on Köln on 27 September and 4 October – and that you survived, borders on a miracle.

I choked when I had Father's report on his 'shovelling action' in the West. I visualised each old man from the Tax and Finance Department waiting for two hours under the German railway direction. That must have been hard on your legs and then to be taken to the Dombunker to listen to the speech of the district leader Schaller. Then after that the marching of the last call-up to the station with music '*Muss i denn, Muss i denn, zim Stadtele hinaus*', and entrained in a cattle wagon. Then your stay in the Erkelenz district in the emergency quarters on straw, in cowsheds and no warm food. On top of that, four days of hanging around because no spades were available. I was quite disgusted about it, especially about the SA people with revolvers supervising you. That is just like Siberia! You should report to the doctor about your thrombosis in both legs, as the marching and the labour tasks are dangerous to your health. For three weeks you were kept there and now you lie at home with ointment and bandages.

From me there is nothing to report until the school begins again. When Frau Kippar and I returned from a brief end of the holiday walk in the woods we met soldiers seeking quarters in the village.

And on your silver wedding anniversary day, Wolfgang and I always had you in our warmest thoughts.

Gertlauken 14 October 1944

My dear Parents

I have not received any news from you and I am really worried. Surely the post will not have been destroyed? Even from Wolfgang I have heard nothing. Oh, if only one could ring up. Fritz has written that perhaps he may be able to visit me, that would be so nice, but we are all waiting for the post so as to be able to comfort each other.

In the evenings we all gather together and have a small party. Frau Stachel, Frau Kippar and Frau Kerwath, all three have no idea as to where their husbands are. Also Frau von Cohs' husband is again working with his spade on the Eastern Wall. She is expecting her baby at any moment. When she comes of an evening, every day, on her cycle, and leaves at 11 o'clock or 11.30, again on her cycle, to ride alone back to her lonely forestry house on the edge of the woods, we often joke when playing cards about the possibility of her having the baby on the way home.

The lessons have begun again but with regard to the older boys, they must either help out at home or find themselves working with spades on the East Wall. The smaller children in their happy uninhibited way are a delight and steer one's thoughts away from the dire happenings of the hour. Also my bigger girls give me so much happiness. At the beginning of the week the new school official rang about his proposed visit here on Thursday. Because of that I asked for a volunteer helper on Wednesday to help clean the classrooms. All the bigger girls from Classes 7 and 8 school years came with buckets, cloths and aprons. So with plenty of floorcloths and water we have cleaned floors, benches and windows. During these chores we chatted and laughed so much that the hours flashed by in an instant. Afterwards there was fruit juice and cakes as a suitable reward.

The new school official is a friendly, reserved man and sat with me during both a German and natural-history lesson, without any interruptions. He sat on a bench at the back and examined my class book entries and found them in order and had no complaints. During our meeting he mentioned how interested the children were in their lessons and had obviously worked hard at them. He discussed the children at length and then came the nicest part. He praised the cleanliness of the classrooms. With his fingers running over the shelves and under the desks, he found no paper, no old pieces of bread and no dust, and then said that in his opinion it was rare to find such cleanliness.

Our No. 3 classroom, formerly the kindergarten, has become the 'rest room'. There the soldiers, all very pleasant and quiet men, draw and write, just as in civil life anywhere.

Something very tragic has occurred in our village. I wrote and told you about the stationing of the forestry guard here, because of the isolated nature of the foresters' work. One night recently one of the farmers went out to check on his cattle, uneasy in their stalls, when he was shot by a forestry guard who took him to be an intruder.

Gertlauken 21 October 1944

My dear Parents

Another huge air attack on Köln and I have heard nothing from you. I am so anxious and feel for certain that the post has been burned. Please give me news at once. Best of all, double it so that I can at least get one letter. I haven't had any news about Osnabrück for there the Americans have been very active in their air attacks. Eventually I received a letter from Wolfgang and you will scarcely believe it, he is stationed in Osnabrück. His company is to be made up to strength, for it was almost decimated. He writes quite lively and will see what he can do to find out how things are going with Aunt Lies and Uncle Hermann.

Fritz arrived here at the beginning of the week and it is lovely to have him here as he came so unexpectedly on Monday.

This Monday Frau Stachel, Frau Kippar and I had planned something nice. I have told you previously about the Ratsstube and the Raten, who are very cultured and musical people. Recently one of them asked Frau Stachel if he might, for one occasion, play her violin. Then an idea came to me that we should get up a musical evening and it was to be on Monday.

At first Frau Stachel would accompany Frau Kippar, who has a wonderful voice, singing Brahms and Loewe *Liedern* [songs]. After that the soldiers would play Chopin. In Frau Stachel's living room we placed lots of stools and lit as many candles as we could find. The warm room with its tiled stove was almost in half-light and the guests came in.

Later, there was a ring, and I went to the door and there stood Fritz with a beaming face. He also took part in our concert and it was a moving, beautiful evening. I am not musical and Fritz, I believe, is not especially musical, but it was an unbelievably wonderful atmosphere. The world was shut out and at the close, one of the soldiers played a piece by Ravel, after which no one spoke for a long time.

Gertlauken 26 October 1944

My dear, dear Parents

At last, news from you. I did not receive your card but still the detailed letter of 16 October came today and you are alive, that is the main thing. Now our living block has suffered and the neighbour's house knocked down as far as the first storey and all the interior has collapsed. Who also was dead as well as Heinze? It was so lucky that Gunter and Arno were at home and could help put out the fire. The water from the Rhein was used to quell the fire, and all around bright, burning fires, and carpets of bombs on the Siegburger Strasse. And then the day once again further bomber raids with one carpet of bombs after another. Craters close together, one huge expanse of rubble, burning cars and trams, defective high towering rail tracks, no light, no water, dust and chaos. Please, why stay in Köln? Pack your things and go to Aunt Minchen in Spenge.

I can scarcely write any more because I am so agitated about your plight, and it is so helpful for me to have Fritz still here with me. Please go away from Köln and Fritz is also of that opinion.

Your news is shattering. What have you had to go through! How good it is to know that you are at present with Aunt Minchen in Spenge. But why has Father gone back to Köln? Nothing remains there and he is living with the Schunemanns in the cellar in Merheim. There is nothing there to eat and Father is so awkward. How can he cope?

My dear Mother, I can understand that you have come to the end of your tether. You must therefore reckon on our house as no longer existing. For three weeks you have continually been in an air-raid shelter, no sign of life, no water and no light. Father too must be exhausted by it all and then this terrible journey to Spenge taking thirty hours in rain and snow, weighed down with cases and hand bags, getting on and off transport eight times and always the fear of low-flying attacks by the enemy planes. But now, dear, dear Mother, don't brood on what is lost. You are alive and all the rest we can endure.

In any case you must now recover and please don't have any worries about me. We have a permanent accommodation system in the village and also a constantly changing one. Frau Kippar has now people from the TODT organisation billeted in her house. Frau Stachel's husband has found himself on the Bodensee and Frau Kippar has not heard from her husband since the summer and is quite often in despair. Also Frau Kerwath does not know the present location of her husband. Herr von Cohs is back from his spadework on the Eastern Wall and his wife has had a small baby girl, and I shall be godmother to it.

Fritz is again in Gross-Born in Pommern. He took with him a large case of clothing from Frau Stachel to deliver to relatives living in Schneidemuhl. Herr Beckmann took us in his horse and cart to Mauern and then on to Laukischken because there was no train. It was a lovely sunny autumn day and the roads were full of armed-forces vehicles. Fritz eventually got a lift in one of them, so we returned to the village.

For some time now the German House in Laukischken has been used as a hospital and for the past three weeks I've travelled there to work in the kitchen. I work for two afternoons per week. Frau Schulz is greatly worried about her husband but her children thrive splendidly.

My dear Mother and dear Father (in case you are in Spenge)
I don't know if you received my Christmas letter but I take it that
Father is spending the Christmas holiday with you. It is so good to
know you have managed to get some space. Naturally it is difficult
no longer being the owner of your own house and to be at the
mercy of relatives, but you are so brave and efficient. I can well
imagine you with your talent for needlework, being most acceptable
in any home in which you find yourself. Almost magically you can
turn a piece of cloth into a child's coat.

Certainly the nights are bad and the thoughts one has about so
many things. If only we know something about Wolfgang. Fritz is
still in Gross-Born and I would actually like to travel at Christmas
to see him, but we are not allowed to leave our place of duty,
otherwise we'd be considered deserters.

I told you about the wonderful baptism ceremony with the
family von Cohs in my last letter but I never know if sometimes
I never receive a letter you have sent to me or some of mine fail
to reach you. Therefore I shall mention the baptism once again. I
often think of that particular day I liked so much and my lovely
small godchild, Franka. She is so sweet and was so bravely well
behaved in church. The baptism took place on 10 December in
Laukischken. With regard to the questions of the minister to me as
I held the small infant, I was quite, quite dim. It was the first time
for me to know about the obligations of a godparent. It was my
first godchild and my heart was full of the best intentions and the
desire to undertake my tasks in an earnest manner.

Frau von Cohs was a radiantly beautiful mother and her two sons
were present. The eldest is Wolfgang in Class 1 school year, the
second Eberhard will come to school next year. Both boys romped
about quite excitedly among the many people attending, most of
whom were quiet forestry folk. The von Cohs have six cows in their
stalls and a large poultry yard that belonged at one time to another
forestry official. So you can imagine what there was available to eat
and drink, just like as in the real peacetime. The relatives of Frau
von Cohs from Mosel could not attend, but from his side of the
family quite a few were present, besides the neighbours and the other
forestry workers. For the day of the baptism, a Sunday, the mother

and child had the pleasure and benefit of a car. The others came in their carts.

At Christmas we shall roast a goose and each person in the village has invited soldiers to attend. To Frau Stachel and myself will come a major from Saxony and a lieutenant from Schlesien. The latter has expressed a wish for potato dumplings. Every day he studies the maps very carefully to note the position of the front line. He is fearful about his family, and his youngest child is still a baby. I have learnt much about the ways of men since the military personnel have been billeted here. It is most interesting and constructive what one can learn in their company. Almost all the soldiers quartered at times with Frau Kippar fall in love with her. One, from Wien, sang to her in verses. Another told her yearning fairy stories. Many become quite impassioned and effusive. A sign of the times we live in, I suppose.

On some fantastic situation or another, or because of something we've read, Frau Stachel and I burst out in merriment. Besides, you can scarcely imagine your daughter, every morning in the half-light, still unwashed, wrapped in warm gear, and in wooden clogs, getting hold of a petrol lamp and feeding the geese in their stall.

Gertlauken 17 January 1945

My dear Mother

I am writing to Spenge and hope that Father is there also. Since 14 December I haven't had any more news and the greatest happiness was getting post from Wolfgang on 16 and 25 December. He was deeply involved in the mess in the Ardennes offensive. On 25 December with a stub of a pencil and by candlelight he wrote to me.

As I have already written, our Christmas party went off in an unbelievably happy way. I shall never forget the picture of Frau Stachel with Helma and Peter on Christmas Eve before the Christmas tree. She had her arms looped round the children, the tiled stove sent out its warmth, the Christmas tree lights glowed and sparkled in the candlelight and it was so peaceful with the four of us. The huge meal on the first day of Christmas ended on a bad note. Our lieutenant even had a bad stomach ache because he had eaten so much.

Yesterday I helped the evacuee lady from the third teacher's quarters to pack her cases. Mothers and children are to be allowed to go to Central Germany. Frau Stachel, Frau von Cohs, Frau Berkan and Frau Kerwath did not want to come with us and none of their relatives were travelling either. Our evacuee lady took it all in her stride as she had already had to give up her previous house in the Elchniederung district. The other evacuee lady did not want to travel with us and had already obtained a horse and cart, and gone off and left the rest in the lurch. But the Polish man helper took us directly to Mauern after the lessons. I was literally amazed at the station, for the carriages were warm and clean, and there were coaches for mothers and children, and Sisters of Mercy helped the embarking on the train, that was half empty.

'If the soldiers at the front can't hold, then we, as a party, will do so,' as the area leader Koch recently intoned. We find his talk ridiculous. Is the position so serious as he said, that special trains for the evacuation are arranged and then leave half empty, because the population has not been informed? This train, in any case, is on its peaceful way.

When I returned to the village Frau Stachel was sitting in front of the kitchen window in the twilight and Frau Kippar was standing near her. 'No, one cannot just leave home with two cases and travel into the unknown,' said Frau Stachel. Frau Berkan, who comes from Hamburg, was unable to come to a decision. I myself have no choice, neither has Frau Kippar. I could not simply leave my friends and the children.

Now, don't have any worries about me, dear Mother. If it should become very serious, we shall be informed very early and in good time.

Penig in Sachsen 27 January 1945

My dear Mother

I hope this letter reaches you very soon, because you must have been very worried about the Armed Forces Reports of the last few weeks. Over eight days ago I wrote to you from Gertlauken and I could not imagine what was going to happen from one day to another.

Friday 19 January began as any other day. After school finished I went to a meal with the Beckmanns. I still had the afternoon lesson to do and as I came back the young Frau Strupat stood in the schoolroom quite distraught. 'Have you heard yet?' she said. 'We should prepare ourselves to be ready for the notice to pack and leave.'

I could not believe it and accepted it as a rumour. So I cycled at once to the Forestry Office Department in Liedtkes from where the district leader's message had come, and found it to be correct. I couldn't contact the school official and rushed quickly to Frau Beckmann to give her the terrible news. She went as white as a sheet and it seemed as if she would faint and was speechless. On the way I met an agitated mother about to fetch her children from school.

I then handed the children their savings books and sent them all home. After that I went to Erika Stachel who was very quiet. In a short time all the rooms were completely changed. We first packed a box with all the good crockery, then rolled up three sets of bedding in the dining-room carpet – a large, unshapely bundle it made. Two large cases were filled with clothing and a small case packed with important papers. We stuffed shoes in a sack and washing on top of them, then in a bag were placed foodstuffs. We did not know how much we were to take – perhaps we would be limited to hand luggage only. As far as the most important item went – news of what was to happen – we knew nothing. Especially how we were to get away. We waited and hoped something positive would happen, but nothing did we see nor hear. We were all left to our own devices and rumours abounded. The talk was all of the Russian breakthrough.

It became evening, it became night-time, and we waited always for information, but still it did not come, and long empty hours passed. We could not sleep and it was very cold. The land covered in snow, the sky clear and starlight, the wide, vast East Prussian sky where in the East the horizon was red. We heard, alarmingly clear, the noise from the front and in the morning, unbroken long lines of horses and wagons trailing through the village. The French prisoner of war helped with the loading, tightened the saddlery and led them off.

I went once again to the Beckmanns and there too was a jumble of confusion ready for departure. Herr Beckmann was not in the house and the old, loving grandmother gave all instructions. Horses and wagons stood ready. They had recently slaughtered the necessary foodstuffs to be taken and bedding, clothing and cooking items all prepared for transportation.

On the way back to the school the snow crackled beneath my

feet. A sledge came towards me with Herr von Cohs seated on it. With a quick wink he said, '*Auf Wiedersehen*. See you in Heaven!' He had had to go back and be with the *Volkssturm* [German people's levy – armed forces]. The forestry people had tractors and trailers and with them travelled Frau von Cohs with her children. They left about 3 o'clock in the direction of Königsberg where her elderly in-laws lived.

The military came through the village and went in a different direction. A general who rested overnight in the schoolhouse wanted to take Erika Stachel and her children with them, as they, the military, left – but, naturally, without baggage. We stayed and waited and it was 4 a.m., in the morning. Like most people in the village, we were helpless.

At daybreak, further soldiers came through the village, and the sound of the shooting from the front line became louder. The sky over Kruzingen was coloured red. A couple of coaches of the TODT organisation halted in the school grounds, obviously no firm instructions were given out. I spoke with an officer and he was ready to take us in his bus to the railway station at Labiau. On the top of the bus was a luggage rack and the driver, a friendly Frenchman, piled our cases, the carpet containing the rolled bedding and my accordion on the rack. Eventually, my cycle was thrown on the top.

When the people heard about the transport, the women came with their children and baggage, and stormed the two coaches. Close to me sat Frau Stachel and Frau Kippar. Those who remained behind were told that two transports would come for them. The transport later returned but whether other transport managed to return I do not know. It was all an indescribable confusion on the streets.

Our coach went at midday on Saturday 20 January and we travelled over frozen fields because all the roads were blocked by predominantly army vehicles. The wagons of the evacuees built up in a congested flow and attempted to pull themselves across the fields. Along the entire way there were ownerless wagons with luggage strewn around, unattended cattle, and people searching for each other. Many attempted to mend their broken wagon shafts themselves. Frau Berkan was there with the cart with our evacuee lady from Elchniederung and their Polish man, and overtook us on the trek from Gertlauken. Christel Beckmann winked at me.

After a rough journey with a broken window we arrived at Labiau station, where we were set down. One saw thereabouts, evacuees, carts, luggage, ownerless possessions, and horses wandering about. The people of Labiau were surprised at it all. Since there was no train, the evacuees were taken to makeshift shelters in schools, churches and private houses. Frau Stachel stayed in the church with her children, and Frau Kippar and I stayed on the station with our things. We wandered up and down, above us the star-studded sky and it was bitterly, penetratingly, cold – minus twenty degrees.

Finally we spent three hours with acquaintances of Frau Kippar, who we had roused from their sleep by our ringing. What we reported to them they found inconceivable and they thought we were exaggerating things. At least we were able to rest together on a sofa for a few hours.

At 8 a.m. we were again on the station exactly as two goods wagons rolled in. We quickly packed our baggage in one wagon and informed Frau Stachel. Soon all the people streamed to the station, because the news of the arrival of the wagons had soon got about. Frau Kerwath came with her children and we all stayed together and sought our seats. Then further wagons were attached and finally, to our great, lasting relief, a locomotive came. The people pushed themselves forward and everything was filled to breaking point, and many had to stand in open wagons.

About fifty persons were packed in our wagon. There was no room to sit and I was glad to stand with Frau Kippar at the open door, through which cold air blew. The air in the carriage was unbearable. After several hours the train set off in motion, with often long halts before we came to Königsberg. Frau von Cohs had heard that an evacuee lady would meet the evacuees from Labiau and she was on the station to meet us. She had her dachshund in her arms and told us that all was quiet in Königsberg, and no one had thought of fleeing. She was very sad that her children were not with her. Instead they would be travelling with us.

In the evening we arrived in Marienburg where we were switched to a siding where we waited the entire night. With Frau Kippar I crossed the railway tracks to the station waiting room where hundreds of evacuees pushed and jostled there. The Red Cross people had their hands full supplying hot drinks and slices of bread. I became afraid as I saw that these people were all South

East Prussians who had had to leave their homes. Many women were dressed only in nightdresses with a coat over them. Children there had school satchels on their backs. Retreating soldiers had warned them, 'Make sure you get away. The Russians are only a few kilometres distant.' Rumours ran riot. 'The Russians had already reached the railway line at Konitz,' 'The Weichselrucke [bridge] was blown up,' and so on.

With hot coffee and a carton of bread and butter we returned to our wagon. Nervousness and fearfulness were everywhere. Had we been forgotten? Would we reach the west bank of the Weichsel river? We waited and finally after seven hours, release of the tension – our train at long last got moving. We travelled over the Weichsel Bridge during the night of Sunday and Monday. On Thursday we arrived in Penig. Always I saw again people in open wagons, mothers desperately trying to get milk for their small children. A few children had died from frostbite or weakness.

Dear Mother, I have got through everything and survived. You need not have any worries about me. We have been brought to this school and soon hope to be accommodated in private houses. I hope all goes well with you. Is Father still in Köln? The Americans are still on the other side of the Rhein. I think about Wolfgang always. When you next receive news from him, please write to me at once.

THE HOMECOMING
Diary
January–June 1945

I am sitting in a classroom in the school at Penig. All along the walls straw is spread, sleeping places for over thirty persons. An hour ago I walked over the white snow-covered school playground to visit Frau Stachel in her new private quarters. She has a large, spacious room, the cases lay opened on the floor and clothes hanging on the door. The unknown future, the worry about her relatives, and the look of utter loneliness in her gaze.

With Frau Kippar I went a little way down the street. Each now is alone. At 8 a.m. this morning I was in the gymnasium and helped the sports teachers get their baggage lying there in order. Sacks, buckets, boxes and cases. What else may have been lost? On the way a wagon was overturned.

My eyes burn from tiredness. I have become accustomed to the straw bed, so that I shall sleep quite well there. But tomorrow there will be something else to be worried about.

30 January 1945

After my breakfast a room was allotted to me at No. 3 Schillerstrasse with Frau Werner. With Frau Kippar I went there at once in order to look at it. It is a lovely room. Together with Frau Stachel and her children we went to a barn where a lot of baggage lay, and after just one search we found our things. We helped Frau Stachel move them into her room and saw it to be so much more comfortable with carpet and the lovely embroidered table coverings. Together we then went to Christel Kippar and her small room is now looking quite homely. We were quiet when we thought of the beautiful home she had lost. It is a pity that we are now living so apart from each other, each in our own part of the town.

I went back alone through the wintry town and in the snow was heard only the rustling of the leaves. On the other side of the River Mulde the town layout before me. Terraces standing upon each other and houses all pressed up against each other. All the roofs and the trees white and the waters of the Mulde gurgled a quiet song. Other than that it was quite still everywhere.

Now I am lying in my bed, full of food and at last freshly washed and feel myself to be newly born. Only the frost in my toes to complain about. During the evacuation I wore my boots for seven unbroken days and nights, and in Penig, because of the snow, they are always soaked through. But tomorrow I can look for other shoes.

5 February 1945

Outside it has become most uncomfortable, windy, wet and splashy. Fine rain drives into one's face. The Mulde river has awakened now with the melting snow, the water powers over the weir with a roaring sound. I end the day mostly with a solitary walk through the town at night. Sometimes there is a small light on in the windows. I think of Gertlauken where the sky above me was everywhere.

I can't write to anybody any more. All connections have been broken. In the West the Americans are again going quickly forward and the enemy planes control the air and land. And in the East the Russians storm onwards. East Prussia, Schlesien, all have been lost. The Armed Forces Report mentions already Küstrin on the River Oder and battles about Schneidemuhl.

How is it going with Fritz? Whether Father is again in Köln? I hear from no one any more. The inevitable alarms me and I live my life as if through a veil. We have nothing to do. When possible we go to the cinema in order to lessen the time and to displace the reality of our situation. One hears nothing but terrible reports.

Frequently now we have air-raid alarms. Yesterday a huge attack on Chemnitz. It must have been very bad. The towns here are full of evacuees. Women from Penig have lived through it and came back on foot, muddy and exhausted. The railway lines have been destroyed.

16 February 1945

For two days I was in Leipzig to look up acquaintances who were quartered with us in Gertlauken, with many greetings from Frau and Frau Kippar! I wandered through the dark, half-destroyed town and found the dwelling place of Family B where I was allowed to stay overnight. I was so tired that during the night I took no notice of the air-raid alarm. There was nothing I could find out in the way of experience. All relationships have disintegrated. No one knows where the men or the sons are to be found. I visited the People's War Memorial, a massive building 91 metres high with a large, clear view of the town and its entire surroundings. Unfortunately I was disturbed by an air raid so that for over two hours I had to stay on a small spiral staircase between walls of granite six metres thick. My hands and feet were frozen.

Few trains are running and there is always the difficulty with getting on one and endless waiting at railway stations. The next morning I was again in Penig and my one final wish was to sleep. Then I heard of the terrible things that had occurred in Dresden.

20 February 1945

Mother has written. Her letter has actually got through. I am so happy that I can hardly express it. She is still in Spenge with Aunt Minchen, and Father is still in Köln. From Wolfgang she has heard nothing.

27 February 1945

Today is Wolfgang's birthday. A year ago he was with me in Gertlauken, together with Fritz. On the Saturday evening we had a party with the Neumanns and on Sunday evening again invited to a party, and Paula's examination work typed. That was a year ago. And today? How will everything go? Almost every afternoon I spend with Frau Stachel. I love my homecoming in the evening through the still, quiet town and beneath it all there is the rustling of the River Mulde and the waterfall to listen to.

2 March 1945

Yesterday was a difficult day for Penig. For the first time bombs fell in the town. A great deal of damage was done and much destroyed, with about thirty people dead. I went straight away to. Christel Kippar who sewed and cleaned my shoes. As soon as the first wave of bombers had gone, there was a roaring overhead with the planes' engines making a different sound, and that to Christel meant another wave of bombers were overhead. Already there were crashing and roaring sounds and we ran to the cellar. I ran without socks and still held my shoes in my hand.

It was a shock to Penig and brought much sorrow to its people who up until now have felt secure. This morning we again had an alarm but no bombs fell. Outside it is raining and snowing and the wind howls.

Last week saw the beginning of springtime and the birds sang.

6 March 1945

We now have air raids daily, mornings, midday and evenings, and sometimes at night. It is a case of running to the cellar and back again. I do feel so sorry for the children. At 5 a.m. Frau Werner woke me and we went to the police station and to the reception centre for the evacuees and those who have been bombed out. We helped with the provisions and worked for hours on end. Our sympathy was aroused by all the people around us whose faces are full of sorrow and uncertainty. The whole of Germany is on its last legs, the homeless scattered in every direction under heaven. Frau Stachel's parents arrived and her sister with the small Uta [child]. We are all very happy for the moment.

For two days now I have been giving lessons in the Penig school. I've got the fourth school year boys and girls from all parts of Germany – forty-nine children in all. In addition the third school year with boys from Penig – a very unruly class. The lesson is for the moment about paper production, a period about the town of Leipzig, also classroom work.

4 April 1945

Yesterday I was in Chemnitz, but no train was to be had for the return journey, so I went on the *Autobahn* [highway], It was full of traffic with military vehicles going in both directions. I got a lift in a loaded wagon and suddenly there was an air-raid alarm and the roar of bombers in the immediate vicinity. We then saw the enemy planes flying above us in different directions.

Nearby was a small wood and I don't know how I managed to cross the fifteen metres between it and the road. The planes were ground-strafing and as I hugged the earth, foliage and earth sprang up. I pressed my face to the earth with my heart hammering. 'Soon, I must with Thee meet,' I thought.

After the raid was over I lifted my head and nearby on the Autobahn at a junction stood a line of five evacuee wagons. One wagon was burning and six horses were dead, and two so terribly wounded they had to be shot. One man was severely wounded and our goods truck had many bullet holes.

5 April 1945

I am so alone – my hand is so tired from writing. What will happen? Wolfgang is dead. Nothing more can I say. How empty I am inside. On the letter I wrote to him which was returned to me, it was marked *'Gefallen fur Gross Deutschland'* [Fallen for Great Germany]. My God, what a mockery it all is to me. Where? When? Did he suffer? Did Mother and Father know? They too must have received the similar news. Poor Mother! Also Frau Kippar has learnt that her eldest brother is dead, the second brother is dead already and she has not heard anything more about her husband.

Today I have become twenty-four years old. When the war began I was eighteen. A year ago, for the last time, I was together with Wolfgang. I can still not grasp that I shall never see him again.

Yesterday the Americans entered the town as we were all in the cellar. Here and there one heard shooting. The prisoners were set free at once, even the Russian and Polish skilled workers. Food shops, shoe and clothing shops were broken into and looted. I saw terrible things happen on the street. Finally it was forbidden by the Americans and we, Germans, have a curfew that allows us to be out on the street from 7 to 9 in the morning, and four to six in the afternoon.

Whit Sunday 20 May 1945

For a long time now I have not been able to write. The terrible happenings have paralysed me. The monstrous things done in the concentration camps, about which we heard, I wanted not to believe it, the horror of it all is beyond my imagination. Who could do such devilish things, or even think of doing them? I cannot fathom it out.

And still the horror reports from Böhmen. When the war finished on 8 May, the terrible things commenced. The delight in murdering an entire people. The murdering of innocent women and children. The evacuees were horrified to face it all. To me it was as if I had lived in a strange world. What here in the East, innocent people have experienced and witnessed will stay with me day and night.

The Americans have engaged Herr Rieder to act as interpreter and I am to be his secretary and our office is in the school. The role is to act as an advice centre for the evacuees, foreigners, announcements, food ration cards, etc. I am glad I have a task and not to have afterthoughts.

In order to fetch foodstuffs cards from Rochlitz, I have been given a special authorisation and a special identity certificate from the commandant. So I have some freedom of movement and I am able to cycle alone through the empty streets. It gives me the opportunity to make quite an original plan. I did not give the identity-card authorisation back. And nobody has asked for its return.

For two days now I have been at home once again. On 12 June I set off from Penig. Already for several days, the Russians had a security post on the bridge across the River Mulde. Then I heard that the Americans would arrive and the Russians would withdraw. I gave thought to everything – the streets appeared to be unsafe for travel and it was possible I would be placed in an Assembly Camp. But I had to get away, so I packed all the necessary things on my cycle and, early the next morning, I set off on my great journey.

I felt utterly free and by evening time I was in Leipzig. I went to the Beckerts who let me stay overnight. In Halle I could not find the house of the person to whom I was to give greetings from a person in Penig, who had given the Halle address to me. No houses were standing in the street in question. I spent the night in an air-raid shelter and early the next morning I set off again. Up until then all had gone well, the land was quiet and the streets empty. Only here and there the odd traffic passed. The sentry posts in the small towns were friendly when they heard my few words in broken English, 'I am going to see my aunt – will be back very soon.' All was then OK. Whenever I was asked for a pass, I produced my special pass from the commandant in Penig. It was an English form and a stamp. They were enough, nothing else was needed.

On the streets on the way to Aschers Leben stood rows of trees full of cherries and I really ate my fill of them. In a paper factory I entered I found a bed in the sickroom bay, and the doorkeeper there acquired some food for me. By the next afternoon I was in Quedlinburg and by evening in Bad Harzburg, where I sought the mother of Fräulein Heifer, the latter being a colleague of mine in Penig. She, the mother, was very pleased to have news of her daughter and I was made so welcome that I stayed there for two days and was able to get some sound sleep.

From Bad Harzburg I went on my way again and reached Hildesheim and rode through its wreckage in the direction of Hameln. In a village I was invited to a midday meal by a woman teacher. I received much ready help all along my journey. Along the River Weser I went, a journey lasting fifteen hours, through Rinteln. Now, Spenge was not too far distant and perhaps I could make it there by evening. With sheer pleasure I dashed along the *Autobahn* to Oeynhausen. The whole town must have been occupied for some time, for the English military swarmed all over the place.

At 10 o'clock in the evening I was in Spenge and it was utter and sheer joy. Aunt Lies was also there but I didn't meet Mother, as she had gone back to Köln a week before. I stayed in Spenge for ten days and looked for all our relatives there, and in Osnabrück. Everywhere there were families waiting for their husbands and sons from whom they had heard nothing for many months.

Uncle August took me to Hamm in his tradesman's van. From there I could travel by train to Düsseldorf – a rough, unbroken stretch of ruins. My cycle was packed full of foodstuffs, but unfortunately all along the Rhein it was not good travelling.

In Deutz I heard from a former neighbour that Father and Mother were in Köln-Merheirn where they had obtained living quarters. Finally I reached home. For five months we had had no news of each other. Then the name Wolfgang was mentioned. They had not heard anything. Wordless, they sat there and looked at me. Mother cried, her face motionless.

I sit in our garden, between the greenness of the trees and the bushes. Everywhere fruit is hanging and it will be a wonderful year for fruit. Near me, the wreckage of our once pretty garden-house. A bomb destroyed it. We had so loved to sit there, Wolfgang and I.

I think of Gertlauken. How many may still be living? Which fate have they met with? Only the nature there will always be the same – unspoiled by inhumanity. The quiet, dark woods, the dunes, the song of the waves on the beach at the Nehrung and all over, the wide, wide sky.

The End

POSTSCRIPT BY THE EDITOR

'Publisher sought for Letters from East Prussia 1941/45,' was the text of an advertisement in the weekly newspaper *Die Xeit* [*The Times*] in November 1984.

Now, I am certainly not a publisher, and above all nor am I an East Prussian, but despite that, the advertisement appealed to me and invoked curiosity. But then I harboured a huge affection for this former German province whose history went back for 700 years before 1945. Since then, I have considered it to be a stroke of luck that I should be able to have a glimpse of that land, a light thrown on the concept, an idea of the particular way of life that existed before it disappeared behind the Iron Curtain.

In 1943 and 1944 I went to East Prussia fairly frequently but I certainly cannot claim that I learnt very much about the province. My stay there was much too short. Besides which it was wartime, I was a soldier and my visits were duty ones, quite another purpose altogether than to learn about the land and its people. That's why to me, the impressions I received were but faint ones, but the others would be coloured.

This or that impression one gets strangely a considerable time after the war, either a clearer background or a stronger emphasis colouring events. There were books that brought memories back to me each year, two of them especially. One is *The Shattering East Prussia Diary of Grafen* [Count] *Hans von Lehndorf*, and another, a beautiful one, always taken down from the bookshelves for a new reading, *Names* [Reminiscences] *of Those No Longer Known* by Grafin [Countess] Marion Donhoff.

My few East Prussian reminiscences are naturally opportunistic and disordered. Small towns where, in a cobbled market square, stand memorials to the Great Electoral Prince, of old Fritz (Frederick the Great), and tiny villages where a dusty high road with birch trees to the left and birch trees to the right, leads to wide farmyards, and geese doze in the sunshine in the middle of the road, oblivious to any delay they cause. Lush meadowlands with brown horses and black-coloured cows, a high sky full of swallows, and on the distant horizon a church tower or endless woods.

Beneath the aeroplane's cockpit, black woods hemmed around a clear open lake, and still another and then the next on the one after that, an entire chain of lakes shimmering in the woods and morning haze. A forged iron door with golden-tipped lances, leading to a part in which are grassy lawns with rhododendron bushes, and then up to a white castle with a porch and columns, and a coat of arms.

Sandy beaches and shifting dunes, storks' nests on the reed-covered roofs of the fishermen's cabins, a yellow field of buckwheat. The water of the Baltic Sea, if one flew over it at low level, was the same brilliant colour of the backs of the freshly caught Baltic Sea herrings. And on the beach, in the July sunshine, the sand gleamed and dazzled like the freshly fallen snow in the cold sunshine of a January afternoon.

Inland on the banks of a river, metre-thick stone-bricked buildings, ivy-clad stumps of towers, walls with pointed arched window apertures – the ruin of a religious order, symbolic of an East Prussian past.

Such memories were probably as a result of my reading and thinking about the newspaper advertisement, and later with the writing and drafting of the letters, I was given a glimpse of East Prussia's past.

Frau Peyinghaus answered by return of post. A typewritten copy of the thirty or forty letters existed and were sent. The Siedler Verlang [Siedler publisher] was impressed by the sample sent and requested the complete collection of the 382 descriptive pages. From these it was apparent that a book of those letters of special significance could be published.

Who had heard of Gertlauken? Of the Gertlauken where the greater part of the letters had been written? An out-of-this-world, secluded hideout, ten kilometres from the nearest railway station. In spring and autumn it could be reached only on mud-covered roads and in winter, in the deep snow, at best with a horse-drawn sledge. In summer admittedly filled with birdsong, humming bees and the scent of the hay.

In its way, surely an idyllic spot, especially in the middle of the war and most certainly a plot of earth where foxes and hares said goodnight to each other. In this village of about 100 inhabitants, there burst in the late autumn of 1941 a not yet twenty-one-year-old teacher transferred from Köln. A young, unprejudiced girl who found no difficulty in her contacts with the villagers. She found everything to be strange but very interesting, and wrote about her experiences weekly, often more frequently, to her parents in Köln. How she travelled on occasions to Königsberg and its environs and at other times to Tapiau and Laukischken.

Nothing was left out and, without full stop or comma, she wrote in her letters about all her activities undertaken in her leisure time, what she did in school where, as the only trained teacher, she was responsible for teaching over 160 children. Everything she saw, experienced and felt, found itself being described in her letters. What it was that made her happy or even, occasionally, made her annoyed. About her great worries day in and day out, about her parents in the bomb-blasted city of Köln and then soon about her brother at the front.

The child of the great city became surprisingly quickly at home in the flat landscape which asked and received answers, all of which were written about, often by candlelight with quiet radio music in the background, seated next to a warm, tiled stove. Sometimes the young girl's eyes would close as she was writing. It was seldom that she went to bed before midnight. Frequently her letters covered a dozen, sometimes more, pages.

To ascribe a single explanation for her desire to correspond, thus is not possible. Behind it there lies a greater desire on her part, to tell a story with a literary impetus. Recognition of this ability on her part is contained in reference to her father's letters to her when he gently remonstrates that she should write more matter of factly, and omit the flowery adjectives. She is to be praised for not observing these admonitions. Therefore, she continued describing customs, ways of behaviour, village rituals, as well as the greatly loved card parties and the various celebrations to which she was invited. And, just as colourfully and forcibly, she wrote about her cycle tours and hikes in the woods, excursions on the Haff and to the Nehrung. Her visits to Königsberg or to the Masurian Lakes, about the arrival of the first storks in the village, the appearance of the first liverwort in the woods or the first snows.

Included in the saga of events, mention of the twenty-three cakes on tables, of each of the family celebrations, as if in the middle of peacetime with East Prussia so distant from the war itself. And just as these festivities get mentioned, so too do the circumstances when temporarily she had to fetch water from a neighbour's pump because her own pump was either frozen over or a storm had broken the pump's handle. One reads in the letters about the leisure hours with a book in the sunlit garden or of the interminable night-time conversations with her friend Paula, a teacher in another somewhat outlandish village. Additionally we notice, by the way, her concern for the Oldenburgers in wartime, their well-being and survival and particularly in respect of Kinni, a neighbourhood friend of her Köln-Deutz childhood days.

But one reads also of anxiety and sorrow, of the heavy grief felt over the death of the little Elke Berkan. And one learns of her perplexity when confronted with the Jewish ghetto in the Polish town of Plohnen (which in Polish times had another name) and how affected she was by the meeting with the Jewish tailor, who today we know probably met certain death in the gas chambers of Auschwitz.

At present one likes to talk about everyday events. Abbreviated expressions one understands, but this young historian is writing about not only the political, military, economic, cultural and scientific events, but also the views of the participants in this historical era. The so-called world of the little people, those folk who always become the victims of history, such as the farmers, forestry workers, handymen, the baker, the bricklayer, the smithy, and their wives and children. Not to forget the young lady from Köln. By doing so, Marianne Peyinghaus has observed, witnessed and written about this warm-hearted microcosm that has passed into history. She achieved this without the knowledge of hindsight and created an old-fashioned portrait, and in so doing, created an unusual work of everyday history of a time long gone.

The Gertlauken folk are peculiarly attractive as model characters and the specific or typical East Prussian, when looking back, is surprisingly generally accepted to be so different from those encountered and described by Marianne Peyinghaus in her letters.

On the one hand arising from these letters we are given an inside view of the smallest trifle occurring in an unknown village in former East Prussia, and on the other hand inclusive of the visits to Köln there are the several journeys across Germany, meeting with familiar bonds, and over all we have put before us an informative report about life in Germany in the Second World War.

One should remember in this connection the fact that the part of East Prussia in which Königsberg, Tabiau, Labiau and even Gertlauken lie, since 1945 falls within the sphere of Soviet influence and has not been accessible to visitors since that date.

In her letter of 15 January 1944 Marianne Peyinghaus, then still Marianne Günther, reported that during the return journey from Köln she had met on the train a Lieutenant Fritz Peyinghaus. She wrote as follows:

'In 1940 he was shot down near Dunkirk and spent three and a half years in English prisoner of war camps before, as a severely wounded prisoner, he was exchanged.'

It is possibly known that such an exchange took place between the English and Germans, but certainly not as to how it was effected. I asked Herr Peyinghaus if he could explain the manner in which it had occurred and he wrote as follows:

'In the vicinity of Dunkirk at the end of May 1940 the plane in which I was flying as an observer was shot down and I was taken with a British field ambulance unit to England. I remained in a hospital in Woolwich, SE London for a year and in May 1941 was a prisoner in a camp at Grizedale in the Lake District, the North of England. There a large country house was used as an official camp. On account of my injuries, in the spring of 1942 I was posted to a prisoners' exchange camp. The exchange proceeded apparently very sluggishly but one and half years later at the end of September 1943, to all intents and purposes they were ready. About 600 of us, all German wounded, were embarked on a hospital ship in Glasgow, Scotland. The journey took us first to the north, then eastwards to the Norwegian coast and then along the Norwegian coast in a southerly direction to Sweden. The exchange took place in Göteborg, where about 1,000 British prisoners of war had been brought by ship from Stettin. In accordance with the exchange rules the exchanged soldiers were no longer to be employed on Front Line duty, because of the severity of their wounds. I was then treated in a German Air Force hospital in Braunschweig and after a course in Bad Nauheim, on 1 June 1944 I was posted to an artillery school in Mourmelon, France as an instructor/adjutant. However, the school was preparing to move to Gross-Born in Pommern, which it did at the end of August 1944. In January 1945, following the Soviet offensive, we pulled back to Rokitzan in Böhmen. In Bohrnerwald I was taken into American custody as a POW.'

'Quiet Years in Gertlauken'. The village, an island in a sea of war. Far enough from the distant war to be considered safe and comfortable. But so near was it also, through the sorrowful communications from the air-raid shelter in Köln and the appalling nights of bombing. From news about young friends, school companions, a friend or cousin lying wounded somewhere in hospital or lying dead somewhere in Russia. Meanwhile the larger aspects of the course of the war were sketched in concise keywords: Stalingrad, the Landing of the Allies in Italy, the Invasion in Normandy, the 20 July 1944 Assassination Attempt, the grief about the Defeat on the Frontier and the Retreat.

And the triumphant scepticism of the father. He was a finance officer and finally, but after the war, a tax office official. In the Nazi era as an old Social Democrat he had not received any promotion, only demoted and disadvantaged. So much the more bitter for him was that his only son Wolfgang did not finish his schooling to take the German School Leaving Certificate [A levels] necessary for entry to a university, but instead volunteered to join the Waffen SS and was enlisted in the Leibstandarte Adolf Hitler Division. As a section leader he was killed, probably on 31 December 1944 near Vielsalm in Belgium. He is buried in the Soldiers Cemetery in Recogne-Bastogne, Belgium.

In the summer of 1944 it was generally accepted as certain that the end of the Gertlauken idyll was approaching. With the huge breakthrough of the Russian army as far as the River Weichsel and the entire centre of the German Eastern Front torn open, the war drew nearer to the East Prussian border. Enemy planes appeared over the East Prussian towns and the ashes from the burnt buildings in Königsberg drifted over the fields and woods of Gertlauken. As the front drew nearer, all those males from the age of fourteen years upwards and not in employment were ordered to work on the fieldworks on the East Wall. In the summer weather one had heard already the artillery fire in the south-east. In the letter of 20 July 1944 the news of the assassination attempt on Hitler had still not reached the people. It says:

'We went for a long walk, during which time the noise from the front line was heard like background music to the peacefulness of the evening and the countryside.'

But his peace was most certainly becoming fragile, the quiet days were drawing to a close. The eventual fate of East Prussia was noticeable and never in doubt, despite the Greater Germany radio announcements and confident notices hanging on each and every tree, with exhortations to stand fast, and that victory was assured.

Indeed the enemy breakthrough was actually brought to a halt for a few months, but that was only the lull before the storm. But most certainly from the summer of 1944 onwards, something uncanny and almost ghostly enters into the letters, if only between the lines, as it were. Already these letters are so different from those preceding them. With hindsight, one is startled and suspicious to the extent of cold shivers almost running down one's spine when comparison is made with those carefree days. Times of birthday parties, homely card-playing evenings, boat trips on the lagoon, children's baptisms, Sunday excursions to Königsberg, or the very last Gertlauken Christmas party with roast goose and dumplings.

One wants to warn the people, especially the children, to flee from the deadly danger hanging over them. In God's name, flee, go at once, pack your things or leave them there, as long as you reach safety, so long as you have the time to do so.

Belonging to the 382 pages of the manuscript were also a number of letters written by the women and girls from Gertlauken and also by the much-mentioned friend, Paula. As I read these letters in May 1985 there was a detailed account in the press, on radio and TV of the grandiose military parade of the Soviet Union celebrating the 40th anniversary of the Great Fatherland War. Everywhere appeared disturbing pictures of the veterans (both men and women) who took part in the war itself. Their breasts from the shoulder to the stomach were decorated with innumerable orders and medals. But the Germans and others at that time had certainly different experiences.

'On 19 January 1945 we received orders to escape. In the night we loaded our things on a cart drawn by two horses. Grandmother was the bravest. She had already slaughtered turkeys and chickens and given Mother and the rest of us confidence. One saw signs of untidiness everywhere in the rooms, kitchens and food cupboards. Everything lay all mixed up, feathers, chicken's heads, old clothing and other things. Our Aunt Lina did not want to move with us. After the parting from her and the house, farm and the cattle, we set off on our way.' So wrote in June 1946 the fifteen-year-old Christel Beckmann to her former teacher, Marianne Peyinghouse.

It was the fate of the East Prussian people to encounter the hardest winter for years. It froze *'Stein und Bein'* (stone and bone), the storm howled, black ice and snowdrifts impeded those fleeing on the escape route. The peaceful East Prussians once so distant from the war found themselves embroiled in an inferno.

Christel Beckmann continued:

'After two days we reached Mahnsfeld about 16 kilometres to the rear of Königsberg and there at first we stayed. Early on the third day we heard the rumble of artillery fire and at midday the first shell fell in the village. The sky also was full of planes, bombs were falling and there was strafing from the air with machine-guns. The entire village burnt, also the barn in which our horses stood.'

During the following night the Beckmanns reached the Frisches Haff [frozen lagoon],

'We spent three days and two nights on the lagoon in freezing cold and driven-snow. On the Nehrung there were only a few villages but the people there were very strange. Very often we were rejected, even if we only wanted to get warm within the house.'

Finally the family reached Danzig and from there the journey continued to Pommern, Rugenwalde, Kolberg and Koslin. Everywhere the same picture – hunger, cold and massive overcrowding. On 2 March the Beckmanns crossed the River Oder and on 10 March they luckily arrived in Wamckow in Mecklenburg. The family obtained two rooms with a kitchen in a schoolhouse and 'felt quite at home here'. Soon they began to believe that the worst had been overcome and began to make preparations for themselves, but on 3 May, 'within the space of ten minutes' the whole village swarmed with Russians.

'For four weeks we were concealed in a hiding place in a hayloft without anyone finding us. We looked so miserable. Herta's face was covered in scabs. In the night we heard the screaming and crying of the women in the village. Not one man could protect his wife, he would be beaten half-dead if he attempted to do so, and the wife would have a pistol pointed at the breast, and they had to obey. We became almost crazy.'

Half a year later, again in a letter to her former teacher, Christel Beckmann drew up a balance sheet and wrote, 'We have had news from Aunt Lina in Gertlauken. Hildegard Schustereit and other girls were abducted and died in the Urals in Russia. Almost all the old people in the village are dead. My cousin Ingrid Iwahn is also dead, as well as Aunt and Uncle Matschull and my school comrade Lotte Jakobeit and her mother, Lies Wallat and Eva Gronwald. Siegfried Schwarm is likewise dead, the mother of the latter buried him in a grave in the street. Herr von Cohs is dead and Frau von Cohs returned to the village and died from Typhus fever. Her children are no longer together, the smallest Franka is with Frau Kather, the young boy with Frau Schwarm and the others with Frau Frose. My dear cousin Herta was frequently raped, as were the other women. The Russians behaved very badly in Mecklenburg, but at home it was still as bad.

'The farming community business is all destroyed. The land is devastated, only thistles and thorns. All must work in Deimehoh, even Gertrud Beckmann and my cousin Herta. As far as animals are concerned we have only dogs, cats, mice and rats. Neither cows, pigs, nor hens. All have lost everything, the last bed, clothing, shoes, everything. They have only the rags that they carry on them.'

So one could quote from letters, pages long, from Christel Beckmann and other women and girls from Gertlauken. A chronicle of misery, pain and death.

But in between, the few lucky ones who made their immediate escape, the first to go, and among those was the former friend Paula. She travelled on her cycle to Königsberg and from there to Pillau:

345

'In a school I obtained from the German Navy a passenger pass permitting me to board a ship. I had to hurry as my name would be called. It was dark when I eventually found my ship and they didn't want me to embark. The ship was dreadfully overcrowded and I should therefore try my luck with another ship. I went back, met a naval officer and poured out my distress to him. He took me with him, discussed the matter with a sentry on the gangway and then pushed me high up onto the gangplank. Then he made a quick hand movement, indicating that I should quickly dash away. I hurried up above, and in the darkness was not seen by the sailors. But, I was aboard the ship. In a corner I found room for a place on the floor and as the morning dawned, we were on the high seas.'

Ten days later Paula stood in front of her parents' house:

'As I opened the large entrance door, my father stood before me. I flung my arms round his neck. "Is it really you?" he asked, and cried out to the house behind him, "Paula is here! Our Paula is here again!"'

Gunther Elbin – May 1985, Louisendorf

The schoolhouse in Gertlauken, 1993.

Cologne (Köln) in May 1945.

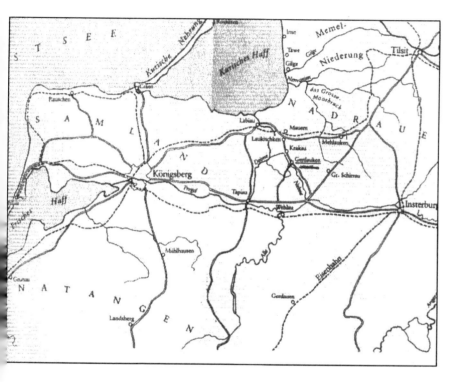

Map of Könisberg District (Gertlauken is underlined).

The authoress, Marianne Peyinghaus in 1941.

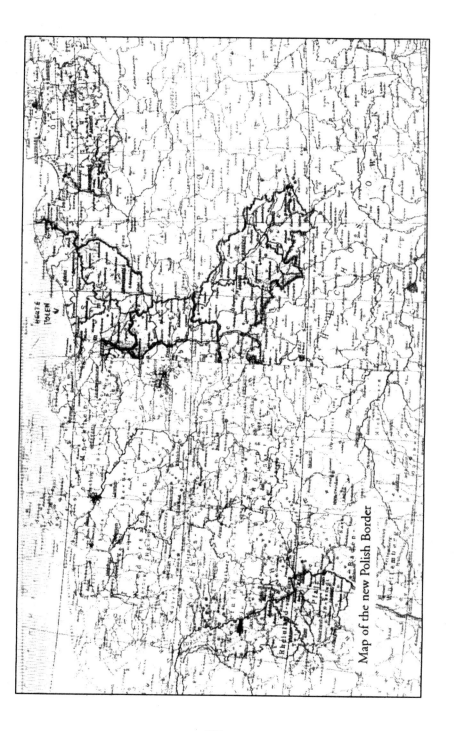

Map of the new Polish Border